DIOCESE OF CHICHESTER

A CATALOGUE OF THE RECORDS OF THE BISHOP, ARCHDEACONS AND FORMER EXEMPT JURISDICTIONS

Compiled by

FRANCIS W. STEER, M.A., F.S.A.
Archivist to the Diocese of Chichester

and

ISABEL M. KIRBY, B.A.

With a Foreword by The Rt. Rev. The Lord Bishop of Chichester
and
A Preface by Marc Fitch, F.S.A.

Issued by
THE WEST SUSSEX COUNTY COUNCIL
COUNTY HALL, CHICHESTER
1966

© West Sussex County Council, 1966.

CONTENTS

EP.VII. THE ARCHDEACONRY OF HASTINGS

EP.VIII. THE DEAN OF BATTLE'S PECULIAR

FOREWORD

If it is true that beneath the soil of England lie many treasures of historical interest still awaiting discovery by the archaeologist, the written records of past centuries—in private ownership or public custody—must surely be much richer. Before records can become available to the historian, there is a hard preliminary task to be done in collecting and classifying them.

Much historical source material, particularly of ecclesiastical concern, is still untapped. Many parish records are still in the keeping (it is to be hoped the safe keeping) of incumbents and churchwardens: but a whole range of records, episcopal and otherwise, has today been assembled and put in the care of archivists. To sort and list these documents so that they may become available for thorough research and exposition is an immense project, but under the auspices of the Marc Fitch Fund a start on the publication of lists of episcopal and capitular archives has been made with the present volume. It is an exhaustive piece of work which redounds greatly to the credit of all concerned in its production.

A detailed list of records, such as is here contained, has primarily a specialist appeal: but this volume offers a double promise. First, it is to be hoped that it will stimulate fresh local study of the history of the Church and community in Sussex; secondly, that from the experience of this volume will come a number of similar diocesan undertakings elsewhere. For this reason we must be grateful for the initiative shown by the Council of Management of the Marc Fitch Fund, and equally for the assistance given by the County Council of West Sussex. We may rightly ask the public to support these actions by purchasing copies of this book.

The Palace, Chichester   ROGER CICESTR:
January 1966

PREFACE

Ecclesiastical archives probably constitute one of the largest English archive groups which remain relatively untapped by the historian. For this there are several reasons but the most important is both simple and interesting. In the Middle Ages, and indeed for some time after, the government of life was more or less equally divided between Church and State and the records reflect this. Down to the last century, however, access to both groups was difficult and restricted. Then came the great Victorian drive to gather the Public Records together and to arrange them, publish them, and make them available. This was a State activity from which, with some exceptions, ecclesiastical records, like private records, were excluded. The Church, lacking such financial resources, was unable to do for its own records what the State has done for secular public records. The enormous size of the consequent gap in historical knowledge was first brought home to many students by the (still unpublished) survey of ecclesiastical archives made under a scheme sponsored by the Pilgrim Trust in 1946.

When the Council of the Fund of which I am Chairman considered the desirability of making this immense store of historical evidence available it became apparent that the Diocese of Chichester offered peculiar advantages. The diocese was an ancient one, exemplifying ecclesiastical policy and administration from medieval to modern times; it was of manageable size—an important consideration in a first venture; some work had already been done on the lines that were envisaged; and, finally, the deciding factor was that my friend, Mr. Francis Steer, was Archivist of the County of West Sussex and of the Diocese of Chichester and resident in Chichester. Had a search to find the ideal editor for this work been needed, I venture to think few would have been found to fit the requirements more perfectly.

Miss Kirby was engaged by the Marc Fitch Fund to work under the direction of Mr. Steer. To her has fallen the task of examining, describing and listing the documents in this *Catalogue*. It has been the joint object of Mr. Steer and Miss Kirby to provide as perfect a key as possible to the records of the Diocese of Chichester, and it is my belief that their work has culminated in a model, *mutatis mutandis*, for other dioceses. The Fund does not anticipate being able to complete the great task of covering all the dioceses in the country, but its Council hopes that if others find this *Catalogue* acceptable they will endeavour to follow on similar lines. Meanwhile, work has commenced on the archives of the Diocese of Gloucester, a Henrician foundation, thus providing, it is hoped, an example of a more recent type of ecclesiastical organization.

London   MARC FITCH
January 1966

INTRODUCTION

On 21 July 1949 the Bishop of Chichester, acting in accordance with the Parochial Registers and Records Measure, 1929, established a Record Office for his Diocese with the agreement of the County Council of West Sussex. In February 1951, Dr. Bell arranged for the deposit of his episcopal archives in the Diocesan Record Office at Chichester on "permanent loan" under the care of the County Archivist. It is those records which are described in this *Catalogue* which, in itself, is in the nature of an experiment in the production of a workmanlike list for a single ecclesiastical territory. The term "experiment" is used advisedly because this is the first list to be prepared under the scheme proposed by the Council of Management of the Marc Fitch Fund for assisting some Dioceses and Deans and Chapters in the arrangement and publication of their vast holdings of historical documents. As each collection of episcopal and capitular records is processed, so the value of each earlier list will be enhanced, and such errors of classification or even of description which may occur (it is hoped only infrequently) in this present book will be lessened or eliminated. This remark is not offered by way of apology, but to emphasize that one of the difficulties in dealing with records so diverse as those under consideration is the terminology used by registrars or other officials in various parts of the country for certain classes of records: this will be mentioned again later on.

As this book is designed to be an addition to the historian's equipment and not a book for the general reader, it is unnecessary for it to be furnished with a long introduction. The history of the Diocese of Chichester and the architectural development of the Cathedral have received attention from many writers whose works are listed in the select bibliography on pp. xv–xxi, so anything further on these subjects (and in any case the Cathedral is more the concern of the Dean and Chapter than the Bishop) would be repetitive or incomplete. The aim of this book is to present the historian with a full list of all the surviving material—mainly up to the middle of the 19th century—relating to the administration of the Diocese of Chichester and of the estates forming the endowment of the See; it is hoped that these records will be used by scholars to make, in the first instance, contributions to the better understanding of episcopal and archidiaconal administration in a Diocese which has always been almost coterminous with the County of Sussex. With the detailed examination of the records of individual Dioceses and their comparsion with each other, a true picture for the entire kingdom will be eventually obtained.

The scope of the archives of the Diocese of Chichester (excluding parish records which are not included in this volume) is shown in the list of contents on pp. iii–ix. The areas of jurisdiction are given on pp. xxii, xxiii. An examination of certain sections of these records will disclose many gaps, especially for the earlier periods; whether the loss may be attributed to the sacking of the Cathedral during the Civil War, or to the neglect of generations of registrars, or to the wanton destruction of "old papers", we shall never know, but of the three possibilities the second is the least likely. The absence of medieval documents is, however, a cause for regret. The accumulation over the centuries of enormous quantities of miscellaneous papers (e.g. Ep.I/15, see pp. 20, 21), many of them in an exceedingly fragile state, present a heavy burden of listing in the future; at present, these documents have been sorted into chronological order so far as is possible. No spectacular discoveries have been made in the course of preparing this *Catalogue*, although it must be admitted that there may be treasures to be found when every paper and every page has been scrutinized.

To assist the user of this *Catalogue* and partly to overcome the lack of standard terms for certain classes of records, brief notes have been provided on diocesan administration only so far as it is relevant to, and explains, the documents in the collection.

The previous sortings to which the documents have been subjected and the fact that they received numbers which have been quoted in print has increased the difficulties in preparing this volume. In brief, however, documents have only been transferred from one class to another in cases where it was unavoidable because of earlier mis-sorting. The original groupings made in the 1950s (Ep.I/1–57, II/1–37, III/1–13, IV/1–13, V/1–18, VI/1–60 and VII/1–7) have been retained although they sometimes include unrelated documents; the index should solve any problems arising from such errors in the original classification. New numbers have been added (Ep.I/58–88, II/38–43, III/14–17, IV/14, V/19–21, VII/8 and VIII) to provide references to "stray" documents and later accessions.

A figure in round brackets after a catalogue reference indicates the number (sometimes only approximate) of documents in each bundle where such information may be helpful. Where there is obviously one document for each parish (e.g. Ep.I/42A) this detail has been omitted. Many volumes have been foliated or paginated more than once, but it is advisable always to follow the pencil foliation when using a book in the collection; it has been a rule in compiling this *Catalogue* to use what is believed to be the most recent foliation. A higher folio or page number preceding a lower (e.g. ff.10–3, pp. 312–260) indicates that the volume has been used from both ends.

Different hands have made notes in or on these records for various purposes, especially in the 19th century, when users of documents did not always reverence them as we do (or should) today and selfishly marked what they particularly required or thought important regardless of the difficulties they were creating for future custodians. It should be emphasized that the printed catalogue mark under which any records are described is the one which should be quoted; the earlier (and often confusing) catalogue marks, if they are found on documents, should be ignored. Seals and types of binding have only been noted if they are of special interest. No distinction has been made between records which have been received at different times. There still remains at the Diocesan Registry some records (e.g. Bishops' Registers and Faculty Papers) which overlap in date some others described in this book.

Access to certain documents may be restricted either because of their content or their recent date, or because of their age and fragile condition.

Miss Kirby has been responsible for sorting many of the records and for compiling the *Catalogue* and the index; much credit is due to her for tackling such a large job as the first in her professional career. But any shortcomings in this book are my responsibility as the editor; I do not expect it to be beyond adverse criticism because ideas on the presentation of such works as this are individual, and archivists, like some antiquaries and historians, have to be pioneers and accept the inevitable censures from their colleagues and from reviewers.

I welcome this opportunity of expressing my gratitude to all who have directly or indirectly furthered the production of this *Catalogue*. In particular I would mention the late Dr. G. K. A. Bell, Bishop of Chichester from 1929 to 1958, and his successor, Dr. R. P. Wilson, for their support and lively interest in the work of the Diocesan Record Office. The constant help and friendship of the Archdeacon of Chichester, the Venerable Lancelot Mason (who has represented the Bishop of Chichester on the County Records Committee since 1947) is invaluable. The gift from the Pilgrim Trust in 1955 to assist in carrying out urgent repairs to some of the ecclesiastical records was most encouraging and this book may be regarded as another milestone in the survey of such records which the Trust inaugurated in 1946.

I must also pay tribute to those members of the Record Office staff who, by their knowledge and skills, have contributed in one way or another to the better preservation of these archives, and mention must also be made of the voluntary work done by the late Dr. Hilda Johnstone and which is still being done by Mr. W. D. Peckham whose knowledge of Chichester Cathedral and the Chapter records in particular is unrivalled. But the County Records Committee, the Diocesan officials, scholars and I as Archivist owe the greatest debt of all to Mr. Marc Fitch whose munificence has enabled this *Catalogue* to be produced much sooner than would otherwise have been possible; I am personally very gratified that he and the Bishop of Chichester should have consented to writing commendations of this book.

Chichester   FRANCIS W. STEER
March 1966

SELECT BIBLIOGRAPHY

The compilation of this bibliography of 147 entries has presented many difficulties. To have listed all the general works bearing on the subject of this book would have been a major undertaking and would have included numerous books with which scholars will be familiar already. Some distinction has been made between books and articles dealing with the Diocese and Bishop of Chichester on the one hand and with the Cathedral and Dean and Chapter of Chichester on the other; references to the latter (e.g. Act Books, the biographies of Deans), although obviously relating in some way to the former, will be more appropriate in the forthcoming Catalogue of the Capitular Archives.

The bibliography is mainly drawn from books and periodicals of Sussex interest. While it does not claim to be comprehensive, it is hoped that it will be useful as a guide. Additions, especially references to articles in periodicals, will be welcomed.

COUNTY OF SUSSEX

J. Dallaway, *A History of the Western Division of the County of Sussex*, esp. Vol. 1 (1815).

T. W. Horsfield, *The History, Antiquities, and Topography of the County of Sussex* (1835).

M. A. Lower, *A Compendious History of Sussex* (1870).

W. Page (ed.), *The Victoria History of the County of Sussex*, vol. 2 (1907).

CHICHESTER CATHEDRAL AND CITY

A. Hay, *The History of Chichester* (1804).

M. E. C. Walcott, *Memorials of Chichester* (1865).

W. R. W. Stephens, *Memorials of the South Saxon See and Cathedral Church of Chichester* (1876).

C. A. Swainson, *The History and Constitution of a Cathedral of the Old Foundation* (1880).

W. R. W. Stephens, *The South Saxon Diocese, Selsey—Chichester* (1881).

A. Ballard, *A History of Chichester* (1898).

H. C. Corlette, *The Cathedral Church of Chichester . . . with an Account of the Diocese and See* (1901).

I. C. Hannah, 'The Vicars' Close and Adjacent Buildings, Chichester', in *Sussex Archaeological Collections*,[1] vol. 56 (1914), pp. 92–109.

I. C. Hannah, 'Houses in the Close at Chichester', in *S.A.C.*, vol. 68 (1927), pp. 133–158.

W. D. Peckham, 'Some former Parishes in Chichester', in *S.A.C.*, vol. 68 (1927), pp. 266–268.

T. G. Willis, *Records of Chichester* (1928).

W. D. Peckham, 'The Parishes of the City of Chichester', in *S.A.C.*, vol. 74 (1933), pp. 65–97.

---

[1] Abbreviated hereafter to *S.A.C.*

L. F. Salzman (ed.), *The Victoria History of the County of Sussex*, vol. 3 (1935).

R. S. T. Haslehurst, 'A Short History of Chichester Theological College', in *The Cicestrian*, vol. 10 (1939), pp. 81–100.

A. S. Duncan-Jones and F. W. Steer, *The Story of Chichester Cathedral* (1955).

L. Fleming, *The Little Churches of Chichester* (Chichester Paper No. 5, 1957).

F. W. Steer, *The Heraldic Ceiling at the Bishop's Palace, Chichester* (Chichester Paper No. 10, 1958).

W. D. Peckham, 'Chichester Cathedral in 1562', in *S.A.C.*, vol. 96 (1958), pp. 1–8.

W. K. Lowther Clarke, *Chichester Cathedral in the Nineteenth Century* (Chichester Paper No. 14, 1959).

F. W. Steer, *The Arms of the County Councils of East and West Sussex and the Diocese of Chichester* (1959).

F. W. Steer, 'Repairs to the Bishop's Palace', in *Chichester Cathedral Journal* (1961), pp. 14–18.

A. Bouquet, *A History of the Diocese of Chichester (from the foundation to the end of the 18th century)* (n.d.).

THE ARCHIVES

W. H. Blaauw, 'Episcopal Visitations of the Benedictine Nunnery of Easebourne', in *S.A.C.*, vol. 9 (1857), pp. 1–32.

M. E. C. Walcott, 'The Medieval Registers of the Bishops of Chichester' and 'Kalendar of the Episcopal Registers of Chichester', in *Transactions of the Royal Society of Literature*, vol. 9 (second series) (1870), pp. 215–255.

E. H. W. Dunkin, 'Contributions towards the Ecclesiastical History of the Deanery of South Malling', in *S.A.C.*, vol. 26 (1875), pp. 9–96.

M. E. C. Walcott, 'The Early Statutes of the Cathedral Church of the Holy Trinity, Chichester, with Observations on its Constitutions and History', in *Archaeologia*, vol. 45 (1877), pp. 143–234.

Historical Manuscripts Commission, *Report on Manuscripts in Various Collections*, vol. 1 (1901), pp. 177–186.

F. G. Bennett, R. H. Codrington and C. Deedes, *Statutes and Constitutions of the Cathedral Church of Chichester* (1904).

W. C. Renshaw, 'Ecclesiastical Returns for 81 parishes in East Sussex made in 1603', in Sussex Record Society, vol. 4 (1905), pp. 1–17.

C. Deedes, 'Extracts from the Episcopal Register of Richard Praty, S.T.P., Lord Bishop of Chichester, 1438–1445', in Sussex Record Society, vol. 4 (1905), pp. 83–236.

W. C. Renshaw, 'Notes from the Act Books of the Court for the Deanery of South Malling', in *S.A.C.*, vol. 50 (1907), pp. 41–46.

C. Deedes (ed.), *Register of Robert Rede, Bishop of Chichester, 1397–1415* (Sussex Record Society, vols. 8, 11 (1908, 1910)).

W. C. Renshaw, 'Witnesses from Ecclesiastical Deposition Books, 1580–1640', in *S.A.C.*, vol. 56 (1914), pp. 1–15.

W. D. Peckham, 'Some lost Chichester Charters', in *Sussex Notes and Queries*,[1] vol. 1 (1926–27), pp. 115, 116.

W. D. Peckham, 'Ceadwalla's Charter and the Hundred of Manhood', in *S.N.Q.*, vol. 1 (1926–27), pp. 233, 234.

W. D. Peckham, 'The Text of Ceadwalla's Charter', in *S.N.Q.*, vol. 2 (1928–29), pp. 45–47.

W. D. Peckham, 'The Missing Leaves of Liber E', in *S.N.Q.*, vol. 2 (1928–29), pp. 105, 108.

'Dunkin Collection, British Museum', in *S.N.Q.*, vol. 2 (1928–29), p. 158.

'A Lewes Priory Charter', in *S.N.Q.*, vol. 2 (1928–29), pp. 251–254; vol. 4 (1932–33), p. 25.

W. D. Peckham, 'A Diocesan Visitation of 1553', in *S.A.C.*, vol. 77 (1936), pp. 93–105.

H. Johnstone, 'An Early Medical Certificate', in *S.N.Q.*, vol. 9 (1942–43), pp. 157, 158.

W. D. Peckham, 'A Chichester Court Diary of 1675', in *S.N.Q.*, vol. 12 (1948–49), pp. 37–39.

W. D. Peckham, 'Bishop Sherburne', in *S.N.Q.*, vol. 12 (1948–49), p. 66.

H. Johnstone (ed.), *Churchwardens' Presentments (17th century)* (Sussex Record Society, vol. 49 (1949), Archdeaconry of Chichester; vol. 50 (1950), Archdeaconry of Lewes).

W. D. Peckham, 'Bishop Mitford's Register', in *S.N.Q.*, vol. 13 (1950–53), p. 40.

L. M. Midgley and P. M. Ward, *Survey of the Principal Collections of Archives of the Church of England* (The Pilgrim Trust, 1952).

A Descriptive Report on the Quarter Sessions, other Official, and Ecclesiastical Records in the custody of the County Councils of East and West Sussex (1954).

W. D. Peckham, 'A Chichester Inventory of 1653', in *S.N.Q.*, vol. 14 (1954–57), pp. 243–245.

C. R. Cheney, 'The Earliest English Diocesan Statutes', in *English Historical Review*, vol. 75 (1960), pp. 1–29.

H. Mayr-Harting (ed.), *The Acta of the Bishops of Chichester, 1075–1207* (Canterbury and York Society, 1964).

BISHOPS[2]

A. Anscombe, 'The Ring of Eolla, Bishop of Selsey, *circa* A.D.720', in *S.N.Q.*, vol. 1 (1926–27), pp. 136–139.

M. E. C. Walcott, 'The Bishops of Chichester from Stigand to Sherborne', in *S.A.C.*, vol. 28 (1878), pp. 11–58; vol. 29 (1879), pp. 1–38.

H. Mayr-Harting, *The Bishops of Chichester, 1075–1207* (Chichester Paper No. 40, 1964).

---

[1] Abbreviated hereafter to *S.N.Q.*

[2] The entries in this section are arranged, so far as it is possible, in chronological order of the holders of the office.

H. Hall, 'Stigand, Bishop of Chichester', in *S.A.C.*, vol. 43 (1900), pp. 88–104.

W. D. Peckham and E. E. Barker, 'The Successors of Bishop Stigand', in *S.N.Q.*, vol. 10 (1944–45), pp. 112–117, 163, 164.

H. Mayr-Harting, 'Hilary, Bishop of Chichester (1147–1169) and Henry II', in *English Historical Review*, vol. 78 (1963), pp. 209–224.

F. H. Arnold, 'Notes on a Biography of Simon de Wells, Bishop of Chichester (1204–1207)', in *S.A.C.*, vol. 22 (1870), pp. 178–184.

M. R. Capes, *Richard of Wyche, Labourer, Scholar, Bishop and Saint (1197–1253)* (1921).

L. F. Salzman, 'Some Sussex Miracles [refs. to St. Richard and Gilbert de Sancto Leofardo], in *S.N.Q.*, vol. 1 (1926–27), pp. 215–218.

C. M. Duncan-Jones, *S. Richard of Chichester* (1953).

A. Rye, *A Yeoman Bishop (St. Richard of Chichester)* (1953).

W. H. Blaauw, 'Will of Richard de la Wych', in *S.A.C.*, vol. 1 (1848), pp. 164–192.

J. H. Cooper, 'Some Notes on the Life of Saint Richard of Chichester', in *S.A.C.*, vol. 44 (1901), pp. 184–203.

A. O. Jennings, 'St. Richard de Wych and the Vicarage of Brighton', in *S.A.C.*, vol. 68 (1927), pp. 158–170.

J. R. H. Moorman, 'Saint Richard of Chichester (*circa* 1197–1253)', in *Theology*, vol. 56 (1953), pp. 51–54.

'Bishop Robert Rede', in *S.N.Q.*, vol. 6 (1936–37), pp. 57, 58.

'Adam Moleyns, Bishop of Chichester', in *S.N.Q.*, vol. 2 (1928–29), p. 27.

John Lewis, *The Life of the Learned and Right Reverend Reynold Pecock, S.T.P.* (1744).

V. H. H. Green, *Bishop Reginald Pecock* (1945).

E. F. Jacob, 'Reynold Pecock, Bishop of Chichester', in *Proceedings of the British Academy*, vol. 37 (1951), pp. 121–153.

F. W. Steer, *Bishop Edward Story and the Chichester City Cross* (Chichester Paper No. 1, 1955).

F. W. Steer, *Robert Sherburne, Bishop of Chichester: Some Aspects of his Life Reconsidered* (Chichester Paper No. 16, 1960).

W. D. Peckham, 'Bishop Sherburne and Shulbrede Priory', in *S.N.Q.*, vol. 3 (1930–31), pp. 5–9.

H. Ellis, 'Notices of Richard Curteys, Bishop of Chichester, 1570 to 1582', in *S.A.C.*, vol. 10 (1858), pp. 53–58.

F. M. G. Higham, *Lancelot Andrewes* (1952).

J. G. Bishop, *Lancelot Andrewes, Bishop of Chichester* (Chichester Paper No. 33, 1963).

P. A. Welsby, *Lancelot Andrewes, 1555–1626* (1958).

W. D. Peckham, 'The Acts of Bishop Montague', in *S.A.C.*, vol. 86 (1858), pp. 151–154.

F. W. Steer, 'Bishop Montague's Personal Accounts, 1636–8', in *S.A.C.*, vol. 95 (1957), pp. 28–41.

R. Berman, *Henry King & the Seventeenth Century* (1964).

L. R. C. Agnew, *Robert Grove, Bishop of Chichester* (Chichester Paper No. 21, 1961).

W. R. W. Stephens, *A Memoir of Richard Durnford* (1899).

J. B. Atlay, *The Life of the Right Reverend Ernest Roland Wilberforce first Bishop of Newcastle-on-Tyne and afterward Bishop of Chichester* (1912).

M. Moore, *Winfrid Burrows, 1858–1929* (1932).

F. Bentham Stevens, 'Hugh Maudslay Hordern, Bishop', in *S.N.Q.*, vol. 12 (1948–49), p. 159.

ESTATES

G. A. Clarkson, 'Notes on Amberley, its Castle, Church, etc.', in *S.A.C.*, vol. 17 (1865), pp. 185–239.

W. D. Peckham (ed.), *Custumals of the Manors of the Bishop of Chichester* (Sussex Record Society, vol. 31, 1925).

W. D. Peckham, 'Fairs & Markets of the Bishop of Chichester' in *S.N.Q.*, vol. 1 (1926–27), p. 78.

W. D. Peckham & A. Mawer, 'The Hundred of Typenoak and its Tythings', in *S.N.Q.*, vol. 1 (1926–27), pp. 249, 250; vol. 7 (1938–39), pp. 123, 124.

M. S. Holgate, 'The Manors of the Archbishops in Sussex', in *S.A.C.*, vol. 68 (1927), pp. 269–272.

W. D. Peckham, 'Two Domesday Book Freeholds' [Aldingbourne and Ferring], in *S.N.Q.*, vol. 2 (1928–29), p. 17.

W. D. Peckham, 'A Drungewick Heriot', in *S.N.Q.*, vol. 2 (1928–29), pp. 17, 18.

W. D. Peckham, 'Courts, Hallmotes, Views of Frankpledge and Hundreds of the Bishop of Chichester', in *S.N.Q.*, vol. 2 (1928–29), pp. 82, 83.

A. H. Allcroft, 'The Bishops' Park, Selsey', in *S.N.Q.*, vol. 2 (1928–29), p. 95.

W. D. Peckham, 'An Amberley Manor Document', in *S.N.Q.*, vol. 2 (1928–29), pp. 123, 124.

M. S. Holgate, 'The Canons' Manor of South Malling', in *S.A.C.*, vol. 70 (1929), pp. 183–195.

F. R. H. du Boulay, 'The Pagham Estates of the Archbishops of Canterbury during the Fifteenth Century', in *History*, vol. 38 (1953), pp. 201–218.

B. C. Redwood and A. E. Wilson (eds.), *Custumals of the Sussex Manors of the Archbishop of Canterbury* (Sussex Record Society, vol. 57, 1958).

CLERGY AND BENEFICES

J. Le Neve, *Fasti Ecclesiæ Anglicanæ* (1716).

Henry Edward Manning, *The Preservation of Unendowed Canonries: A Letter to William, Lord Bishop of Chichester* (1840).

W. H. Blaauw, 'Subsidy collected from the Clergy of Sussex, in 30 Richard II (A.D.1380)', in *S.A.C.*, vol. 5 (1852), pp. 229–243.

J. Le Neve, corrected and continued by T. Duffus Hardy, *Fasti Ecclesiæ Anglicanæ* (1854).

M. E. C. Walcott, 'Early Presentations to Sussex Incumbencies', in *S.A.C.*, vol. 17 (1865), pp. 104–107.

W. D. Cooper, 'Crown Presentations to Livings', in *S.A.C.*, vol. 21 (1869), pp. 44–72.

F. E. Sawyer, 'Proceedings of the Committee of Plundered Ministers relating to Sussex', in *S.A.C.*, vol. 30 (1880), pp. 112–136; vol. 31 (1881), pp. 169–200; vol. 36 (1888), pp. 136–159.

E. H. W. Dunkin, 'Admissions to Sussex Benefices (*temp*. Commonwealth) by the Commissioners for the Approbation of Public Preachers', in *S.A.C.*, vol. 33 (1883), pp. 213–224.

F. E. Sawyer, 'Crown Presentations to Sussex Benefices (*temp*. Charles II)', in *S.A.C.*, vol. 35 (1887), pp. 179–188.

George Hennessy, *Chichester Diocese Clergy Lists* (1900).

J. H. Cooper, 'A Religious Census of Sussex in 1676', in *S.A.C.*, vol. 45 (1902), pp. 142–148.

W. Hudson, 'The Ancient Deaneries of the Diocese of Chichester', in *S.A.C.*, vol. 55 (1912), pp. 108–122.

W. C. Renshaw, 'Some Clergy of the Archdeaconry of Lewes and South Malling Deanery', in *S.A.C.*, vol. 55 (1912), pp. 220–277.

E. B. Ellman, *Recollections of a Sussex Parson* (1912).

V. J. B. Torr, 'An Elizabethan Return of the State of the Diocese of Chichester', in *S.A.C.*, vol. 61 (1920), pp. 92–124.

S. Leslie, *Henry Edward Manning, his Life and Labours* (1921).

'Clergy List for Sussex', in *S.N.Q.*, vol. 3 (1930–31), pp. 248–250.

A. G. Matthews, *Calamy Revised* (1934).

W. D. Peckham, 'The Vicars Choral of Chichester Cathedral' in *S.A.C.*, vol. 78 (1937), pp. 126–159.

W. D. Peckham, 'Ordinations by Bishop Brideoake', in *S.N.Q.*, vol. 8 (1940–41), p. 61.

W. D. Peckham, 'Hennessy's Clergy List', in *S.N.Q.*, vol. 8 (1940–41), pp. 170–172.

H. Johnstone, 'Richard Bowchier, Archdeacon and Antiquary', in *History*, vol. 31 (1946), pp. 1–8.

A. G. Matthews, *Walker Revised* (1948).

C. E. Welch, 'Commonwealth Unions of Benefices in Sussex', in *S.N.Q.*, vol. 15 (1958–62), pp. 116–120.

J. M. Horn (comp.), *John Le Neve, Fasti Ecclesiæ Anglicanæ, 1300–1541*, vol. 7 (Chichester Diocese) (1964).

Crockford's Clerical Directory (in progress).

Chichester Diocesan Directory (in progress).

R. A. Waters, *Church Life in Sussex* (n.d.).

C. M. Duncan-Jones, *The Anglican Revival in Sussex* (n.d.).

WILLS AND ADMINISTRATIONS

W. H. Hall (comp), *Calendar of Wills and Administrations in the Archdeaconry Court of Lewes . . . the Archbishop of Canterbury's Peculiar Jurisdiction of South Malling and the Peculiar of the Deanery of Battle* (from earliest extant to temp. Commonwealth) (Index Library, vol. 24, 1901).

E. A. Fry (ed.), *Calendar of Wills in the Consistory Court of the Bishop of Chichester, 1482–1800* (Index Library, vol. 49, 1915).

E. A. Fry (ed.), *Calendar of Administrations in the Consistory Court of the Bishop of Chichester 1555–1800; Wills and Administrations in Peculiar of the Archbishop of Canterbury, 1520–1670; Wills and Administrations in the Peculiar Court of the Dean of Chichester, 1577–1800* (British Record Society, vol. 64, 1940).

W. D. Peckham, 'Intestate Administrations, 1559', in *S.N.Q.*, vol. 14 (1954–57), pp. 235, 236.

BISHOPS' TRANSCRIPTS

W. H. Challen, ' "Bishop's Transcripts": Archdeaconries of Lewes and Hastings', in *S.N.Q.*, vol. 10 (1944–45), pp. 9–13, 42.

W. H. Challen, 'Parish Registers and "Bishop's Transcripts": Archdeaconry of Chichester', in *S.N.Q.*, vol. 10 (1944–45), pp. 27–33, 56, 57, 82–85, 100, 101, 128–131, 150–153, 174–177, 193–199.

MARRIAGE LICENCES

The following Calendars of Sussex Marriage Licences have been published by the Sussex Record Society:—

E. H. W. Dunkin (ed.), Archdeaconry of Lewes, 1586–1643 (vol. 1).

E. H. W. Dunkin (ed.), Archdeaconry of Lewes, 1670–1729, and Deanery of South Malling, 1620–1632 (vol. 6).

E. H. W. Dunkin (ed.), Archdeaconry of Chichester, 1575–1730 (vol. 9).

E. H. W. Dunkin (ed.), Deanery of Chichester, 1583–1730, and Deanery of Pagham and Tarring, 1579–1730 (vol. 12).

E. W. D. Penfold (ed.) and E. H. W. Dunkin (comp.), Archdeaconry of Lewes and Deanery of South Malling, 1772–1837. Part I (A–L) (vol. 25); Part II (M–Z) (vol. 26).

D. Macleod (ed.) and E. H. W. Dunkin (comp.), Archdeaconry of Chichester, 1731–1774 (vol. 32); 1775–1800 (vol. 35).

NONCONFORMITY

W. P. Peckham, 'Chichester Recusants, 1621' in *S.N.Q.*, vol. 4 (1932–33), pp. 244, 245.

N. Caplan, 'Original Records of Nonconformity in Sussex', in *S.N.Q.*, vol. 15 (1958–62), pp. 217–221.

N. Caplan, 'Visitation of the Diocese of Chichester in 1724', in *S.N.Q.*, vol. 15 (1958–62), pp. 289–295.

N. Caplan, 'Sussex Non-Parochial Registers', in *S.N.Q.*, vol. 15 (1958–62), pp. 334–338.

AREAS OF JURISDICTION

Ep.I. THE DIOCESE OF CHICHESTER was coterminous with the County of Sussex except for:—

(1). Four peculiar jurisdictions, i.e. that of the Dean of Chichester, the exempt deanery of Pagham and Tarring, that of the Dean of Battle, and the exempt deanery of South Malling. These were abolished 1 Jan. 1846 (Order in Council, 8 Aug. 1845) when the first two became part of the Archdeaconry of Chichester and the other two part of the Archdeaconry of Lewes.

(2). North and South Ambersham which were detached portions of Steep parish (co. Hants., dio. Winchester) transferred to Selham in Sussex in 1844 (7 & 8 Vict. c. 61) but not to the Diocese of Chichester until 1916 (*London Gazette*, 18 Aug. 1916).

(3). Tunbridge Wells (King Charles the Martyr) which was created a consolidated chapelry in the Diocese of Canterbury in 1889 partly out of the parish of Broadwater Down and later transferred to the Diocese of Rochester.

The area of the ARCHDEACONRY OF CHICHESTER has remained unchanged except for (1) and (2) above and by an Order in Council (15 Aug. 1929) when the parishes of Colgate St. Saviour, Crawley with West Crawley, and Ifield were transferred from the Archdeaconry of Lewes to that of Chichester, and Bramber with Botolphs was transferred from Chichester to Lewes. In 1943, Lower Beeding was transferred from Chichester to Lewes.

Until the mid-19th century the four Rural Deaneries in the Archdeaconry of Chichester were those of Arundel, Boxgrove, Midhurst and Storrington; there are now nine as listed in the *Chichester Diocesan Directory*.

Ep.II. The area of the ARCHDEACONRY of LEWES was the rest of the county until the creation of the Archdeaconry of Hastings in 1912. The changes in the Archdeaconry are referred to under the Diocese and Archdeaconry of Chichester (Ep.I above). The four Rural Deaneries until the mid-19th century were those of Dallington, Hastings, Lewes and Pevensey; there are now nine as listed in the *Chichester Diocesan Directory*.

Ep.III. THE DEAN OF CHICHESTER'S PECULIAR comprised the Chichester parishes of St. Andrew, St. Bartholomew, St. Martin, St. Olave, St. Pancras, St. Peter the Great [Subdeanery], St. Peter the Less [incorrectly known as St. Peter-*juxta*-Guildhall], and New Fishbourne, Rumboldswyke and the precinct of the Close. The peculiar was not subject to visitation by the Archdeacon; jurisdiction was vested in the Bishop during a vacancy. The peculiar jurisdiction was abolished 1 Jan. 1846 (see Ep.I above). For an explanation of the parish boundaries, and in particular of the confusion over the various parishes of St. Peter, see W. D. Peckham, 'The Parishes of the City of Chichester', in *Sussex Archaeological Collections*, vol. 74, pp. 65–97.

Ep.IV. THE EXEMPT DEANERY OF PAGHAM AND TARRING was in the hands of the Archbishop of Canterbury and comprised the following parishes and chapelries: South Bersted, Chichester All Saints, Durrington,

Heene, East Lavant, Pagham, Patching, Slindon, Tangmere, West Tarring and Plaistow in Kirdford. Other areas of jurisdiction were:—

Chichester: The Headacre, in parish of St. Pancras [in 1705 described as "the Fourteen houses in the parish of St. Pancrass which are within the peculiar Jurisdiccon of the Archbishop of Canterbury"[1]].

Chichester: The Vintry ["infra wardā vocat' le ventr' Cicest' jurisdictionis peculiaris"[2] (1590].

Horsham: The Bishoprick [also frequently called Bishopsbridge].

Bognor St. John: site of proposed chapel (in parish of South Bersted) consecrated 1822, and first curate appointed 1839.

This peculiar was never inhibited and was abolished 1 Jan. 1846 (see Ep.I above).

Ep.V. THE EXEMPT DEANERY OF SOUTH MALLING, also in the hands of the Archbishop of Canterbury, comprised Buxted, Edburton, Framfield, Glynde, Hadlow Down, Isfield, Lewes St. Thomas-at-Cliffe, Lindfield, Mayfield, Ringmer, South Malling, Stanmer, Uckfield and Wadhurst, with chapelries at [East] Chiltington, Hartfield, Withyham and Wivelsfield. A very small part of East Grinstead was also included in this jurisdiction which was never inhibited and was abolished 1 Jan. 1846 (see Ep.I above).

Ep.VII. THE ARCHDEACONRY OF HASTINGS was created by Order in Council, 24 June 1912, and was to 'comprise and consist of the Rural Deaneries of Pevensey I, Pevensey II, Hastings I, Hastings II and Dallington and the parishes of Frant, Tidebrook and Wadhurst'. The area now comprises seven rural deaneries as listed in the *Chichester Diocesan Directory*.

Ep.VIII. THE DEAN OF BATTLE'S PECULIAR was the lowey, or liberty, of Battle Abbey. Although the incumbent of Battle is still styled the Dean of Battle, the peculiar jurisdiction was abolished 1 Jan. 1846 when the deanery became part of the Archdeaconry of Lewes; since 1912 it has been in the Archdeaconry of Hastings. The parish register transcripts are Ep.II/16/10 (Battle) and II/16/138 (Netherfield).

[1] Ep.IV/4/12. Site unknown.
[2] Ep.IV/4/13. Possibly in Upper St. Martin's Lane or Crooked S Lane.

RECORDS OF THE BISHOPS AND ARCHDEACONS OF CHICHESTER

Ep.I/1 EPISCOPAL REGISTERS, 1397-1792

Calendars of Ep.I/1, 2, 3 and 4 (taken from the marginal notes) have been printed by Mackenzie Walcott in *Transactions of the Royal Society of Literature*, 2nd series, vol. 9 (1870), pp. 215–244. Brief extracts also appear in *Historical Manuscripts Commission, Various Collections*, vol. 1, pp. 177–178. Other indexes to the registers are in Ep.I/2 and Ep.I/52. Documents relating to Easebourne nunnery have been printed in *Sussex Archaeological Collections*, vol. 9, pp. 1–32. Crown presentations to Sussex benefices (taken from the Patent Rolls) have been calendared in *Sussex Archaeological Collections*, vol. 17, pp. 104–107, vol. 21, pp. 44–72 and vol. 35, pp. 179–188. Microfilmed copies of these registers are in the East Sussex Record Office. Later registers from the episcopate of Bishop Gilbert (1842-1870) are in the Diocesan Registry.

I/1/1 REDE 179 ff. parchment and 10 ff. paper.[1] Most of the contents of this volume, originally known as Register R, have been calendared by Canon C. Deedes in *Sussex Record Society*, vols. 8 and 11. See also *Transactions of the Royal Society of Literature*, 2nd series, vol. 9, pp. 216–224.

f.i, part of an illuminated medieval MS; ff.1–24, commissions and mandates issued by the bishop before his primary visitation, Feb. 1396/7–Mar. 1414; ff.25–39, episcopal visitations, 1397 and 1402; ff.39*v.*–63, commissions, mandates, ordinations and memoranda, 1398–1412 (not chronological); ff.64–159, commissions, institutions, collations, ordinations, resignations, exchanges of benefices, confirmation of elections and a visitation, Mar. 1396/7–Mar. 1414/5; ff.160–178, visitations, admissions, institutions, collations, ordinations and memoranda (not chronological), June 1409– Apr. 1414; ff.179–184, list of contents, 17th cent.; f.187, modern inaccurate typescript copy of two deeds.

I/1/1a 55 ff. parchment repaired and filed. These leaves, some with illuminated and coloured initial letters, were originally pasted together to form the boards of Ep.I/1/1; they are all from medieval books and most, with extensive glosses, come from one volume.

I/1/2 PRATY 118 ff. parchment and 8 ff. paper.[1] Extracts from this volume, originally known as Register E, were printed by Canon C. Deedes in *Transactions of the Royal Society of Literature*, 2nd series, vol. 9, pp. 224–230; f. 1 *r.* is in Bishop Barlow's hand.

ff.i–ii, part of an illuminated medieval MS.; f.1, contemporary index and list of contents; ff.2–43a, admissions, institutions, collations, resignations and exchanges of benefices, July 1438—Aug. 1445; ff.43b–60, royal and episcopal mandates and commissions, 1438–1441 (not chronological); ff.61–70, monastic elections, 1438–1445; f.71, a petition by the Lord of Poynings and the people of Crawley; ff.72–73, episcopal visitation, 1441; ff.84–106, installation of the bishop, 1438, commissions, augmentations of vicarages and memoranda, 1438–1445; ff.107–115, ordinations, 1438–1444; ff.116–117, an index of admissions in this register, compiled in the late 17th cent.; f.124, part of an illuminated medieval MS.

I/1/2a 62 ff. parchment repaired and filed. These leaves were originally pasted together to form the boards of Ep.I/1/2; they are all from medieval

---

[1] Repaired and rebound at the Public Record Office in 1936.

books, except f.60, which is the flyleaf of a copy of Bishop Sherburne's Donations (see Cap.I/14).

I/1/3 STORY 200 ff. parchment and 6 ff. paper.[1] This volume was originally known as Register D. The Cathedral statutes on ff. 71–72 are printed in Bennett, Codrington and Deedes, *Statutes and Constitutions of the Cathedral Church of Chichester* (1904), pp. 18–22; f. 200 *r.* is in Bishop Barlow's hand. See *Transactions of the Royal Society of Literature*, 2nd series, vol. 9, pp. 230–239.

ff.1–32, primary episcopal visitation, 1478; ff.33–96, visitations, commissions, mandates, admissions, institutions, collations, ordinations, resignations and memoranda, 1478–Mar. 1501/2; ff.97–158, royal and episcopal mandates, Dec. 1483–July 1502; ff. 159*v.*–176, statutes of the hospital of the Holy Trinity, Arundel, compositions and augmentations of vicarages, 1453–1502; ff. 177–199, ordinations, Mar. 1483/4–Dec. 1502; f.200*r.*, notes concerning entries on ff.159–176; f.200*v.*, an institution; f.201, part of a 17th cent. index.

I/1/3a 94 ff. parchment repaired and filed. These leaves were pasted together and formed the boards and cover of Ep.I/1/3; they are all from medieval books, including a treatise on baptism.

I/1/4 STORY; FITZJAMES; SHERBURNE 111 ff. parchment.[1] In 1936 the early folios were rearranged in chronological order. This volume was originally known as Register A. See *Transactions of the Royal Society of Literature*, 2nd series, vol. 9, pp. 239–244.

ff.1–36, admissions and collations, Jan. 1480/1–Feb. 1502/3; ff.37–45, mandates to induct, admissions and collations, Feb. 1503/4–Jan. 1505/6; ff.46–64, admissions and a resignation, Apr. 1523–Jan. 1535/6; ff.65–74, collations and a resignation, Apr. 1523–Jan. 1535/6; ff. 75–78, assignations of pensions, Dec. 1523–Aug. 1529; ff.79–89, augmentations of vicarages and unions of benefices, 1524–June 1534; ff.90–102, episcopal visitations, 1524–1527; ff.103–111, royal and episcopal mandates, Jan. 1522/3–Jan. 1535/6; f.111*v.*, part of a contemporary index.

I/1/4a 16 ff. parchment guarded and bound inside the original cover; they consist of four sheets of an illuminated medieval service book, two sheets of another medieval book and fragments of late 16th cent. accounts and deeds found inside the original cover.

I/1/5 SHERBURNE 146 ff. parchment and 10 ff. paper.[1] This volume was originally known as Register C. f.153 *r.* and some marginal notes on ff.35–37 are in Bishop Barlow's hand; f.68 is printed in *Sussex Notes and Queries*, vol. 2, pp. 251–254, and ff.141–142 in *Sussex Archaeological Collections*, vol. 9, pp. 61–66.

ff.i–ii, two fragments of documents from the original binding; ff.3–22, admissions, Jan. 1508/9–Mar. 1522/3; ff.23–34, collations and resignations, Dec. 1508–Feb. 1522/3; ff.35–51, monastic elections and assignations of pensions (not chronological), 1516–1521; ff.52–84, appropriations, 1249–1521; ff.85–107, episcopal visitation, 1521; ff.108–108a, purgation of a criminous clerk, June 1509; ff.109–114, testaments, Mar. 1517/8–July 1520; ff.115–132, royal and episcopal mandates, Nov. 1509–Dec. 1532; f.133, manumissions, Feb. 1522/3–July 1536; f.134, royal licences, 1518 and 1526; ff.135–136, compositions, Dec. 1511–July 1514; ff.137–140, statutes of the hospital of the Holy Trinity, Arundel; ff.141–142, injunctions to religious houses,

---

[1] Repaired and rebound at the Public Record Office in 1936.

1518; f.142v., list of the testaments on ff.109–114; ff.143-144, 17th cent. index of the admissions and collations on ff. 3–34; f.153, contemporary index of entries on ff.52–84.

I/1/6 SAMPSON; DAY; SCORY   122 ff. parchment.[1] This volume was originally known as Register B. ff.9–25, 32–51 and 117 were part of a copy of Bishop Sherburne's Donations (see Cap.I/14); these folios were scraped, and further gatherings were forced into the original cover to provide the registrar with a new volume. A few institutions for 1556 and 1557 appear in Ep.I/10/10. ff.71, 116 r. and some marginal notes are in Bishop Barlow's hand. For a note on f.115 see *Sussex Notes and Queries*, vol. 9, pp. 37–40.

ff.i–v, late 16th cent. accounts found loose in the volume; ff. 1–8, memoranda, Aug. 1536–Mar. 1540/1; f.10, installation of Bishop Day, 1543; ff.11–83, episcopal commissions and mandates, admissions, collations and memoranda, May 1543–Jan. 1551/2; ff.84–85, installation of Bishop Scory, 1552; ff.85v.–114, royal and episcopal mandates, admissions, collations and assignations of pensions, Aug. 1553–Apr. 1556; f.115, augmentation of the vicarage of Henfield, 1576; f.116, part of a contemporary index.

I/1/6a   6 ff. parchment and the original cover of Ep.I/1/6 repaired and filed. These leaves are fragments of medieval books and some of Bishop Sherburne's accounts, which formed part of the original cover.

I/1/7 CHRISTOPHERSON; BARLOW; CURTEYS; BICKLEY   95 ff. parchment and 8 ff. paper.[1] This volume was originally known as Register F. Institutions and memoranda from Sep. to Nov. 1571 appear in Cap.I/12/1, ff.1–8. See also Ep.I/10/10. Some marginal notes on ff.9–12 are in Bishop Barlow's hand.

f.i, memoranda; f.1, installation of Bishop Christopherson, 1557; ff.2–13, admissions, collations and memoranda, Nov. 1557–Apr. 1559; ff.14–15, installation of Bishop Barlow, 1560; ff.15–27, admissions, collations and memoranda, Jan. 1559/60–July 1568; ff.27v.–30, election of Richard Curteys as Dean of Chichester, 1566; ff.30–37, installation of Bishop Curteys, 1570, and admissions and collations, May 1570–Jan. 1571/2; f.38, union of benefices, Nov. 1572; ff.39v.–43; admissions and collations, Mar. 1577/8–July 1582; ff.44–56, admissions and collations, June 1586–Apr. 1596; ff.56v.–57, royal mandate, 1638; ff.81–85, union of benefices, appointment of officers and memoranda, 1664–1666; ff.86–87, archbishop's ordinances, 1587; ff.89–94, ordinations, Apr. 1560–June 1586.

I/1/8 WATSON; ANDREWES; HARSNETT; GUNNING   105 ff. parchment.[1] This volume was originally known as Register G. The original parchment cover is preserved as end-papers.

ff.1–27, admissions and collations, Sep. 1596–Mar. 1604/5; ff.28–29, ordinations Mar. 1599/1600–Oct. 1603; ff.30–33, causes concerning presentation to benefices, 1596–1598; ff.33v.–44, admissions and collations, Feb. 1605/6–Oct. 1609; ff.46–50, causes concerning resignations, Mar. 1605/6–Oct. 1609; f.51v., licences to preach, Feb. 1605/6–Oct. 1609; f.53, certificates of recusants, July 1606–Aug. 1609; f.54, ordinations, Oct. 1607 and Sep. 1609; ff.54v.–55, institutions, Mar. 1604/5–Oct. 1605; f.56, list of deprived preachers, Apr. 1605; f.56v. part of a list of institutions; f.57, list of licences to preach, to curacies, to teach, and to a painter; f.57v., list of admissions; ff.58–73, admissions and collations, Dec. 1609–Aug. 1619; f.74, admissions, Apr. 1624 and Feb. 1639/40; ff.79–98, admissions, collations, ordinations, resignations, licences, caveats and sequestrations, Nov. 1670–Feb. 1674/5; ff.102–104, contemporary index.

---

[1] Repaired and rebound at the Public Record Office in 1936.

I/1/8a WATSON; ANDREWES; MONTAGU 74 ff. repaired and rebound. This volume was originally known as Register H. ff.31–48 are missing; ff.1–28 and 49–61 are a copy of Ep.I/1/8, ff. 1–44 and 51–55.

ff.1–27, institutions and collations, Sep. 1596–Mar. 1604/5; f.27v., ordinations, Mar. 1599/1600–Oct. 1603; f.28, causes concerning institutions, Feb. 1596/7 and Aug. 1597; ff.30, 49–59, institutions and collations, Feb. 1605/6–Oct. 1609; f.60, cause concerning resignation, June 1606; f.60, licences to preach and to curacies, Feb. 1605/6–Oct. 1609; f.61, institutions and collations, Mar. 1604/5–Oct. 1605; ff. 62–66, clerical subsidy, n.d.; ff.66v.–72, register of orders, 1635–1638.

I/1/9 MONTAGU 13 ff. parchment.[1] The original parchment cover is preserved as end-papers. Another section of Montagu's register is in the Bodleian Library (Bodleian MS. Ashmole 1144). Both volumes and the Bishop's certificates in the Public Record Office have been printed in *Sussex Archaeological Collections*, vol. 86, pp. 141–154.

f.3, institutions and collations, Oct.–Dec. 1628.

I/1/10 BRIDEOAKE; LAKE; PATRICK; GROVE; WILLIAMS; MANNINGHAM 111 ff. parchment and paper.[1] This volume was originally known as Register I. Bishop Brideoake's ordinations are printed in *Sussex Notes and Queries*, vol. 8, p. 61, but the folio on which they were written has not reached the Diocesan Record Office. The indexes are contemporary.

ff.2–6, election and installation of Bishop Brideoake, Mar. 1674/5; ff.6v.–15, institutions, collations, caveats, causes and memoranda, July 1675–July 1678; f.15v., index to ff.6v.–15; ff.17–21, institutions, collations and ordinations, Oct. 1685–July 1687; f.22, index to ff.17–21; f.25, an institution, Feb. 1787; ff.28–32, institutions, collations and ordinations, Dec. 1689–June 1691; f.35, index to ff. 28–32; ff.37–43, institutions, collations, ordinations, licences to teach and caveats, Aug. 1691–Sep. 1696; f.44, index to ff.37–43; ff.46–66, institutions, collations, ordinations, resignations, licences to preach, teach and to curacies, and causes, Mar. 1696/7–Apr. 1709; ff.66v.–67, index to ff.46–66; ff.68–83, institutions, collations, ordinations, resignations, licences to preach, teach and to curacies, and causes, Nov. 1709–Aug. 1722; f.84, index to ff.68–83; ff.85–86, union of benefices, Dec.1764 and Jan.1768; ff.89–86,[2] letters patent, June 1671, Apr. 1691, Oct. 1700 and Dec. 1687; ff. 90–91, union of benefices, Sep. 1768 and Aug. 1770; ff.91v.–93, mortgages, Oct. 1780 and Feb. 1780; ff.96–97, lease of Harting parsonage, May 1668 (begins f.97v., then f.96r.; f.97r. is the latter part of another lease; f.96v. contains causes about St. Mary's Hospital and the rectory of Pulborough); ff.98–100, institutions, collations, caveats and causes, Mar. 1675/6–June 1677; ff.101–103, a dispute about cutting wood in Houghton Chace, Dec. 1677; ff.104–110, index to ff.46–66.

I/1/11 BOWERS; WADDINGTON; HARE; MAWSON; ASHBURNHAM 126 ff. parchment, and 2 paper.[3] This volume was originally known as Register K.

f.1, index of institutions and collations, 1722–1752; f.2, list of ordinations, 1722–1752; ff.3–7, list of licences and ordinations. 1753–1791; ff.9–13, list of institutions and collations, 1753–1792; ff.14–17, institutions, collations, ordinations, licences to teach and to curacies, causes and assignment of a residentiary house, Oct. 1722–Aug. 1724; f.17, list of contents of ff.14–17; ff.19–21, institutions, collations, ordinations, resignations, dispensations and licences to preach and teach, Nov. 1724–Feb. 1726/7; ff.21v.–22, lease of Harting rectory, Mar. 1726/7; ff.22v.–23, institutions, collations,

---

[1] Repaired and rebound at the Public Record Office in 1936.

[2] When foliations are given as from a large number to a lesser one, it indicates either that the book has been begun from both ends or that some leaves have been written on upside down in one or more parts of the volume. This tiresome practice seems to have been popular with the creators of many ecclesiastical archives.

[3] Repaired and rebound at the Public Record Office in 1936.

ordinations, resignation, licences to curacies and to teach, and union of benefices, Apr.–Aug. 1727; ff.23v.–25, episcopal mandates, Sep. 1727; ff.26–31, institutions (including to the Deanery of Battle, 1731), collations, ordinations, resignations and licences to curacies, Sep. 1727–July 1731; ff.32a–40, institutions, collations, ordinations, resignations, licences to curacies, assignment of a residentiary house and Dean Hayley's subscription to the liturgy (Jan. 1735/6), Jan. 1731/2–Dec. 1739; ff.41–60, institutions, collations, ordinations, resignations, licences to curacies, union of benefices and list of proctors for the diocese elected to convocation (1741), Nov. 1740–Feb. 1754; ff.60v.–111, institutions, collations, ordinations, resignations and licences to curacies, Apr. 1754–June 1792.

This register also contains the following later entries:—

ff.112–113, Order in Council raising the bishop's income, July 1837; ff.114–115, concerning the advowson of Salehurst, July 1815; ff.116–119, concerning the building of St. Clement's chapel, Halton, Hastings, Dec. 1838; f.120, concerning the advowson of Hartfield, Feb. 1830; f.121, concerning Shipley church rates, Dec. 1831; ff.122–125, conveyances, 1807–1811; f.126, concerning the advowson of Bletchington, Apr. 1744; f.127, list of licences, 1722–1752.

Ep.I/2 OFFICIAL INDEXES TO THE EPISCOPAL REGISTERS, 17th–19th centuries

These official indexes were compiled by officers of the court; other indexes and notes on the registers made by J. B. Freeland[1] are in Ep.I/52.

I/2/1 16 ff. unbound and written in a 17th cent. hand. Index to Ep.I/1/1, 2, 3, 4, 5, 6 and 7.

ff.1–5, appropriations of churches, testaments; ff.6–13, institutions and collations (by parishes); ff.13v.–15, cathedral clergy (by title).

I/2/2 28ff.; mid-18th cent. copy of I/2/1.

I/2/3 28 ff.; 19th cent. copy of I/2/1.

I/2/4 10 ff.; written in a late 17th cent. hand.

ff.1–4, presentations and advowsons relating to Earnley; f.10, correction cause before the bishop, June 1677.

I/2/5 17 ff.; A. C. Ducarel,[2] *A Repertory of the Endowment of Vicarages,* 1763, taken from the registers, cartularies and other sources.

I/2/6 18 ff.; 18th cent.

ff.4–11, summary of the registers, Ep. I/1/1, 2, 3, 4, 5, 6, 7, 8, 8a, 9, 10, subscription books and others; ff.14–17, Canon W. Clarke's[3] list of episcopal records, 1750.

I/2/7 30 ff.; 18th cent.

ff.2–6, Canon W. Clarke's list of episcopal records, 1750; f.7, appropriation of Fletching and Alfriston by Michelham priory; ff.26–25, summary of the registers; ff.29–27, list of the bishops of Chichester, 1070–1798.

---

[1] Deputy Diocesan Registrar, 1841–52, and a local antiquary.

[2] Andrew Coltee Ducarel, D.C.L., F.S.A., F.R.S., 1713–85. Keeper of the Lambeth Library, 1757–85. He printed a similar work for the dioceses of Canterbury and Rochester in 1782.

[3] William Clarke, M.A., 1696–1771, Prebendary of Hova Villa (1728–71), Chancellor of the Cathedral (1770–1). For his list of capitular records see Cap.I/21/7; both lists are also in Cap.I/1/5.

Ep.I/3 GENERAL SUBSCRIPTION BOOKS AND PAPERS, 1635–1859

Subscriptions and declarations before the ordinary or commissary were required by statute and ecclesiastical law of all candidates for ordination, all clergy before admission to any benefice or ecclesiastical office and of schoolmasters, surgeons, apothecaries and midwives before receiving episcopal licence (see Act 3 Hen. VIII. c. 11). In most cases the oaths and declarations were written out in full only once in each book, but those listed as [3,5] and [6] below were usually copied by each person. In the later volumes there are occasional notes of ordinations and often, in the case of an incumbent, the names of his predecessor and patron, and the cause of vacancy. Subscriptions taken on commission (i.e. when the signatory could not attend at Chichester) were either pasted into these books later, or kept separately, as in Ep.I/4/1–2. Many volumes have a modern typescript index of surnames attached to the fly-leaf. Unless otherwise stated these volumes include only the archdeaconries of Chichester and Lewes; there is one subscription book for Lewes alone (Ep.II/1/1). "Curates" here refers to stipendiary curates only, and "apothecaries" includes all branches of the medical profession. Oaths and declarations were made as follows:

[1] the oath of supremacy, 1558 (1 Eliz. I c. 1).

[2] the oath of canonical obedience, prescribed by ecclesiastical law (see Francis Clerke, *Praxis*, tit. 91, which is in Ep.I/51/6, p. 62).

[3] the three articles of the 36th Canon (1603), acknowledging the sovereign's position as 'supreme governor' of the Church of England, the Book of Common Prayer and the Thirty Nine Articles of Religion.

[4] the declaration of obedience contained in the Act of Uniformity, 1662 (13 & 14 Chas. II c. 4).

[5] subscription to the Thirty Nine Articles of Religion, required by the Act 13 Eliz. I c. 12 (1570).

[6] the declaration of conformity to the liturgy, required by the Act 13 & 14 Chas. II c. 4 (1662).

[7] the oath of allegiance, 1688 (1 Will. & Mary c. 8); reaffirmed 1714 (1 Geo. I stat. 2 c. 13).

[8] the oath of supremacy, 1688 (1 Will. & Mary c. 8); reaffirmed 1714 (1 Geo. I stat. 2 c. 13).

[9] the oath against simony, required by Canon 40.

[10] the oath of residence, prescribed by ecclesiastical law (see Francis Clerke, *Praxis*, tit. 91, which is in Ep.I/51/6, p. 62).

[11] the oath of a prebendary to observe the Statutes, Ordinances and Laudable Customs of Chichester cathedral.

[12] the oath of abjuration, 1714 (1 Geo. I stat. 2 c. 13).

[13] the declaration against transubstantiation, 1672 (25 Chas. II c. 2).

I/3/1   39 ff.; includes the Dean of Chichester's Peculiar, the Deanery of Pagham and Tarring, and Chancellor of the diocese; see *Sussex Notes and Queries*, vol. 4, p. 245, for a note on f.25.

f.3[1,2]; f.5[3]; ff.5v.–14, curates, schoolmasters and apothecaries[3], Oct. 1635–Feb. 1641; ff.14v.–26, incumbents, curates, schoolmasters and apothecaries[3], May 1661–Jan. 1684/5.

I/3/2 354 ff.; repaired and rebound at the Public Record Office in 1936, but the original folios have not been replaced in chronological order.

ff.1–20, incumbents and ordinands[4], Feb. 1664/5–June 1668; f.21, memoranda; f.22[4]; ff.27–40, incumbents and ordinands[4], Nov. 1662–Jan. 1664/5; ff.41–83, incumbents and ordinands[4], Aug. 1668–Sep. 1678; f.241, affidavit on the ordination of John Newman, June 1680; ff.354–241, incumbents, curates and ordinands[3], Nov. 1662–Sep. 1678.

I/3/3 109 and 6 ff.

ff.2–34, incumbents, curates and ordinands[4], Jan. 1678/9–Apr. 1685; ff.106–76, incumbents, curates and ordinands[3], Jan. 1678/9–Apr. 1685, Oct. 1690; f.109, caveats, Dec. 1684–Jan. 1684/5; f.1a[3]; ff.1a–1b, incumbents, curates and schoolmasters[3], Jan. 1699/1700, Nov. 1703, June 1705, May 1708.

I/3/4 90 ff.

ff.2–3, contemporary index to ff.4–25; ff.4–25, incumbents, curates and ordinands [3–5], Oct. 1685–July 1689; f.27, contemporary index to ff.27v.–31; ff.27v.–31, incumbents, curates and ordinands[3, 5, 6], June–Dec. 1690; ff.32–41, ordinands[3, 6], May 1697–July 1704; f.42, contemporary index to ff.32–41; f.43, contemporary index to ff.65–44; ff.65–44, incumbents, curates and schoolmasters[3, 6], Mar. 1696/7–Sep. 1704; f.66, contemporary index to ff.81–66; ff.81–66, incumbents, curates, ordinands and schoolmasters[3, 6], Aug. 1691–Sep. 1696; ff.87–82, incumbents, curates and ordinands[3, 6], Sep. 1690–July 1691; f.87v.[3]; f.88, contemporary index to ff.87–82; f.88v., directions for the subscription of incumbents; f.89[2, 7–10]; ff.89v.–90, accounts, Jan. 1723/4; f.90[11].

I/3/5 143 ff.

f.2, scriptural passages supporting Canons 39, 41, 43, 47 and 67; f.3, directions for the subscription of incumbents; ff.3v.–4, Canon 36; f.5[2, 7–11]; ff.7–8, forms of institution and collation, and of dispensation to hold livings in plurality; ff.10–24, incumbents[3, 6], Feb. 1704/5–Apr. 1709; ff.24–25, contemporary index to ff.10–24; ff.25v.–53, incumbents[3, 5, 6], Nov. 1709–Aug. 1722; ff.53v.–54, contemporary index to ff.25v.–53; ff.55–60, incumbents and officials[3, 6], Oct. 1722–Aug. 1724; ff.72–73, forms of licence to curates, schoolmasters and absentees; ff.74–76, curates and schoolmasters [3, 6], Dec. 1704–Sep. 1708; f.76v., contemporary index to ff.74–76; ff.77–84, curates and schoolmasters[3, 5, 6], Nov. 1709–Sep. 1721; ff.85–86, curates and schoolmasters[3, 6], Oct. 1722–July 1723; ff.124–105, ordinands[3, 5, 6], Nov. 1709–Sep. 1723; f.124v., contemporary index to ff.139–125; ff.139–125, ordinands[3, 6], Dec. 1704–Feb. 1708/9; ff.141–140, directions for ordination[3, 7]; f.142, scriptural passages supporting Canons 31–37.

I/3/6 192 ff.

Flyleaf, caveats, Nov. 1725, Jan. 1725/6, Feb. 1728/9 and Sep. 1739; ff.1–6, index of benefices; ff.9–11, caveats, Mar. 1742–May 1753; ff.13–14, Canon 36; ff.15–16[2, 7–11], form of subscription; ff.17–182, incumbents, curates and ordinands[3,5,6], Nov. 1724–Feb. 1754; ff.187–188, index of ordinands; f.189, memoranda; ff.190–191, list of institutions, 1735 and 1781; f.192, letter concerning a caveat, Aug. 1748.

I/3/7   160 ff.

ff.1–6, index of benefices; f.11[3]; f.12[2,7–11]; ff.14–155, incumbents, curates, ordinands and schoolmasters[3,5,6], Apr. 1754–Dec. 1772; ff.157–156, caveats, May 1754–May 1771; ff.159–160[7,8,12,13].

I/3/8   136 ff.; this volume includes the Deanery of Battle.

f.1, note of Bishop Ashburnham's consecration; f.2[3]; f.3[2,7–11]; ff. 6–131, incumbents, curates and ordinands[3,5,6], Jan. 1773–Feb. 1787; ff. 132–135, index of benefices, priests and deacons; f.136v., caveats, Feb. 1773 and Feb. 1783.

I/3/9   161 ff.

ff.1–6, index of benefices; f.11[3]; ff.11v.–12[2,7–11]; ff.13–161, incumbents, curates and ordinands[3,5,6], Feb. 1787–Dec. 1800.

I/3/10   199 ff.

ff.1–6, index of benefices; f.10[3]; ff.10v.–11[2,7–11]; ff.12–199, incumbents, curates, ordinands and schoolmasters[3,5,6], Jan. 1801–Dec. 1814.

I/3/11   137 ff.

f.2[3]; ff. 2v.–3[2,7–9,11]; ff. 4–127, incumbents, curates and ordinands[3,5,6], Jan. 1815–Feb. 1829; ff.129–134, index to benefices.

I/3/12   280 ff.

ff.1a–1b[2,7–9,11]; ff.1d–1j, index to benefices; ff.1–260, incumbents[3,5,6], May 1829–June 1846; ff.262–269, index of incumbents.

I/3/13   266 ff.

ff.1a–1b[2,7–9,11]; ff.1c–1h, index of benefices; ff.1–248, incumbents[3,5,6], July 1846–Nov. 1859; ff.250–256, index of incumbents.

I/3/14   (10); loose subscription papers[3,5–8], 1592–1798, one certificate of subscription (1798) and an unused form for a stipendiary curate's subscription [19th cent.].

Ep.I/4   CURATES' SUBSCRIPTION BOOKS, 1799–1855

Some of the volumes have a modern typescript index of surnames attached to the flyleaf. "Curates" here refers to stipendiary curates only. I/4/1–2 were for curates who subscribed on commission, the first for the Lewes archdeaconry only. I/4/2–4 include both archdeaconries and the Dean of Chichester's Peculiar, and I/4/5 covers the whole diocese.

[1–13] For key to these numbers, see p. 6.

I/4/1 80 ff.

f.1[2, 7, 8]; ff. 3–19, curates and a schoolmaster[3, 5, 6], Apr. 1799–Aug. 1821.

I/4/2 141 ff.

f.2[3]; f.2v.[2, 7, 8]; ff.4–49, curates and schoolmasters[3, 5, 6], Jan. 1815–Nov. 1830.

I/4/3 252 ff.

ff.9–239, curates[3, 5, 6], June 1829–Oct. 1842.

I/4/4 212 ff.

Flyleaf[2, 7, 8]; ff.2–212, curates[3, 5, 6], Nov. 1842–Dec. 1849.

I/4/5 200 ff.

Flyleaf[2, 7, 8]; ff.1b–1g, index of curates; ff.1–190, curates[3, 5, 6], Dec. 1849–Dec. 1855.

Ep.I/4A ORDINANDS' SUBSCRIPTION BOOK, 1829–1862

This volume continues from Ep.I/3/11 and gives dates of ordination and subscription to nos.[3, 5] and [6]. A modern typescript index of surnames is attached to the flyleaf.

I/4A/1 88 ff.

f.1[3]; ff.2–86, Feb. 1829–Dec. 1862.

Ep.I/5 ORDINANDS' EXAMINATION PAPERS

These papers are only occasionally dated, but they cover at least the years 1813–1824.

I/5/1 (400); examination papers written in Greek, Latin and English by ordination candidates.

I/5/2 (6); printed and manuscript question papers.

Ep.I/6 PRESENTATIONS, 1544–1934

(1,401); a presentation was a written request[14] from the patron (or such person as had the right of presentation) to the ordinary to institute a particular clerk to a void benefice or preferment. The document usually included the name of the previous clerk and the cause of the vacancy, and was often endorsed with the dates of admission and institution. Annexed to many of these presentations are grants of next presentation, resignations, institution and resignation bonds, proxies for resignation and letters testimonial, details of which may be found in the typescript calendar

---

[1-13] For key to these numbers, see p. 6.

[14] Before the Statute of Frauds, 1677 (29 Chas. II c. 3), presentations could also be made verbally.

available in the Diocesan Record Office (Ep.I/88/1). This class includes presentations to rectories and vicarages in both archdeaconries, to the Deanery of Battle and the Mastership of St. James' Hospital, Chichester, Crown and archiepiscopal presentations to Cathedral preferments, and presentations to the bishop during vacancy of the Deanery of Chichester. For nominations to perpetual curacies see Ep.I/6C/2, and for patrons' presentations of themselves see Ep.I/69/5. For 1933 and 1934 there are also bundles of correspondence between the diocesan registry and patrons, old and new incumbents, sequestrators, the Church of England Pensions Board and Queen Anne's Bounty Office.

Year	No.	Year	No.	Year	No.	Year	No.
1544	1	1617	9	1711	10	1774	3
1545	3	1618	7	1712	1	1775	3
1546	3	1619	4	1713	9	1776	1
1547	1	1661	4	1714	10	1777	3
1548	1	1662	1	1715	1	1778	2
1549	3	1663	8	1716	6	1779	4
1550	1	1664	14	1717	6	1781	1
1552	6	1665	2	1718	14	1782	3
1553	5	1666	9	1719	12	1783	4
1554	15	1667	2	1720	12	1784	14
1555	4	1668	13	1721	6	1786	4
1556	4	1669	6	1722	9	1787	4
1557	10	1670	4	1723	5	1788	6
1558	23	1671	8	1724	5	1789	1
1559	4	1672	3	1725	10	1790	7
1560	1	1673	5	1727	8	1791	6
1562	1	1674	6	1728	7	1792	4
1567	9	1675	5	1729	5	1793	6
1568	4	1676	5	1730	13	1794	11
1570	9	1677	15	1731	3	1795	6
1571	9	1678	6	1735	2	1796	7
1572	2	1679	30	1737	5	1797	5
1573	5	1680	12	1738	7	1798	6
1574	9	1681	18	1739	10	1799	5
1575	9	1682	18	1740	6	1805	1
1576	11	1683	8	1741	11	1811	1
1577	3	1684	3	1742	15	1819	3
1578	2	1685	8	1743	6	1820	1
1579	4	1686	8	1744	12	1821	1
1580	12	1687	12	1745	5	1822	1
1581	1	1688	3	1746	21	1833	5
1582	1	1689	8	1747	3	1855	7
1583	1	1690	21	1748	6	1879	1
1585	1	1691	7	1749	11	1909	2
1586	9	1692	7	1750	7	1911	1
1587	11	1693	6	1751	10	1912	2
1588	7	1694	6	1752	11	1921	1
1589	10	1695	11	1753	7	1922	1
1590	21	1696	6	1754	7	1923	2
1591	2	1697	6	1755	10	1924	6
1592	7	1698	11	1756	1	1925	6
1593	11	1699	10	1757	1	1926	6
1594	2	1700	5	1759	2	1927	5
1595	8	1701	8	1760	1	1928	3
1596	1	1702	6	1763	2	1929	6
1609	3	1703	4	1764	4	1930	9
1610	19	1704	6	1766	1	1931	12
1611	13	1705	11	1767	1	1932	8
1612	14	1706	10	1768	2	1933	20
1613	9	1707	6	1770	3	1934	8
1614	13	1708	7	1771	4		
1615	12	1709	6	1772	4		
1616	16	1710	7	1773	1		

and 18 undateable documents.

Ep.I/6A GRANTS OF NEXT PRESENTATION, 1542–1611

(21); patrons could grant to another person or corporate body the right to present at the next vacancy, or specified number of vacancies, or at all vacancies occurring in a term of years. Written evidence of this grant had to be produced before the bishop would admit and institute the clerk; grants were therefore often attached to the presentations themselves, as in Ep.I/6. A typescript calendar of these documents is available in the Diocesan Record Office (Ep.I/88/1).

1542	1	1565	1	1576	2	1589	1
1543	1	1566	2	1577	1	1591	1
1558	1	1570	5	1583	1	1611	1
1560	1[1]	1573	1	1587	1		

Ep.I/6B PAPERS RELATING TO ADVOWSONS, 1574–1920

These documents relate to cases in which the proprietorship of an advowson was in dispute. A typescript calendar of these papers is available in the Diocesan Record Office (Ep.I/88/1).

I/6B/1 (38); abstracts of title to advowsons, many with letters and court papers attached; others are in Ep.I/6.

1874	1	1886	2	1903	1	1913	1
1876	1	1887	3	1906	2	1914	3
1879	3	1893	1	1909	1	1916	4
1883	1	1894	3	1910	1	1917	2
1885	1	1895	4	1912	1	1920	2

I/6B/2 (2); quitclaim of advowsons of Northiam, Beckley, Iden and Playden, 1574, and revocation (1617) of a presentation to Iden made in 1550.

I/6B/3 (2); letter requiring George Green and William Holland to show their title to the advowson of Sidlesham (2 Sep. 1591) and letter resigning title to that of Beckley (23 Sep. 1599).

I/6B/4 (2); (i) conveyance, 13 Oct. 1662, for £150, of the advowson of West Blatchington, from Thomas Carre, vicar of Oving, 1623–1663, and George Butler of Broadwater, rector of Blatchington from 1628, to Sir John Stapley, bt., of Patcham; (ii) conveyance, 20 Mar. 1706/7, for £300, of the same advowson from Edward Pelling, rector of Petworth, 1691–1718, and Thomas his son, to trustees, for the purpose of uniting the churches of West Blatchington and Brighton and conveying the patronage of West Blatchington to the bishops of Chichester.

I/6B/5 (1); caveat (Stedham *with* Heyshott), 1746.

Ep.I/6C NOMINATIONS, 1550–1933

For nominations to stipendiary curacies see Ep.I/68/1; a typescript calendar of these papers is available in the Diocesan Record Office (Ep.I/88/1).

---

[1] See *Sussex Record Society*, vol. **58**, no. **617**, for note on the archbishop's option.

I/6C/1 (9); prebend of Highleigh:[1] 1550, 1581, 1684, 1701, 1730, 1768, 1776, 1797, 1930.

I/6C/2 (31); Perpetual Curacies. In a parish where the rectory was appropriated and there had been no endowment of a vicarage the appropriator was bound to nominate a curate, known as a perpetual curate, to be licensed by the bishop; in more recent times, ministers of new churches with separate parishes, of ecclesiastical districts and consolidated and district chapelries, are also perpetual curates. For licences to perpetual curacies see Ep.I/68/4 and I/69/1. Some of these nominations have letters testimonial and other papers attached.

1687	2	1770	1	1799	2	1909	1
1689	1	1776	1	1820	2	1927	2
1739	1	1778	2	1834	1	1929	1
1751	1	1781	1	1855	5	1933	1
1763	1	1787	1	1870	1		
1766	1	1792	1	1877	1		

I/6C/3 (1); Mastership of Midhurst Free School: John Wooll nominated by the trustees, 5 Nov. 1799.

I/6C/4 (2); prebend of Bargham:[2] 1676, 1694.

Ep.I/7 INDUCTION REGISTERS AND MANDATES, 1621–1848

After the institution of a new incumbent, possession of the temporalities of the benefice was vested in him by induction. (Prebendaries and Cathedral dignitaries were installed; for installation mandates see Cap.I/8.) The bishop or his commissary issued a mandate to induct to the archdeacon, who usually commissioned a neighbouring incumbent to act for him, or made a general mandate to all clergy within the archdeaconry. These documents all relate to the Chichester archdeaconry and from 1846 include the former peculiar jurisdictions.

I/7/1 40 ff.

f.i, legal opinion on the archdeacon's right to induct, n.d.; ff.1–19, register of archdeacon's mandates to clergy to induct on his behalf, July 1626–Aug. 1646; ff.39–36, list of stewards for archidiaconal visitations, 1621–1641. (From 1677–1678 the mandates are registered in Ep.I/51/7, pp. 56–58).

I/7/2 30 ff. bound in part of a contemporary deed.

ff.1–21, register of archdeacon's mandates, with some caveats, Nov. 1686–Nov. 1733.

I/7/3 (513); episcopal mandates for induction, 1637–1848. These documents usually give the name of the previous incumbent and the patron, and the cause of vacancy. They are occasionally endorsed with the date of the archdeacon's mandate and a certificate of induction. Mandates issued by the Archbishop of Canterbury *sede vacante* are included here.

---

[1] It was in the nomination of the Dean and Chapter from 1497 and annexed to the upper mastership of the Prebendal School by Bishop Story. For the foundation statutes of the Prebendal School (*Statuta Scholae Cicestrensis*) see Cap.I/1/3, pp. 73–86. The two offices were dissociated in 1930.

[2] For the foundation of this prebend by Bishop Sherburne in 1524, and the right of nomination by the Dean and Chapter, see Cap.I/14/1, ff.41v.–43.

Year		Year		Year		Year	
1637	1	1755	5	1785	5	1819	10
1638	3	1756	2	1786	8	1820	2
1639	2	1757	4	1787	2	1821	4
1680	1	1758	1	1788	10	1822	4
1699	1	1759	7	1789	6	1823	6
1704	1	1760	1	1790	2	1824	5
1707	2	1761	6	1791	3	1825	1
1710	1	1762	1	1792	6	1826	7
1729	1	1763	3	1793	1	1827	2
1734	2	1764	4	1794	10	1828	5
1735	7	1765	3	1795	9	1829	5
1736	7	1766	7	1796	8	1830	4
1737	5	1767	4	1797	7	1831	3
1738	1	1768	2	1802	2	1832	10
1739	10	1769	1	1803	7	1833	11
1740	4	1770	1	1804	6	1834	4
1741	2	1771	3	1805	10	1835	1
1742	11	1772	4	1806	9	1836	6
1743	4	1773	3	1807	4	1837	7
1744	4	1774	4	1808	1	1838	5
1745	2	1775	3	1809	6	1839	3
1746	8	1776	8	1810	1	1840	6
1747	5	1777	2	1811	1	1841	4
1748	1	1778	7	1812	4	1842	2
1749	7	1779	3	1813	9	1843	4
1750	6	1780	3	1814	2	1844	3
1751	7	1781	5	1815	4	1845	3
1752	7	1782	4	1816	5	1846	2
1753	3	1783	3	1817	2	1847	2
1754	4	1784	3	1818	1	1848	4

Ep.I/8 MARRIAGE LICENCE REGISTERS, 1701–1916

These registers contain brief notes of licences issued, usually giving the names of the parties, the parish and date, but occasionally only the number of blank licences sent to a particular surrogate. From 1575 to 1676 the licences were registered in the Diaries amongst the probate and episcopal records (STC III/B–L and Ep.I/31/2–4) and there is an index of licences (by parishes) in Ep.I/34/8, ff.23–42. I/8/1, 3 and 4 all relate solely to the Chichester archdeaconry, which from 1846 includes the former peculiar jurisdictions.

I/8/1 79 ff. ff. 1–77, Dec. 1701–June 1743.

I/8/2 123 ff. ff.2–100, Chichester, June 1743–Aug. 1822; ff.101–121, Chichester and the Dean of Chichester's Peculiar, Sep. 1822–Dec. 1844.

I/8/3 134 ff. ff.2–134, Jan. 1845–Dec. 1868.

I/8/4 422 pp. pp. 2–420, Jan. 1869–July 1916.

Ep.I/8A MARRIAGE LICENCES, 1678–1856

27 marriage licences, including 4 special licences; all but two of these relate to marriages solemnized in Storrington church during the incumbency of William Bradford. Copies of marriage licences from Sep. 1822–Oct. 1823 are attached to the bonds and affidavits in Ep.I/9.

1678	1	1840	2	1847	2	1853	1
1814	1	1841	1	1848	2	1855	2
1816	1	1844	3	1849	1	1856	1
1838	4	1845	1	1850	1		
1839	1	1846	1	1852	1		

Ep.I/9 MARRIAGE LICENCE BONDS AND AFFIDAVITS, 1605–1937

(20,333); from 1605–1753 the documents represent only the bonds on marriage licences. In 1753 Lord Hardwicke's Act, 26 Geo. II c.33, provided that all marriages, except those of Jews and Quakers, should be performed in the parish church after the publication of banns or by licences, and consequently from March 1754 onwards affidavits were required to prove residence in the parish for four weeks by at least one of the contracting parties, to declare that there was no known impediment to the marriage and to show the consent of the parents or guardians of minors. The Marriage Act of 1822, 3 Geo. IV c. 75, which was effective from 1 September 1822 to 31 October 1823, required certified copies of the baptismal entries of both parties to be attached to the bond and affidavit, and in the Chichester archdeaconry copies of the marriage licence itself are also attached. Between 1 April and 31 October 1823 there are no copies of baptismal entries or licences, and it was not until 1 November of that year that the new Marriage Act, 4 Geo. IV c.76, came into effect, requiring only an affidavit to be sworn before the licence could be issued, and abolishing bonds, thus superseding the provisions of Canon 101. The bonds and affidavits give the names, occupation, status and often the precise ages of the contracting parties, their parish of residence at time of marriage and intended place of marriage, and occasionally, in the case of a minor, a letter of parental consent is annexed. The documents for 1605, 1691 and a few for 1693 are parchment; those for 1692 and almost all from 1694 onwards are on printed paper forms. Bonds and affidavits relating to the same parties are here counted as two documents up to and including 1780; from 1781 they were folded together and are therefore counted as one. Bonds contracted with the Archbishop of Canterbury *sede vacante* are included here. Marriages have been calendared in *Sussex Record Society*, vols. 9 (1575–1730), 32 (1731–1774) and 35 (1775–1800).

1605	21	1710	61	1730	92	1750	105
1691	41	1711	74	1731	118	1751	87
1692	7	1712	68	1732	102	1752	80
1693	34	1713	72	1733	113	1753	28
1694	46	1714	61	1734	102	1754	52
1695	45	1715	72	1735	103	1755	152
1696	8	1716	78	1736	126	1756	161
1697	38	1717	70	1737	111	1757	170
1698	44	1718	95	1738	101	1758	158
1699	61	1719	96	1739	96	1759	187
1700	73	1720	82	1740	71	1760	224
1701	78	1721	101	1741	73	1761	207
1702	75	1722	130	1742	92	1762	165
1703	27	1723	102	1743	90	1763	156
1704	69	1724	89	1744	88	1764	176
1705	27	1725	110	1745	101	1765	220
1706	67	1726	111	1746	79	1766	162
1707	74	1727	121	1747	59	1767	184
1708	71	1728	134	1748	98	1768	212
1709	30	1729	130	1749	74	1769	184

1770	186	1812	81	1854	58	1896	16
1771	190	1813	92	1855	61	1897	13
1772	200	1814	92	1856	81	1898	27
1773	206	1815	77	1857	65	1899	13
1774	232	1816	79	1858	70	1900	13
1775	246	1817	56	1859	57	1901	14
1776	244	1818	76	1860	60	1902	21
1777	192	1819	68	1861	64	1903	22
1778	220	1820	61	1862	48	1904	20
1779	233	1821	66	1863	70	1905	15
1780	157	1822	66	1864	55	1906	18
1781	101	1823	53	1865	41	1907	23
1782	85	1824	48	1866	44	1908	27
1783	117	1825	60	1867	60	1909	27
1784	103	1826	47	1868	55	1910	36
1785	99	1827	70	1869	51	1911	31
1786	92	1828	75	1870	47	1912	28
1787	101	1829	62	1871	43	1913	30
1788	98	1830	62	1872	34	1914	54
1789	97	1831	65	1873	38	1915	221
1790	82	1832	75	1874	39	1916	243
1791	91	1833	55	1875	35	1917	307
1792	92	1834	53	1876	43	1918	375
1793	99	1835	59	1877	34	1919	268
1794	83	1836	54	1878	29	1920	139
1795	85	1837	47	1879	32	1921	81
1796	77	1838	61	1880	41	1922	105
1797	73	1839	57	1881	28	1923	69
1798	90	1840	75	1882	25	1924	76
1799	115	1841	67	1883	25	1925	55
1800	92	1842	63	1884	34	1926	76
1801	117	1843	62	1885	22	1927	61
1802	80	1844	69	1886	18	1928	57
1803	110	1845	58	1887	30	1929	74
1804	94	1846	64	1888	23	1930	50
1805	66	1847	60	1889	27	1931	53
1806	72	1848	66	1890	13	1932	49
1807	79	1849	62	1891	24	1933	53
1808	71	1850	58	1892	24	1934	53
1809	79	1851	64	1893	15	1935	58
1810	77	1852	64	1894	24	1936	58
1811	90	1853	71	1895	17	1937	39

Ep.I/9A NULLITY BONDS, 1605

2 bonds entered into by Edward Gibbons of Sidlesham and Joan his wife
on the annulment of their marriage, 1 June 1605.

Ep.I/9B MARRIAGE LICENCE PAPERS, 1670–1933

I/9B/1 (41); rough memoranda of the issue of marriage licences, 1670–
1680.

I/9B/2 (40); letters and papers relating to the granting of marriage
licences *sede vacante* (1870), marriage between English and French subjects
(1885), the re-marriage of divorced persons and marriage within the
prohibited degrees (1916–25), a marriage licence caveat (1927), Chancellors' opinions on the marriage of British subjects with foreigners (1904–33)

and on residence qualifications in parishes divided into several ecclesiastical districts (1894); papers concerning the appointment of surrogates (1901 and later); and table of the prohibited degrees (n.d.).

Ep.I/10 INSTANCE BOOKS, 1506–1798

Ep.I/10–17 are the records of the Chichester consistory court; see notes to Ep.I/15. Instance causes for Mar. 1538/9–Oct. 1541 are in Ep.I/17/2; after 1798 they were entered in the detection books (Ep.I/17/43–47). 10/5 and 10 contain causes of the bishop's (or archbishop's *sede vacante*) audience. Unless otherwise stated all volumes relate solely to the Chichester archdeaconry.

I/10/1   118 ff.   ff.1–118[1-3], Sep. 1506–July 1509.

I/10/2   137 ff.   ff.1–137[1, 2, 4-6], Jan. 1519/20–Jan. 1520/1.

I/10/3   48 ff.; includes the Dean of Chichester's Peculiar. ff.1–48[1-4], Jan. 1523/4–Apr. 1525.

I/10/3a   11 ff.   ff.1–11[1-3], June–Nov. 1525 or 1531.

I/10/4   48 ff.   ff.1–48[1-4], Sep. 1526–Mar. 1527/8.

I/10/5   141 ff. See *Sussex Notes and Queries*, vol. 12, p. 66, for note on schedule to f.7; see also *Sussex Archaeological Society*, vol. 95, pp. 59–70, for notes on three heresy trials recorded in this book. ff.1–141[1-3,5], Apr. 1533–Feb. 1537/8.

I/10/6   37 ff.   ff.1–37[1-3], July 1533–Oct. 1534.

I/10/7   28 ff.   ff.1–28[1-4], Feb. 1536/7–Mar. 1537/8.

I/10/8   137 ff. bound in part of an early medieval MS.   ff.1–22[1, 3, 7], Jan. 1544/5–Aug. 1545; ff.22v.–31, Liber Cleri (general chapter), Sep. 1545; ff.31v.–137[1, 3, 7], Sep. 1545–May 1550.

I/10/9   22 ff.   ff.1–22[1, 3], Dec. 1550–Mar. 1550/1.

I/10/10   49 ff.   ff.1–2[8], no date; ff.3–49[1, 3, 9], Sep. 1556–Nov. 1557.

I/10/11   36 ff; includes the Deaneries of Pagham and Tarring.   ff.1–36[1, 3], May–Nov. 1560.

I/10/12   99 ff.   ff.1–99[1-3], Oct. 1563–May 1567.

I/10/13   27 ff.   ff.1–27[1, 2, 5], Jan. 1567/8–Apr. 1568.

[1] Instance causes.   [2] Correction causes.   [3] Probate acts.   [4] Testaments.
[5] Depositions.   [6] Other acts.   [7] Detection causes.   [8] Visitation articles.
[9] Institutions, *sede vacante*.
[10] From I/10/15 the contents of the volumes are solely instance causes.

I/10/14 33 ff. ff.1–14[1,2], June–Oct. 1576; ff.15–19, Liber Cleri and [4], 1576; ff.17–33[1,2], Oct.–Dec. 1576.

I/10/15 165 ff. ff.1–161[10], Mar. 1582–July 1586.

I/10/16 199 ff. ff.3–198, Mar. 1585/6–Feb. 1588/9.

I/10/17 283 ff. ff.3–283, Apr. 1589–Oct. 1591.

I/10/18 38 ff. ff.1–38, Oct. 1591–Mar. 1591/2.

I/10/19 322 ff. ff.3–318, Apr. 1592–July, 1596; f.320v., memoranda.

I/10/20 214 ff. ff.2–212, Sep. 1596–July 1600.

I/10/21 188 ff. ff.1–188, Oct. 1600–May 1603.

I/10/22 120 ff. bound in part of a contemporary deed. ff.1–120, June 1603–Mar. 1603/4.

I/10/23 42 ff. ff.1–41, Mar. 1603/4—Sep. 1604.

I/10/24 73 ff. ff.1–73, Oct. 1604–June 1605.

I/10/25 135 ff. ff.1–134, June 1605–June 1606.

I/10/26 56 ff. ff.1–56, July–Dec. 1606.

I/10/27 28 ff. ff.1–28, Jan.–Mar. 1606/7.

I/10/28 253 ff. ff.1–2, Nov. 1605; ff.3–252, Oct. 1607–Sep. 1609.

I/10/29 244 ff. ff.2–244, Sep. 1609–Nov. 1612.

I/10/30 118 ff. ff.1–118, May 1612–July 1613.

I/10/31 84 ff. bound in part of a contemporary deed. f.1v., memoranda; ff.2–83, Sep. 1613–Oct. 1614.

I/10/32 191 ff. bound in interrogatories in a Chancery suit. ff.1–191, Oct. 1614–Oct. 1616.

I/10/33 291 ff. f.1, memoranda; ff.2–290, Oct. 1616–Dec. 1619.

I/10/34 329 ff. ff.2–328, Jan. 1619/20–Feb. 1621/22.

I/10/35 386 ff. ff.3–384, Mar. 1621/2–Mar. 1623/4.

I/10/36 277 ff. f.1, memoranda; ff.2–277, Apr. 1624–Mar. 1625/6.

I/10/37 274 ff. f.1, memoranda; ff.2–274, Mar. 1625/6–Oct. 1628.

[1-10] For key to these numbers, see p. 16.

17

I/10/38 286 ff. ff.2–286, Nov. 1628–Sep. 1630.

I/10/39 338 ff. ff.1–2, memoranda; ff.3–335, Oct. 1630–Apr. 1633; f.338, memoranda.

I/10/40 56 ff. ff.1–56, May 1633–July 1634.

I/10/41 377 ff. ff.1–377, May 1633–Feb. 1637/8.

I/10/42 67 ff. ff.1–67, Oct. 1635–Sep. 1636.

I/10/43 23 ff. ff.1–23, no date [?1630–40].

I/10/44 88ff. ff.1–88, June 1637–Apr. 1638.

I/10/45 298 ff. ff.2–210, Feb. 1637/8–May 1642; ff.212–298, Dec. 1660–July 1668.

I/10/46 48 ff. bound in part of a medieval Old Testament. ff.1–47, Dec. 1660–Feb. 1662/3.

I/10/47 91 ff. ff.1–91, Jan. 1664/5–Aug. 1672.

I/10/48 58 ff. ff.1–58, Sep. 1672–Feb. 1675/6.

I/10/49 77 ff. ff.1–77, Feb. 1675/6–Oct. 1678.

I/10/50 102 ff. ff.1–102, Jan. 1681/2–Mar. 1688/9.

I/10/51 74 ff. bound in an original testament (1627). ff.1–73, Mar. 1688/9–Oct. 1696.

1/10/52 87 ff. ff.1–87, Oct. 1696–Feb. 1703/4.

I/I0/52a 13 loose folios, 17th cent. ff.1–13 (unidentified).

I/10/53 168 ff. bound in part of a contemporary deed. ff.1–168, Mar. 1703/4–Dec. 1709.

I/10/54 75 ff. bound in part of a contemporary deed. ff.1–75, Dec. 1709–Mar. 1714/5.

I/10/55 144 ff. bound in part of a contemporary deed. ff.1–144, May 1715–Sep. 1722.

I/10/56 186 ff. ff.1–186, Oct. 1722–Aug. 1728.

I/10/57 184 ff. f.i, memoranda; ff.1–181, Sep. 1728–Sep. 1741.

I/10/58 184 ff. f.i, form of oaths of a witness, of a party principal and on costs taxed; ff. 1–182, Sep. 1741–Aug. 1772.

I/10/59 139 ff. ff.1–58, Sep. 1772–Dec. 1798.

Ep.I/11 DEPOSITION BOOKS, 1557–1694

See notes to Ep.I/15; for earlier depositions see Ep.I/10 and I/17/2.

I/11/1 97 ff., in separate gatherings. ff.1–26, Mar. 1556/7–Oct. 1557 and Jan. 1567/8–Jan. 1571; ff. 27–31, July–Nov. 1573; ff.32–71, Feb. 1573/4–Mar. 1574/5; ff.72–97, July 1575–Mar. 1575/6.

I/11/2 29 ff. ff.1–29, July 1572–June 1573.

I/11/3 49 ff. ff.1–49, June 1576–Apr. 1579.

I/11/4 37 ff. ff.1–28, Apr. 1580–Apr. 1581; f.31, memoranda.

I/11/5 138 ff. ff.1–138, Mar. 1581/2–Nov. 1588.

I/11/6 182 ff. ff.3–181, June 1589–Apr. 1592.

I/11/7 182 ff. ff.2–180, July 1592–May 1597.

I/11/8 161 ff. ff.2–153, May 1597–Mar. 1598/9.

I/11/9 277 ff. ff.2–277, Apr. 1599–Nov. 1603.

I/11/10 291 ff. ff.1–290, Dec. 1603–Apr. 1607.

I/11/11 274 ff. ff.2–265, May 1607–June 1611.

I/11/12 231 ff. ff.2–230, Nov. 1611–Jan. 1617/8.

I/11/13 283 ff. bound in part of a medieval MS. ff.1–280, Jan. 1617/8–Mar. 1625/6.

I/11/14 276 ff. ff.3–274, Mar. 1625/6–Mar. 1630/1.

I/11/15 302 ff. ff.1–301, May 1631–Dec. 1636.

I/11/16 286 ff. ff.1–274, Aug. 1637–July 1641; ff.275–282, Oct. 1661–May 1663.

I/11/17 95 ff. bound in part of a medieval Old Testament. ff.1–95, Feb. 1663/4–Oct. 1676.

I/11/18 42 ff. ff.1–40, Oct. 1676–Nov. 1679.

I/11/19 50 ff. ff.1–50, Dec. 1679–Mar. 1683/4.

I/11/20 42 ff. bound in part of a medieval concordance. ff.1–42, Mar. 1683/4–Apr. 1688.

I/11/21 47 ff. ff.1–47, Dec. 1688–Apr. 1692.

I/11/22 39 ff. ff.1–39, Apr. 1692–June 1694.

Ep.I/12 CITATION BOOKS, 1614–1670

See notes to Ep.I/15; other citations are entered in the Probate records (STC IV/1).

I/12/1 41 ff. bound in part of a contemporary deed.
ff. 1–41, citations, Aug. 1614–Apr. 1620.

I/12/2 13 ff.; citations *viis et modis.*
ff.3–6, Sep. 1631–June 1637; ff.7–10, July 1662–July 1670.

Ep.I/13 EXCOMMUNICATION PAPERS, 1612–1811

See notes to Ep.I/15.

I/13/1 (293); excommunication mandates, 1612–1621.

1612	2		1617	54
1613	49		1618	56
1614	25		1619	26
1615	16		1620	26
1616	30		1621	9

I/13/2 12 ff.; lists of persons excommunicated.
ff.1–6, Sep. 1631–Jan. 1637/8; ff.7–12, Feb. 1637/8–July 1665.

I/13/3 (9); excommunication mandates, 1746–1811.
1746, 1748, 1759, 1770, 1771, 1774, 1776, 1803, 1811—one for each year.

Ep.I/14 TAXATION BOOKS, 1606–1773

See notes to Ep.I/15.

I/14/1 18 ff. ff.1–18, Mar. 1605/6–Mar. 1607.

I/14/2 21 ff. ff.2–8, Aug. 1745–June 1773.

Ep.I/15 MISCELLANEOUS COURT PAPERS, 16th century–1850

This is the largest single group of documents (an estimated 25,000) in the episcopal records, and is still to a great extent unsorted. It consists of every type of court paper, as well as working papers and many other documents produced in evidence. A list (I/15/5) of the documents arranged by courts, giving outside dates and the number of documents in each bundle, had at one time been prepared, but as it was thought that a chronological arrangement of the records would be more desirable, this has been done. A detailed list of the whole series will have to be prepared at some future date. The process books and original bundles have been given separate numbers. A few outsize documents, I/15/4, most of them repaired, have been put into a separate group.

A detailed account of the workings of the consistory courts would be out of place in this brief catalogue, but at least an outline knowledge of the procedure from which these documents were evolved is necessary before they can be profitably studied. The best sources for this purpose for the specialist are B. L. Woodcock, *Medieval Ecclesiastical Courts in the Diocese of Canterbury* (1952), pp. 30–102, *The Ecclesiastical Courts* (Report of the Commission on Ecclesiastical Courts, 1951) (1954), pp. 1–22, and R. L. Storey, *Diocesan Administration in the Fifteenth Century* (St. Anthony's Hall Publications, 1959), but for those desiring less detailed information A. J. Willis, *Winchester Consistory Court Depositions, 1561–1602* (1960), pp. 1–3, is recommended.

I/15/1[1] This is the bulk of the collection and consists of 30 boxes of documents sorted into annual bundles (1549–1850) and 11 boxes of documents which are not immediately dateable, but which on closer inspection could probably be dated from internal evidence.

I/15/2/1–46 Process books (1579–1786) contain manuscript copies of all relevant documents and evidence in a case which was to be appealed in the Court of Arches.

1. 9 ff. Agnes Tye *v.* Thomas Furner, Aug. 1579.
2. 8 ff. Humfrey *v.* [illegible], Jan. 1579/80.
3. 5 ff. Rogers *v.* Joanes, Nov. 1580.
4. 4 ff. Elizabeth Backer *alias* Allen *v.* [illegible], Nov. 1581.
5. 18 ff. Thomas Bury *v.* John Fenn, Feb. 1581/2.
6. 12 ff. [Hartby *v.* Hartby?], n.d. [*post* 1586].
7. 12 ff. Yonge *v.* Filder, 1587.
8. 14 ff. Goble *v.* Goble, 1588.
9. 6 ff. Thomas Hartley [Hartby] *v.* [illegible], May 1588.
10. 6 ff. [illegible], Mar. 1588/9.
11. 4 ff. John James *v.* [?]William Rowland, Mar. 1588/9.
12. 18 ff. Richard Lewkenor *v.* Aylwyn, 1588/9.
13. 10 ff. Elizabeth Bruyster *v.* [illegible], July 1589.
14. 4 ff. John Rowland *v.* Margaret James, n.d. [late 16th cent.].
15. 10 docs. Mantle *v.* Mantle, 1601.
16. 10 ff. [Office *v.* Martlett?], Aug. 1601.
17. 14 ff. [illegible], June 1621.
18. 6 ff. Thomas Harrison *v.* Thomas Penn, Oct. 1624.
19. 6 ff. Nicholas Woolgar *v.* Thomas Harrison, Feb. 1624/5.
20. 56 ff. Richard Stamper *v.* Thomas Oliver, Dec. 1637.
21. 24 ff. Thomas Oliver *v.* Richard Stamper, Mar. 1637/8.
22. 12 ff. William Franklin *v.* John Alwin, n.d. [17th cent.].
23. 7 ff. Daniel Gittens *v.* John Alwin, n.d. [17th cent.].

---

[1] It is regretted that the 11 boxes of undated documents are not yet available to readers, and it is only those already arranged in annual bundles which can be consulted.

24. 13 ff. George Moare *v.* William Boys and William Strudwicke, Aug. 1666.
25. 8 ff. Robert Crossingham and John Mickleham *v.* William Knight, Jan. 1679/80.
26. 32 ff. Office *v.* Peregrine Peryham, Mich. 1681.
27. 31 ff. Edward Barnard *v.* Robert Stone, Jan. 1692/3.
28. 20 ff. Maria Smith *v.* Henry and Richard White, July 1694.
29. 10 ff. Sara Hile *v.* Edmund Hile, June 1695.
30. 10 ff. John Crockford, John Day, John Ford and William Matthewes *v.* William Woolgar and Henry Levett, Mar. 1696/7.
31. 10 ff. Office *v.* Lloyd, Oct. 1698.
32. 16 ff. Office *v.* Richard Brereton, Oct. 1703.
33. 8 ff. Office *v.* Richard Brereton, Mar. 1705/6.
34. 14 ff. Elizabeth Hollis *v.* Isaac Duke, Jan. 1707/8.
35. 8 ff. Thomas Scriven *v.* John Styant, Feb. 1710/11.
36. 9 ff. John Browne *v.* Elizabeth Hammond, Mar. 1713.
37. 12 ff. Office *v.* Thomas Peckham, Sep. 1713.
38. 4 ff. Office *v.* William Lickfold, Oct. 1715.
39. 24 ff. Daniel Newell *v.* Martha Pearley, Jan. 1723/4.
40. 12 ff. Maria Glover *v.* William Sherwin, May 1728.
41. 17 ff. Office *v.* Sara Burley, Oct. 1732.
42. 19 ff. Eleanor Stardefield *v.* Catherine Woodland, Mich. 1733.
43. 12 ff. ff. 1–9 Thomas Easton and Dennis Hyland *v.* Francis Winston, Hil. 1741; ff.10–12, Robert Jones *v.* William Thomas, Hil. 1744.
44. 10 ff. Thomas Adams, William Battine, John Hoar and Thomas Taylor *v.* John Jenman, Mich. 1745.
45. 12 ff. ff.1–6, Richard Osborne *v.* John Osborne, Mich. 1757; ff.6*v.*–11, Mary Fielder *v.* William Ewen, Hil. 1758.
46. 12 ff. Office *v.* Thomas Woods, Mich. 1786.

I/15/3 44 bundles of court papers (1570s–1735), each containing 100–300 documents, obviously complete series (in some cases still on original files but not in chronological order and therefore nos. 1, 2 and 28 are described only as being in decades), or so endorsed by the late Dr. Hilda Johnstone after she had examined them.

1, 1570s; 2, 1580s; 3, office causes, 1583–4; 4, 1584; 5, instance causes, 1589; 6, 1589–90; 7, instance causes, 1590; 8, 1593; 9, 1593; 10, 1596; 11, 1597; 12, exhibits, 1597; 13, instance causes, 1599; 14, instance causes, 1600; 15, instance causes, 1602; 16, 1607–8; 17, 1608; 18, 1609; 19, office causes, 1615; 20, appealed cause, 1616–19; 21, instance causes, 1622; 22, office causes, 1622–3; 23, 1623–5; 24, instance causes, 1624; 25, office causes, 1626; 26, office causes, 1627; 27, office causes, 1628–9; 28, 1630s; 29, instance causes, 1631; 30, office causes, 1631; 31, instance causes, 1634; 32, appealed cause, 1635; 33, instance causes, 1635; 34, exhibits, 1635; 35, 1636; 36, office causes, 1637; 37, 1638; 38, 1640; 39, 1640; 40, instance causes,

1662; 41, instance causes, 1665–8; 42, 1674–5; 43, 1702–21; 44, 1728–35.

I/15/4 21 docs. and 10 ff.; outsize papers, all repaired.[1]

I/15/5 Collection of fragmentary documents and covers.[1]

Ep.I/16 EXHIBITS IN CAUSES, 1616–1857

These are mainly documents produced as evidence in causes, but I/16/2 is probably the volume bought by the Dean and Chapter in 1759 (see Cap.I/23/4, f.45), and I/16/3–10 may be related with the Tithe Commutation papers (Ep.I/54).

I/16/1 61 ff. bound in part of a contemporary deed.

ff.1–61, overseers' accounts and rates for St. Andrew, Chichester, 1616–50.

I/16/2[2] 137 ff; a copy of the assessment for the poor of Chichester, 1755.

flyleaf, index of parishes; ff.1–47, Subdeanery; ff.49–55, St. Bartholomew; ff.56–61, St. Olave; ff.62–66, St. Martin; ff.68–83, St. Pancras; ff.85–95, St. Andrew; ff.97–99 the Close; ff.100–105, All Saints; ff.106–112, St. Peter the Less; ff.117–118, list of the poor, 1765.

I/16/3 39 ff.; subdeanery tithe book, 1766–74, with receipts to 1780.

ff.1v.–34, tithes, Sept. 1766–Sept. 1774; ff.34v.—39, receipts, Oct. 1772–Mar. 1780.

I/16/4 144 ff.; Icklesham tithe book, 1818–24.

f.1, memoranda; ff.4–138, tithes, Mar. 1818–Sept. 1824; f.144v., memoranda.

I/16/5 20 ff.

ff.2–19, a survey of the lands in Pagham parish made by order of a vestry held Apr. 1825.

I/16/6 13 ff.

ff.1–13, tithe receipts at Pulborough, June 1849–Dec. 1851.

I/16/7 26 ff.

ff.1–24, tithe receipts at Pulborough, May 1852–Nov. 1856.

I/16/8 (93); Pulborough tithes, 1844–57.

Annual summaries of tithe apportionments, 1847–54; lists of tithes to be paid, tithes left unpaid and receipts, May 1844–Mar. 1857.

I/16/9 (41); Pulborough tithes, 1845–56.

Letters to the Diocesan Registry, chiefly from John Austin,[3] Jan. 1850–Jan. 1857; accounts and memoranda, mainly of John Austin, Dec. 1845–May 1856.

I/16/10 88 ff.; Pagham tithe book, 1807–1819.

ff.1–12, tithes, Sept. 1807–Dec. 1819.

---

[1] It is hoped that all these documents will be listed in detail at some future date.
[2] See note to Diocesan Record Office, Par.35/30.
[3] Rector of Pulborough, 1822–57.

I/16/11 26 ff.; a copy of Sidlesham poor rate, Mar. 1850.

Ep.I/17 DETECTION BOOKS, 1538–1853

In the mid 16th century correction causes came to be called detection causes (see Ep.I/10), and during the 18th century miscellaneous acts replace detection causes. From I/17/37 these are called Books of Office. After 1798 the few instance causes appear here. From I/17/36 onwards consecrations and faculties[1] and licences for dissenters' meeting houses appear here. See notes to Ep.I/15.

I/17/1 10 ff. unbound. ff.1–10, correction causes and probate acts, May 1538–Feb. 1538/9.

I/17/2 62 ff. bound in a mandate for Convocation (1532). ff.1–62, correction and instance causes, probate acts and depositions, Mar. 1538/9–Oct. 1541.

I/17/3 29 ff. bound in part of a London consistory cause appeal process (late 15th cent.). ff.1–29, Nov. 1572–Mar. 1574/5.

I/17/4 79 ff. ff.1–76, Oct. 1579–Feb. 1579/80.

I/17/5 84 ff. ff.1–84, Mar. 1579/80–Oct. 1580.

I/17/5a 8 loose ff. repaired, n.d. [16th cent.].

I/17/6 204 ff. ff.2–202, Mar. 1585/6–Mar. 1588/9.

I/17/7 253 ff. ff.1–253, Apr. 1589–Feb. 1591/2.

I/17/8 366 ff. ff.2–363, Aug. 1592–Sep. 1596.

I/17/9 269 ff. ff.3–268, Sep. 1596–Sep. 1600.

I/17/10 247 ff. and a fragment of a medieval MS. ff. 1–246, Oct. 1600–Sep. 1603.

I/17/11 273 ff. ff.2–272, Oct. 1603–Sep. 1606.

I/17/12 277 ff. ff.3–277, Oct. 1606–Sep. 1609.

I/17/13 225 ff. ff.2–225, Sep. 1609–May 1612.

I/17/14 66 ff. ff.1–66, May 1612–May 1613.

I/17/15 220 ff. ff.1–219, May 1613–July 1615; f.220, memoranda.

I/17/16 67 ff. ff.1–67, July 1615–May 1617.

[1] See annotated *Lists and Indexes No. 3*, now Ep.I/88/3.

I/17/17 180 ff. f.1, memoranda; ff.2–179, Sep. 1615–July 1617.

I/17/18 265 ff. f.1, memoranda; ff.2–263, Sep. 1617–Dec. 1619; f.264, memoranda.

I/17/19 332 ff. ff.3–332, Jan. 1619/20–June 1622.

I/17/20 283 ff., and a fragment of a medieval MS. ff.1–283, June 1622–July 1624.

I/17/21 225 ff. ff.3–223, Oct. 1624–Nov. 1626; f.224, memoranda.

I/17/22 278 ff. ff.1–278, Nov. 1626–Jan. 1628/9.

I/17/23 254 ff. ff.4–254, Feb. 1628/9–Jan. 1630/1.

I/17/24 280 ff. ff.3–276, Feb. 1630/1–June 1633.

I/17/25 375 ff. ff.3–374, July 1633–June 1637.

I/17/26 38 ff. ff.1–38, Oct. 1635–Apr. 1636.

I/17/27 371 ff. ff.2–370, June 1637–Mar. 1640/1.

I/17/28 330 ff. ff.1–50, Mar. 1640/1–Nov. 1641; ff.50*r*.–329, Dec. 1660–Mar. 1666/7; f.330, memoranda.

I/17/29 96 ff. bound in part of a medieval Old Testament. ff.1–96, Mar. 1666/7–July 1669.

I/17/30 121 ff. ff.1–121, Sep. 1669–Apr. 1674.

I/17/31 139 ff. ff.1–139, Sep. 1674–Jan. 1676/7.

I/17/32 138 ff. ff.1–138, Feb. 1676/7–June 1682.

I/17/32a 8 ff. unbound ff.1–8, Dec. 1678–Jan. 1678/9.

I/17/33 175 ff. ff.1–175, June 1682–May 1692.

I/17/34 78 ff. bound in part of a contemporary deed. ff.1–78, Sep. 1692–May 1700.

I/17/34a 4 ff. unbound and unidentified.

I/17/35 92 ff. bound in part of a contemporary deed. ff.1–92, June 1700–June 1707.

I/17/36 135 ff. ff.2–135, June 1707–Sep. 1718.

I/17/37 177 ff.; this and subsequent volumes called 'Books of Office'. ff.1–177, Oct. 1718–June 1729.

I/17/38 183 ff. ff. 1–183, July 1729–Aug. 1733.

I/17/39 229 ff. ff.1–229, Aug. 1733–Oct. 1739.

I/17/40 178 ff. ff.1–178, Oct. 1739–Nov. 1748.

I/17/41 92 ff. ff.1–91, Nov. 1748–Mar. 1756.

I/17/42 140 ff. f.1, oaths[1-8]; ff.2–140, Apr. 1756–Oct. 1776.

I/17/43 150 ff. ff.1v.–2, oaths[1-9]; ff. 3–150, Nov. 1776–May 1801.

I/17/44 174 ff. ff.1v.–2, oaths[1-10]; ff.3–174, June 1801–Jan. 1822.

I/17/45 186 ff. ff.2–176, Feb. 1822–Dec. 1847.

I/17/46 (15); letters of appointment of parish clerks, 1827–43, documents relating to the consecration of St. Mary's chapel, Sennicots, 1829, letters requesting returns of expenditure on churchyard maintenance in the diocese of Chichester and the Deaneries of Pagham and Tarring, 1834.

I/17/47 341 pp. pp.1–341, May 1847–Apr. 1853, with index of places.

[1] of a parish clerk.
[2] of an executor.
[3] of an administrator.
[4] of a guardian.
[5] of absolution.
[6] of a witness.
[7] of a party principal.
[8] of costs taxed.
[9] on exhibiting an inventory and account.
[10] of churchwardens.

Ep.I/18 LIBRI CLERI, 1521–1893

These are the 'call-books' compiled at visitations from lists of persons, both clergy and churchwardens, cited to attend. Some of the 16th cent. volumes are also registers of orders, and some may be lists of clergy attending episcopal synods. The number I/18/1 has not been allocated.

I/18/2 42 ff.; May–Sep. 1521[2].
ff.1–8[4-5]; ff.9–19[6]; ff.20–36[7]; ff.37v.–39[6]; f.42, notarial instrument in a cause concerning an unidentified monastery of St. Mary, 1500.

I/18/3 18 ff.; May 1530–Sep. 1531[2].
f.1, of Easebourne priory, 1530 (see *Sussex Archaeological Collections*, vol. 9, pp. 1–32, for earlier visitations); f.2, of Hardham priory, 1530; ff. 3–7[6]; f.8v., of Rusper priory, 1530; ff.9–11[6]; f.12v., of Easebourne priory, 1531; ff.13–17[7]; f.18, of Michelham priory, Sep. 1531.

[1] Metropolitical visitation.
[2] Episcopal visitation.
[3] Chichester archidiaconal visitation.
[4] Of the cathedral.
[5] Of the Dean of Chichester's Peculiar.
[6] Of Chichester archdeaconry.
[7] Of Lewes archdeaconry.
[8] Receipts for fees for citing churchwardens.

I/18/4 42 ff.; July–Aug. 1543[2].
ff.1–22[5-6]; ff.23–25, of the College of Arundel; ff.26–41[7]; f.42 fragment.

I/18/4a 6 ff.; Apr. 1550[2].
ff.1–6, of the Midhurst deanery.

I/18/5 66 ff.; Nov. 1551–Jan. 1551/2[1].
ff.1–9[4]; ff.10–40[5-6]; ff.41–63[7]; ff.64–65, of the South Malling deanery.

I/18/6 45 ff.; (a copy of part of I/18/5).

I/18/7 42 ff.; Sep.–Oct. 1554[2].
ff.1–3[4]; ff.6–27[5-6]; ff.28–42[7].

I/18/8 42 ff.; Apr.–June 1556[2].
ff.1–2[5]; ff.3–20[6]; ff.21–42[7].

I/18/9 50 ff.; Mar. 1557/8–Apr. 1558[2].
ff.1–4[4]; ff.9v.–10[5]; ff.11–26[6]; ff.27v.–45[7]; ff.47v.–48, detection causes, Archdeaconry of Lewes.

I/18/10 50 ff.; May 1560–Apr. 1566[3] (continued in I/18/12).
ff.1–11, May 1560; ff.12–14, probate and administration acts, May 1560; ff.14–17, Apr. 1561; ff.17v.–25, Apr. 1562; ff.25v.–35, Apr. 1563; ff.35v.–39, Apr. 1564; ff.40–45, Apr. 1565; ff.45v.–49, Apr. 1566.

I/18/11 70 ff.; Jan. 1560/1–Nov. 1562[2] and June–Sep. 1564[2].
ff.2–6[4], Jan. 1560/1; ff.7–8[5]; ff.8v.–22[6]; ff.22v.–37[7]; ff.37v.–38, of the Pagham Deanery; f.39[6], Nov. 1562; ff.41–43[4], June 1564; ff.43v.–44[5]; ff.44v.–54[6]; ff.54v.–66[7]; f.70, memoranda.

I/18/12 43 ff.; May 1566–May 1571[3].
ff.1–3, May 1566; ff.4–5, Apr. 1567; ff.6–15, May 1568; ff.15v.–25 Apr. 1569; ff.25v.–33, Apr. 1570; ff.34–42, May 1571.

I/18/13 41 ff.; June 1570–Mar. 1572/3[2].
ff.1–4[4], June 1570; ff.7–19[6], June 1570; f.20 of St. Mary's hospital, Chichester, Sep. 1570; f.21 of St. James' hospital, Chichester, Sep. 1570; ff.23–26[4], Feb. 1572/3; ff.30–32[6], Feb. 1572/3; f.33[5]; ff.34–41[6], Mar. 1572/3.

I/18/14 21 ff.; June–July 1576[2].
ff.1–10, 13–19[6].

I/18/15 8 ff.
ff.1–4, episcopal synod for Storrington and Arundel deaneries, Oct. 1579.

I/18/16 39 ff.; July 1581[1].
ff.1–13[6]; ff.14–30[7]; ff.35–36, memoranda.

1-8 For key to these numbers, see p. 26.

I/18/17 41 ff.; May–June 1582[2].
ff.1–2[4]; f.7 memoranda; ff.8–9[5]; ff.10–13, 16–30[6]; ff.32–35, 39–41[7].

I/18/18 41 ff.; Sep. 1586[2]; some injunctions for the cathedral are included.
ff.1–9[4]; ff.10–12[5]; ff.13–20[6]; ff.31–40[7].

I/18/19 32 ff. bound in part of a contemporary libel. May 1589[2].
ff.1–3[4]; ff.6–11[6]; ff.12–13[5]; ff.14–20[6]; ff.23 and 27, memoranda.

I/18/20 25 ff.; June–Oct. 1592[2].
ff.1–2[5]; June 1592; ff.3–21[6], June 1592; f.23 of St. Mary's hospital, Chichester; f.24 of St. James' hospital, Chichester.

I/18/21 22 ff.; Apr. 1595[2].
ff.1–4[4]; ff.5–17[6]; f.19[5]; f.21, of St. James' hospital, Chichester.

I/18/22 43 ff. bound in part of a contemporary deed. Sep. 1597[2] and Sep. 1600[2].
ff.1–4[4], Sep. 1597; ff.6–17[6], Dec. 1597; f.20[5], Jan. 1597/8; ff.28–31[4], Sep. 1600; ff.33–43[6], Sep. 1600, continued in 18/25.

I/18/23 6 ff.; Oct. 1598?[3]
ff.1–6, Oct. 1598.

I/18/24 4 ff.; 16th cent.(?) These fragments include the archdeaconry of Chichester and the deaneries of Pagham and Tarring and South Malling.

I/18/25 16 ff.; Sep. 1600[2].
f.1[5]; ff.2–16[6].

I/18/26 18 ff.; 1605[1].
ff.2–5, 7–13, 15–18[6].

I/18/27 26 ff.; Sep.–Oct. 1606[2].
f.1, memoranda; ff.3–7[4]; ff.8–9[5]; ff.10–19, 22–24[6].

I/18/28 46 ff.; episcopal synods of the Chichester archdeaconry.
ff.2–6, Oct. 1607; ff.7–10, no date; ff.10v.–14, Sep. 1609; ff.15–18, Oct. 1611; f.19, heading for Sep. 1612; ff.27–28, Oct. 1614; ff.29–31, Oct. 1617; ff.32–35, Oct. 1618; ff.35v.–38, Sep. 1620; ff.38v.–40, Sep. 1621; ff.41v.–44, Sep. 1623.

I/18/29 22 ff.; July–Aug. 1609[2].
ff.1–10[4], July 1609; f.11[5], Aug. 1609; ff.14–20[6], Aug. 1609.

I/18/30 27 ff.; Sep. 1610–Aug. 1611[2].
ff.1–5[4], Sep. 1610; f.6[5], Sep. 1610; ff.7–17[4], Apr.–Aug. 1611; ff.20–27[6], Sep. 1610.

[1–8] For key to these numbers, see p. 26.

I/18/31   23 ff.; Sep.–Oct. 1613[2].
ff.1–9[4], Oct. 1613; f.10[5], Oct. 1613; ff.11–18[6], Sep. 1613.

I/18/32   25 ff.; Aug.–Sep. 1615[1].
ff.1–11[6], Aug. 1615; ff.11v.–12[5], Aug. 1615; ff.12v.–13, of Pagham and Tarring Deanery, Aug. 1615; ff.14–20[4], Sep. 1615.

I/18/33   26 ff.; Oct. 1616–Aug. 1617[2].
ff.1–11[6], Sep. 1616; f.11[5], Sep. 1616; ff.12–22[4], Oct. 1616–Aug. 1617.

I/18/34   17 ff.; Oct. 1619[2].
ff.1–4[6]; f.4[5]; ff.5–7, 11–16[6].

I/18/34a   10 ff.; May 1619[3].

I/18/35   49 ff.; Sep. 1622–Oct. 1625[2].
ff.2–12[4], Oct. 1622; ff.14–17[6], Sep. 1622; ff.17–18[5], Sep. 1622; ff.19–28[6], Sep. 1622; ff.32–36[4], Oct. 1625; ff.40–42[6], Oct. 1625; f.42[5], Oct. 1625; ff.43–49[6], Oct. 1625.

I/18/36   31 ff. bound in part of a contemporary deed. Oct. 1628[2].
ff.2–8[4]; f.9[5]; ff.16–18, 20–22[6].

I/18/37   29 ff.; Oct. 1631 and Oct. 1635[2].
ff.1–6[4], Oct. 1631; ff.7–9[4], Oct. 1635; f.10[5], Oct. 1631; ff.11–19[6], Oct. 1631; f.20[5], Oct. 1634; ff.21–29[6], Sep. 1634.

I/18/38   9 ff.; 1662[2].
ff.1–8[6]; f.9[5].

I/18/39   6 ff.; 1662[2], churchwardens and sidesmen only.
ff.1–6[6].

I/18/40   6 ff.; 1663[1].
ff.1–6[6].

I/18/40a   10 ff.; Sep. 1666[2].
ff.1–2[4]; ff.3–10[6].

I/18/41   6 ff.; Apr. 1667[?3]; churchwardens and sidesmen only.

I/18/42   6 ff.; May 1669[3].

I/18/43   6 ff.; Apr. 1670[?3]

I/18/44   10 ff.; July–Oct. 1673[2].
ff.1–5[4].

[1–8] For key to these numbers, see p. 26.

I/18/45 21 ff.; Sep. 1675². Boxgrove Deanery also appears in Cap.I/7/1.
ff.1–13⁶.

I/18/46 8 ff.; Apr. 1676³.

I/18/47 10 ff.; May 1677³.

I/18/48 8 ff.; May 1678³, incumbents only.
ff.1–4, incumbents; ff.5–8, procurations.

I/18/49 8 ff.; May 1678²³, churchwardens only.

I/18/50 16 ff.; Sep. 1678², churchwardens only.
ff.1–14⁶, f.16v., of the Deanery of Pagham and Tarring.

I/18/51 18 ff.; bound in part of a medieval theological MS. May 1679²,
churchwardens only.
ff.1–18⁶.

I/18/52 31 ff.; Sep. 1679–May 1682².
ff.1–14⁶, Sep. 1679; ff.15–18⁶, May 1682; ff.18–19⁵, May 1682; ff.20–30⁶,
May 1682.

I/18/52a 8 ff.; June 1680³.

I/18/53 7 ff.; Apr.–May 1681³.

I/18/54 12 ff.; June 1683³.

I/18/54a 2 ff.; June 1683³.
ff.1–2, of the Storrington Deanery.

I/18/55 16 ff. bound in part of a writ, June 1684³.

I/18/56 30 ff.; May 1685²; churchwardens only.
ff.1–2⁵; ff.3–30⁶.

I/18/57 40 ff.; 1686(?)²², churchwardens only.
ff.1–25⁶; ff.26–28⁵; ff.29–38⁶; f.39⁵.

I/18/58 9 ff. bound in part of a contemporary deed. May 1687³.

I/18/59 15 ff.; May 1688³.

I/18/60 8 ff.; Dec. 1688², churchwardens only.
ff.1–8⁶.

I/18/61 12 ff.; May 1689².
ff.1–11⁶; f.12⁵.

¹⁻⁸ For key to these numbers, see p. 26.

I/18/62 34 ff. bound in part of a contemporary deed. June 1690–Sep. 1692[2].

ff.1–10[6], June–July 1690; f.11[5], June–July 1690; ff.12–14[6], June–July 1690; ff.15–25[6], May 1692; f.26[5], May 1692; ff.27–34[6], Sep. 1692.

I/18/63 16 ff.; May 1691[3].

I/18/64 21 ff. bound in part of a contemporary deed. May 1693–June 1694[3].

ff.1–10, May 1693; ff.11–21, June 1694.

I/18/65 5 ff.; 1695[?3].

I/18/66 43 ff. bound in part of a contemporary deed. June 1697–June 1700[2].

ff.1v.–12[6], June 1697; ff.13–24[6], June 1700.

I/18/67 27 ff. bound in a copy of a testament. June 1698–June 1699[3].

ff.1–11, June 1698; ff.12–27, June 1699.

I/18/67a 7 ff.; loose folios from 17th cent. libri cleri.

I/18/68 25 ff.; June 1701–June 1702[3].

ff.1–12, June 1701; ff.13–24, June 1702.

I/18/69 14 ff.; May 1703[2].

ff.1–13[6]; f.13[5]; f.14v.[8].

I/18/70 14 ff.; June 1704[3].

I/18/71 10 ff. bound in part of a contemporary deed. June 1704[3].

I/18/72 11 ff. bound in part of a contemporary deed. May–June 1706[2].

ff.1–5[6]; ff.5v.–6[5]; ff.6v.–11[6].

I/18/73 22 ff.; June 1707–June 1708[3].

ff.1–10, June 1707; ff.11–20, June 1708.

I/18/74 12 ff.; June–July 1709[1] (*sede vacante*).

ff.2–12[6].

I/18/75 14 ff. bound in part of a contemporary deed. June 1710[2].

ff.1–6[6]; f.7[5]; ff.8v.–14[6].

I/18/76 13 ff; June 1711[3].

I/18/77 14 ff. bound in part of a contemporary deed. June 1712[3].

[1–8] For key to these numbers, see p. 26.

I/18/78 12 ff. bound in part of a contemporary deed. July 1713[2].
ff.1–12[6].

I/18/79 12 ff.; May 1714[3].

I/18/80 12 ff.; June 1715[3].

I/18/81 12 ff.; June–July 1716[2].
ff.1–11[6]; f.12[5].

I/18/82 26 ff. bound in part of a contemporary deed. June 1717–June 1718[3].
ff.1–11, June 1717; ff.12–21, June 1718; f.26[8].

I/18/83 13 ff. bound in part of a contemporary deed. June–July 1719[2].
ff.1–10[6]; f.11[5]; f.13v.[8].

I/18/84 22 ff. bound in part of a contemporary deed. June 1720–June 1721[3].
ff.1–11, June 1720; ff.12–21, June 1721; f.22v.[8].

I/18/85 11 ff.; June 1722[2].
ff.1–6[6]; f.6[5]; ff.7–11[6]; f.11v.[8].

I/18/86 27 ff. bound in part of a contemporary deed. June 1723[2] and June 1724[3].
ff.2–14[6]; June 1723; ff.15–24, June 1724; f.25[8].

I/18/87 24 ff. bound in part of a contemporary deed. June 1725[3] and June–Aug. 1726[2].
ff.2–12, June 1725; f.12[8]; ff.13–23[6], June–Aug. 1726; f.24[8].

I/18/88 7 ff.; May–Aug. 1727[2].
ff.1–7[5]; ff.6–7, causes.

I/18/89 30 ff.; June 1727–June 1728[3].
ff.1–10, June 1727; f.10[8]; ff.11–29, June 1728.

I/18/90 18 ff.; June 1729[2].
ff.3–15[6]; ff.14v.–15[8].

I/18/91 40 ff.; May 1730–July 1732[3].
ff.1–13, May 1730; ff.14–27, June 1731; ff.28–40, July 1732.

I/18/92 173 pp.; June 1733–July 1742[1, 2].
pp.1–16[4], June 1733[2]; pp.21–58[6], June 1733[2]; pp.61–64[5], June 1733[2]; pp.69–90[6], July 1737[2]; pp.93–95[5], July 1737[2]; pp.97–112[6], Aug. 1740[1]

[1–8] For key to these numbers, see p. 26.

32

(*sede vacante*); pp.113–115[5], Aug. 1740[1] (*sede vacante*); pp.117–130[6], Aug. 1740[1] (*sede vacante*); pp.132–140[4], July 1742[2]; pp.143–170[6], July 1742[2]; pp.171–173[5], July 1742[2].

I/18/93 approx. 37 ff.; June 1734[3], and lists of those excommunicated, 1622–30.

I/18/94 16 ff.; May 1735[3].

I/18/95 15 ff.; May 1736[3].

I/18/96 12 ff.; July 1738[3].

I/18/97 16 ff.; July 1739[3].

I/18/98 18 ff.; June 1741[3].

I/18/99 14 ff.; June 1743[3].

I/18/100 14 ff.; June 1744[3]. f.12v.[8].

I/18/101 100 ff.; June 1745–July 1798[2].
ff.1–11[6], June 1745; f.12[5], June 1745; f.13[8]; ff.14–24[6], July 1748; f.25[5], July 1748; f.26[8]; ff.27–37[6], July 1751; ff.37v.–38[5], July 1751; f.38v.[8]; ff.39v.–42[4], July 1755; f.45[5], July 1755; ff.46v.–56[6], July 1755; f.56[8]; ff. 57–63[6], July 1758; f.63[8]; ff.63v.–64[5], July 1758; ff.65–70[6], July 1758; ff.71–74[4], July 1798; ff.75–82[6], July 1798; ff.83–84[5], July 1798; ff.85–91[6], July 1798; f.91[8].

I/18/102 12 ff.; July 1746[3].

I/18/103 12 ff.; July 1747[3].

I/18/104 12 ff.; June 1749[3].

I/18/105 16 ff.; June 1750[3].

I/18/106 16 ff.; July 1752[3].

I/18/107 10 ff.; July 1753[3].

I/18/108 10 ff.; July 1754[3].

I/18/109 12 ff.; June 1756[3].

I/18/110 12 ff.; July 1757[3].

I/18/111 12 ff.; June–July 1759[3].

I/18/112 12 ff.; July 1760[3].

I/18/113 12 ff.; July 1761[3].

I/18/114 14 ff.; June–July 1762[2]. ff.1–12[6]; ff.13–14[5]; f.14v.[8].

I/18/115 14 ff.; July 1763[3].

I/18/116 14 ff.; July 1764[3].

I/18/117 17 ff.; May 1765[2]. ff.1–4[6]; ff.15–16[5]; f.17[8].

I/18/118 14 ff.; July 1766[3].

I/18/119 14 ff.; July 1767[3].

I/18/120 16 ff.; July 1768[3].

I/18/121 16 ff.; Sep. 1769[2]. ff.1–13[6]; ff.14–15[5]; f.15[8].

I/18/122 16 ff.; July 1770[3].

I/18/123 17 ff.; July 1771[3].

I/18/124 17 ff.; May 1772[2]. f.1, list of ordinands, Chichester, Dec. 1772; ff.2–16[6], May 1772; f.17[5], May 1772.

I/18/125 19 ff.; July 1773[3].

I/18/126 18 ff.; July 1774[3].

[1–8] For key to these numbers, see p. 26.

I/18/127 18 ff.; May 1775[2].
ff.1–15[6]; ff.16v.–17[5].

I/18/128 18 ff.; July 1776[3].

I/18/129 18 ff.; July 1777[3].

I/18/130 18 ff.; July 1778[3].

I/18/131 18 ff.; May 1779[2].
ff.1–15[6]; ff.16v.–17[5].

I/18/132 18 ff.; July 1780[3].

I/18/133 18 ff.; July 1781[3].

I/18/134 18 ff.; July 1782[3].

I/18/135 18 ff.; May 1783[2].
ff.1–8[6]; ff.9–10[5]; ff.11–17[6].

I/18/136 16 ff.; July 1784[3].

I/18/137 16 ff.; July 1785[3].

I/18/138 16 ff.; July 1786[3].

I/18/139 18 ff.; May 1787[2].
ff.1–8[6]; ff.9–10[5]; ff.11–17[6].

I/18/140 16 ff.; July 1788[3].

I/18/141 16 ff.; July 1789[3].

I/18/142 16 ff.; July 1790[3].

I/18/143 16 ff.; July 1791[3].

I/18/144 16 ff.; July 1792[3].

I/18/145 16 ff.; July 1793[3].

I/18/146 16 ff.; July 1794[3].

I/18/147 16 ff.; July 1795[3].

I/18/148 16 ff.; July 1796[3].

I/18/149 16 ff., July 1797[3]; for episcopal visitations of the cathedral, archdeaconry of Chichester and Dean of Chichester's Peculiar, 1798, see Ep.I/18/101, ff.71–91.

I/18/150 16 ff.; July 1799[2] (*archidiaconatu vacante*).
ff.1–15[6].

I/18/151 32 pp.; June 1800[2] (*archidiaconatu vacante*).
pp.1–29[6].

I/18/152 36 pp.; July 1801[2].
pp.1–15[6]; pp.17–19[5]; pp.20–33[6].

I/18/153 30 and 37 pp.; July 1802–July 1803[3].
pp.1–29, July 1802; pp.1–29, July 1803.

I/18/154 36 pp.; Aug. 1804[2].
pp.1–14;[6] pp.15–17[5]; pp.18–30[6].

I/18/155 92 pp.; July 1805–July 1807[3].
pp.1–31, July 1805; pp.33–60, July 1806; pp.61–91, July 1807.

[1–8] For key to these numbers, see p. 26.

34

I/18/156   33 pp.; July 1808[2].
pp.1–27[6]; pp.29–31[5].

I/18/157   32 pp.; July 1811[2].
pp.1–25[6]; pp.26–28[5].

I/18/158   48 pp.; July 1812–July 1813[3].
pp.1–24, July 1812; pp.25–46, July 1813.

I/18/159   54 pp.; July 1815–July 1816[3].
flyleaf, number of parishes in each deanery, pp.1–22, July 1815; pp.23–43, July 1816.

I/18/160   32 pp.; Aug. 1817[2].
pp.1–24[6]; pp.24–26[5].

I/18/161   52 pp.; July 1818[3].

I/18/162   28 pp.; July 1820[3].

I/18/163   32 pp.; July 1821[2].

I/18/164   28 pp.; July 1822[3].

I/18/165   28 pp.; July 1823[3].

I/18/166   32 pp.; July 1824[3].

I/18/167   134 ff.; June 1825–July 1847[2].
ff.2–5[4], June 1825; ff.8v.–16[6], June 1825; ff.16–17[5], June 1825; ff.17v.–23[6], June 1825; ff.24–30[6], July 1828; ff.31–32[5], July 1828; ff.32–38[6], July 1828; ff.39–45[6], July 1831; f.46[5], July 1831; ff.47–53[6], July 1831; ff.54–68[6], Sep. 1834, ff.69–70[5], Sep. 1834; ff.71–78[6], June 1838; ff.79–80[5], June 1838; ff.80v.–87[6], June 1838; ff.88–102, lists of incumbents and curates, and visitation, 6 Oct. 1844; f.103[5], Oct. 1844; ff.104v.–120[5, 6], July 1847.

I/18/168   28 pp.; July 1832[3].

I/18/169   30 pp.; July 1833[3].

I/18/170   30 pp.; July 1835[3].

I/18/171   32 pp.; July 1836[3].

I/18/172   32 pp.; July 1837[3].

I/18/173   40 pp.; July 1839[3].

I/18/174   40 pp.; July 1840[3].

I/18/175   36 pp.; July 1841[3].

I/18/176   36 pp.; July 1842[3].

I/18/177   32 pp.; July 1843[3].

I/18/178   5 pp.; Oct. 1844[2]; lists of incumbents only[5, 6].

I/18/179   7 pp.; a copy of I/18/178.

I/18/180   34 pp.; July 1845[3].

I/18/181   40 pp.; July 1846[3].

I/18/182   38 pp.; July 1848[3].

I/18/183   46 pp.; July 1849[3].

I/18/184   46 pp.; Aug. 1851[3].

I/18/185   46 pp.; Aug. 1852[3].

I/18/186   12 pp.; 1852[3]; lists of incumbents only[6].

[1-8] For key to these numbers, see p. 26.

I/18/187   24 ff.; a copy of the episcopal visitation of the cathedral, with injunctions, July 1742, taken from Cap. I/7/1, pp.93–103, for the visitation of 1853.

I/18/188   145 ff.; Sep. 1850–July 1859[2].
ff.1–19[5,6], Sep. 1850; ff.20v.–51[5,6], Oct. 1853; ff.52–93[5,6], Oct. 1856; ff.95–132[5,6], July 1859.

I/18/189   26 ff.; Aug. 1854[3].

I/18/190   26 ff.; Aug. 1855[3].

I/18/191   40 ff.; May 1860[3].

I/18/192   46 ff.; June 1861[3].

I/18/193   178 ff.; Oct. 1862–Nov. 1871[2].
ff.1–36[5,6], Oct. 1862; ff.38–74[5,6], July 1865; ff.75–112[5,6], 1868; ff.113–151[5,6], Nov. 1871.

I/18/194   40 ff.; May 1863[3].

I/18/195   46 ff.; 1864[3].

I/18/196   48 ff.; June 1866[3].

I/18/197   47 ff.; June 1867[3].

I/18/198   48 ff.; June 1869[3].

I/18/199   46 ff.; June 1873[3].
ff.1–38, visitation; ff.39v.–41, notes of the visitation address.

I/18/200   96 pp.; Oct. 1875[2].
pp.1–79[5,6].

I/18/201   92 ff.; Oct. 1878–Aug. 1881[2].
ff.1–40[5,6], Oct. 1878; ff.42–83[5,6], Aug. 1881; ff.91v.–92, notes on the visitation address.

I/18/202   66 ff.; July 1879[3].   **I/18/203**   66 ff.; May 1880[3].

I/18/204   250 pp.; May 1882–May 1885[3].
pp.1–81, May 1882; pp.85–165, May 1883; pp.169–249, May 1885.

I/18/205   174 ff.; Aug. 1884–July 1893[2].
ff.1–41[5,6], Aug. 1884; ff.42–82[5,6], July 1887; ff.84–124[5,6], July 1890; ff.126–167[5,6], July 1893.

I/18/206   (5); loose folios from libri cleri, 1695–1734.

[1-8] For key to these numbers, see p. 26.

Ep.I/19 REGISTERS OF ORDERS, *c.*1582–*c.*1675

Every rector, vicar, curate, schoolmaster or any other holder of episcopal licence was obliged to exhibit at the bishop's first visitation, or first visitation after the clerk's admission, his letters of orders, institution and induction and all other dispensations, licences and faculties, to be approved by the bishop and signed and recorded by the registrar (canon 137). Consequently these volumes often provide details of an incumbent's ordination and admission to a benefice, and of previous incumbents and patronage; they do not appear to include curates and schoolmasters. Very few of the volumes are precisely dated; all relate to the Chichester archdeaconry and the Dean of Chichester's Peculiar, as indicated. See Ep.I/1/8a, ff.66*v.*–72, for a register of 1635.

I/19/1 20 ff.[1]; (Bishop Curteys, probably 1582, although some names of incumbents do not correspond with those in Ep.I/18/17 but with the archiepiscopal visitation of 1581 (I/18/16).
ff.1–14[5]; f.15[4]; ff.16–18[3].

I/19/2 12 ff.; [1(?), 5] *post* July 1573.

I/19/3 26 ff.; [1], probably 1597.
ff.1–3[3]; ff.5–22[5]; f.23, memoranda; f.24[4].

I/19/4 18 ff.; visitation[5], 1598 or 1603.

I/19/5 25 ff.; [2(?), 5], probably 1605.

I/19/6 24 ff.; [1], 1606.
ff.1–4[3]; ff.5–6[4]; ff.6–22[5].

I/19/7 8 ff.; draft liber cleri and register for visitation probably 1606.

I/19/8 16 ff.; [1(?)], probably 1610.
f.1[3]; ff.2–3[5]; ff.4–5[4]; ff.5–16[5].

I/19/9 19 ff. bound in part of a contemporary deed.[1] 1628.
ff.1–17[5].

I/19/10 47 ff. bound in part of a royal writ. [1], 1634, revised for [2], 1635, and for [1], 1637.
ff.2–6[3]; ff.7–40[5]; ff.41–42[4].

I/19/11 5 ff.; [1], 1662.
ff.1–2[3]; ff.3–4[5].

I/19/12 6 ff.; [1(?)], probably 1675.
ff.1–6[5].

[1] Episcopal visitation.
[2] Metropolitical visitation.
[3] Of the Cathedral.
[4] Of the Dean of Chichester's Peculiar.
[5] Of the Chichester archdeaconry.

Ep.I/20 VISITATION PAPERS, 1554-1910

The bishop normally held a visitation of his diocese triennially, although the real task of personal inspection of each church devolved on the archdeacon, who usually visited his archdeaconry once a year. During visitations all inferior jurisdictions were inhibited, although for convenience this inhibition was often relaxed. Consequently the papers here include the Dean of Chichester's Peculiar (and, in the case of metropolitical visitations, the Archbishop's Peculiars), and are mostly concerned with citations to appear, as follows (all except the mandates mentioned in footnote 13 relate to episcopal or metropolitical visitations only). Metropolitical visitations are indicated.

[1] Inhibitions from the Bishop to the Dean of Chichester and the Archdeacons of Chichester and Lewes, restraining them from exercising jurisdiction during the visitation, and inhibitions and mandates from the Archbishop to the Bishop.

[2] Mandates from the Bishop to apparitors in each of the four Chichester rural deaneries to cite all clergy in the deanery and the old and new churchwardens to appear before the Bishop, usually in the Cathedral; episcopal mandates for synods.

[3] Mandates from the Bishop to the Dean to cite the dignitaries and prebendaries to appear.

[4] Mandates from the Dean to his virger to cite the dignitaries and prebendaries (individually) to appear (from 1733 all are named together on one document).

[5] Mandates from the Dean to his apparitor in his Peculiar to cite all clergy and churchwardens to appear.

[6] Certificates from the Dean to the Bishop (or Archbishop) that the citations have been served; apparitors' returns of incumbents and old and new churchwardens, and of those not appearing or not exhibiting the required documents (see Ep.I/19).

[7] Articles of enquiry sent to Cathedral clergy and staff, and answers.

[8] Churchwardens' presentments (see Ep.I/22).

[9] Certificates, mostly of appointment of churchwardens and of several neighbouring clergy undertaking to help serve a parish temporarily on behalf of an absent incumbent.

[10] Suspensions of prebendaries absent without excuse from visitations, their petitions for restoration to their stalls, and relaxations of suspension.

[11] Petitions presented to the Bishop (or Archbishop) at visitation by clergy and people, mostly relating to loss of letters of orders, etc., or to alleged ill-treatment; letters of excuse for non-attendance, and appointments of proxies.

[12] Other papers, including memoranda, letters testimonial, a few cause papers and acts of court, and older documents used as covers.

[13] Mandates from the Archdeacon of Chichester to apparitors in each of his rural deaneries to cite all clergy and the old and new churchwardens to appear before him.

I/20/1   (1); [2], Aug. 1554.

I/20/2   (42); [1,4-6,12], Apr. 1582.

I/20/3   (1); [2], Sep. 1589.

I/20/4   (19); [1,3,4,6,9,11,12], Sep. 1597.

I/20/5   (17); [4], Aug. 1603.

I/20/6   (56); [1,4,6-9,11,12], July 1605 (metropolitical).

I/20/7 (68); [1–4, 6, 7, 11, 12], lists of "orders to be observed" at the visitation and the "Sussex Commission for Charitable uses" (39 Eliz. I c.6, 1597, repealed 43 Eliz. c.9, 1601), 1606.

I/20/8 (1); [2], Sep. 1608.

I/20/9 (32); [1, 4, 7], Sep. 1619.

I/20/10 (40); [1, 4, 6, 7, 9, 12], Sep. 1622.

I/20/10a (31); [1, 4, 6, 7, 12], Sep. 1625.

I/20/11 (34); [1, 3, 4, 6], Sep. 1628.

I/20/12 (55); [1–4, 6, 9–12], Sep. 1631.

I/20/13 (32); [1, 4, 6], Aug. 1634.

I/20/14 96 ff.; [1, 4, 6, 10–12], May 1635 (metropolitical); f.48 is printed in *Sussex Notes and Queries*, vol. 9, pp.157–8.

I/20/15 (3); [2], Oct. 1635.

I/20/16 (1); [13], Apr. 1639.

I/20/17 (2); [4], Dec. 1641.

I/20/18 (2); [6], no date [1603 and 1626–9].

I/20/19 (1); [4], Sep. 1662.

I/20/20 (3); [1], Apr. 1663 (metropolitical).

I/20/21 (1); [12], Sep. 1666.

I/20/22 (2); [1, 4], June 1669.

I/20/23 (1); [4], Aug. 1670.

I/20/24 (4); [13], Apr. 1671.

I/20/25 (4); [13], Apr. 1672.

I/20/26 (1); [13], Apr. 1674.

I/20/27 (26); [1, 2, 4, 6, 7], Aug. 1675.

I/20/28 (1); [13], Mar. 1675/6.

I/20/28a (6); [2, 4, 6], Aug. 1678.

I/20/29 (3); [2, 6, 12], May 1679.

I/20/29a (1); Bishop's commission to vicar-general to hold visitation on his behalf, Oct. 1683.

I/20/29b (1); [13], May 1684.

I/20/30 (1); [2], Mar. 1685.

I/20/31 (11); [2, 4], Sep. 1686.

I/20/32 (3); [2], June 1690.

I/20/33 (2); [13], Mar. 1690/1.

I/20/34 (3); [2], May 1692.

I/20/35 (1); [13], Mar. 1692/3.

I/20/36 (3); [13], May 1694.

I/20/37 (1); [12], Oct. 1695.

I/20/38 (4); [13], Apr. 1696.

I/20/39 (3); [13], Apr. 1698.

I/20/40 (1); [13], Apr. 1699.

I/20/41 (1); [13], Apr. 1701.

I/20/42 (2); [13], Apr. 1702.

I/20/43 (1); [2], Mar. 1702/3.

I/20/44 (1); [13], May 1704.

I/20/45 (2); [13], May 1705.

I/20/46 (2); [13], May 1707.

I/20/47 (1); [13], Apr. 1708.

I/20/48 (2); [2], June 1710.

[1–13] For key to these numbers, see p. 38.

I/20/49 (4); [1,2], Apr. 1713.

I/20/50 (1); [13], May 1715.

I/20/51 (1); [2], June 1723.

I/20/52 (2); [1,2], June 1726.

I/20/53 (36); [1,2,6,7,11,12], Sep. 1727.

I/20/54 (1); [13], May 1728.

I/20/55 (7); [2-4], May 1733, with lists of churchwardens.

I/20/56 (4); [13], May 1734.

I/20/57 (1); [13], Apr. 1735.

I/20/58 (1); [13], Apr. 1736, with lists of churchwardens.

I/20/59 (3); [2,9], May 1737.

I/20/60 (2); [13], May 1739.

I/20/61 (5); [2,6,7], no date [1731–40].

I/20/61a (8); [6,7], 1742, 1754, 1755, 1757.

I/20/62 (4); [3,4,6,7], June 1798.

I/20/63 (2); [6,7], *post* 1800.

I/20/64 (1); [6], 1817.

I/20/65 (5); [6], 1821.

I/20/66 (1); [4], June 1847, with verger's endorsement.

I/20/67 12 ff. unbound; copy correspondence between Bishop A. T. Gilbert and Thomas Brown (Prebendary of Highleigh, 1840–78, and perpetual curate of Chichester St. Paul, 1837–78) relating to endowments of parish churches, and capitular patronage, 1848.

I/20/68 (2); [1], June 1858.

I/20/69 (1); notes on procedure for Bishop R. Durnford's first visitation, Nov. 1871, with his comments.

I/20/70 (1); articles of enquiry for rural dean's visitation, Rudgwick, Apr. 1872.

I/20/71 (2); notice of episcopal visitation, Pulborough, Oct. 1875.

I/20/72 (1); notice of archdeacon's visitation, Chichester, 1910, used as a precedent for Lewes.

Ep.I/21 PROCURATION BOOKS AND PAPERS, 1681–1901

The costs of visitation were met by procurations, which were money compositions for the former custom of giving hospitality to the visitor in kind. Procurations (including synodals and indemnities) were payable to the archdeacon annually, even without actual visitation if he was inhibited from so doing by the bishop's triennial visitation; they were also due to the bishop by reason of his visitation. Tenths were payable annually to the bishop by the Cathedral dignitaries, some prebendaries and the

[1-13] For key to these numbers, see p. 38.

deaneries of Boxgrove and Midhurst (see Ep.I/51/3, ff.200–205). No distinction has been made here between episcopal and archidiaconal procurations. All volumes relate to the archdeaconry of Chichester only; they are arranged according to deaneries, and from I/21/29 onwards include the former Peculiar jurisdictions.

I/21/1 8 ff. ff.1–4, procurations, 1681.

I/21/2 6 ff. ff.2–5, procurations, 1687.

I/21/3 6 ff. ff.2–5, procurations, 1688.

I/21/4 12 ff. ff.1–12, procurations, 1696–1702.

I/21/5 16 ff. ff.1–16, procurations, 1703-7.

I/21/6 41 ff. ff.1–40, procurations, 1708–17.

I/21/7 22 ff. ff.1–22, procurations, 1718-23.

I/21/7a 19 ff. ff.1–19, procurations, 1723–27.

I/21/8 28 ff. ff.1–28, procurations, 1728–34.

I/21/9 1 parchment membrane; tenths, 1728.

I/21/10 19 ff. f.1v., arrears of tenths; ff.2–12, tenths, **1731**; ff.17–19, accounts for Bishop Waddington's funeral, 1731.

I/21/11 8 ff. ff.1–6, tenths, 1732.

I/21/12 6 ff. ff.1–6, tenths, 1734–5.

I/21/13 7 ff. ff.1–6, tenths and procurations, 1736–9.

I/21/14 6 ff. ff.1–6, tenths and procurations, 1740–3.

I/21/15 8 ff. ff.1–8, tenths and procurations, 1743–5.

I/21/16 4 ff. ff.1–4, tenths and procurations, 1742–6.

I/21/17 8 ff. ff.1–7, tenths and procurations, 1750–2; f.8, collection for the Society for the Propagation of the Gospel, 1752.

I/21/18 8 ff. ff.1–7, tenths and procurations, 1759–60.

I/21/19 7 ff. ff.1–7, tenths and procurations, 1760–1.

I/21/20 8 ff. ff.1–4, procurations, no date.

I/21/21 8 ff. ff.1–7, tenths, 1765–72.

I/21/22 8 ff. ff.1–8, tenths and procurations, 1773–9.

I/21/23 8 ff. ff.1–8, tenths and procurations, 1780–9.

I/21/24 8 ff. ff.1–4, tenths, 1790–1801, ff.5–8, episcopal visitations, 1798–1806.

I/21/24a (3); account of tenths due, Christmas 1790, 1791 and 1792.

I/21/25 4 ff. ff.1–4, procurations, 1798–1806.

I/21/26 7 loose ff.; accounts for visitations, 1801–1808.

I/21/27 2 ff. ff.1–2, procurations, no date (early 19th cent.)

I/21/28 1 f.; tenths, 1833–41.

I/21/28a (34); procurations, 1843–1867 (later called 'Archdeacon's account').

I/21/29 10 ff. ff.1–10. tenths and procurations, 1862.

I/21/30 18 ff. ff.1–18, tenths and procurations, 1863–5.

I/21/31 8 ff. ff.1–8, procurations, 1864–8.

I/21/32 20 ff. ff.1–13, tenths and procurations, 1866–7.

I/21/33 48 ff. ff.1–48, procurations, 1868–87.

I/21/34 34 ff. ff.1 -34, procurations, 1888–1901.

I/21/35 8 ff. ff.1–8, procurations, n.d. [late 19th cent.].

I/21/36 10 ff. ff.1–10, procurations, n.d. [late 19th cent.].

EP.I/22 CHURCHWARDENS' PRESENTMENTS, 1573–1917

Churchwardens and "sidemen" were required[1] to present offenders against ecclesiastical law at least once a year (usually twice, at Easter and Michaelmas) and at visitation; they could also make "voluntary presentments" at any time. Presentments were written out by the churchwardens on single sheets of paper or were in the form of answers to a set of articles of visitation and enquiry sent by the archdeacon, bishop or archbishop before visitation.[2] In the 18th century the answers were written in the margin of printed books of articles,[3] and by the 19th century on printed

---

[1] By Canons 109–119 and Canon 26.

[2] Photostat copies of articles issued by bishops of Chichester in 1586, 1600, 1628, 1631, 1637 and 1638, and by archdeacons in 1635 and 1640, are in the West Sussex Record Office Library.

[3] The articles were prefaced by the churchwardens' and sidemen's oath: "You will swear, that you will diligently enquire, and true Presentment make, of all Defaults and Offences committed in your Parish, against the Ecclesiastical Law of this Realm, to the best of your Skill and Knowledge".

forms. Although most of the single folio presentments are merely certificates that there was "nothing presentable" in the parish, the answers to the articles give much valuable information about the clergy and church officers, services, church fabric, behaviour of the parishioners, and the number of schools, hospitals, schoolmasters, doctors and midwives. By the 19th century the more detailed returns are concerned primarily with the conduct of the clergy, with the services and the fabric and finances of the church. Dating is often uncertain; in the 17th century sometimes only the date of the articles was given, which could be several years before the presentment, as the same set might be used throughout one episcopate. Single presentments were dated for either the year about which, or the year in which, the churchwardens were writing. Many of the documents are bundled apparently according to rural deaneries, but this was a later arrangement and is not always accurate. Other presentments exhibited in the consistory courts, will be found in Ep.I/15, some among the visitation papers (Ep.I/20) and some are written on the same sheets as the bishop's transcripts (Ep.I/24). From 1850 the former Peculiar jurisdictions are included.

I/22/1 4,918 loose presentments, a calendar of which is available in the Diocesan Record Office (Ep.I/88/1).

1573	1	1677	29	1745	1	1783	18
1584	59	1678	47	1746	17	1784	87
1592	1	1679	1	1749	2	1785	60
1597	1	1680	13	1750	2	1786	100
1598	1	1681	2	1751	1	1787	34
1602	3	1682	1	1753	12	1788	48
1604	1	1684	1	1754	1	1789	30
1606	1	1685	2	1755	32	1790	28
1624	1	1686	43	1756	2	1791	25
1626	1	1688	1	1758	121	1792	8
1628	2	1697	1	1762	108	1793	43
1636	29	1698	2	1765	43	1794	37
1640	69	1701	1	1766	66	1795	131
1641	1	1703	1	1767	91	1796	156
1662	150	1711	3	1768	61	1797	15
1663	67	1712	1	1769	108	1798	1
1664	67	1716	1	1770	5	1799	102
1665	107	1725	1	1771	51	1800	171
1666	65	1726	45	1772	66	1806	1
1667	123	1727	1	1773	13	1821	1
1668	139	1728	4	1774	68	1825	11
1669	97	1729	25	1775	116	1828	102
1670	18	1730	6	1776	79	1845	1
1671	43	1731	1	1777	5	1847	1
1672	138	1733	39	1778	67	1850	5
1673	104	1737	49	1779	55	1853	125
1674	82	1741	4	1780	3	1868	111
1675	45	1742	89	1781	139	1873	1
1676	111	1744	34	1782	72		

and 102 undateable documents.

I/22/2 Bound volumes of presentments, presumably complete, except for 1850, for which there are others in I/22/1. Some of the loose presentments for 1868 are duplicated here.

1838	1858	1868	1892
1850	1859	1888	1894
1856	1862	1889	1895
1857	1865	1891	1896

1897	1902	1907	1911
1899	1904	1908	1912
1900	1905	1910	1917
1901			

I/22/3 (8); printed articles of enquiry to churchwardens, filled in, but with dates and parishes missing [18th cent.], and one copy of articles exhibited in the diocese of Canterbury, 1827.

I/22/4 (1); unused form of articles of enquiry to churchwardens, 1903.

Ep.I/22A MINISTERS' ARTICLES OF ENQUIRY, 1804–1903

Similar articles of visitation and enquiry (see Ep.I/22) were sent to incumbents, asking for information about curates, services held, church fabric and finance, schools and dissenters. See Ep.V/16a for the 1875 return for West Tarring.

I/22A/1 Bound volumes of returns from incumbents throughout the diocese; these are arranged alphabetically by parishes, presumably complete, in three volumes for each year.

1878	1884	1890
1881	1887	1893

I/22A/2 Returns from the Chichester archdeaconry. All are bound, and presumably complete, except 1825, 1828, 1853 and some for 1850; a calendar of the loose papers is available in the Diocesan Record Office (Ep.I/88/1).

1825	3 docs.	1850	1 vol. & 9 docs.	1862		1898
1828	62 docs.	1853	113 docs.	1865		1903
1844		1856		1868		
1847		1859		1875	2 vols.	

I/22A/3 (18); letters and papers, 1804–1810, on the state of church fabric, and abstracts of answers to ministers' articles of enquiry, whole diocese.

I/22A/4 (1); "Observations" on "Ministers' Returns" from the archdeaconry of Chichester, 1862, noting unsatisfactory answers.

I/22A/5 (1); unused form of ministers' articles of enquiry, 1903.

Ep.I/23 REGISTERS OF PRESENTMENTS, 1571–1682

All positive presentments were entered in these registers, arranged according to rural deaneries; names of churchwardens are only occasionally given. In the case of answers to the articles of enquiry the number of the article is given in the margins; for original presentments see Ep.I/22. I/23/8 is printed in *Sussex Record Society*, vol. 49.

I/23/1 86 ff.; July and Sep. 1571.

I/23/2 28 ff.; 1573.

I/23/3 24 ff.; Sep. 1573.

I/23/4 47 ff.; Dec. 1573–Dec. 1574.

I/23/5 67 ff.; 1579.

I/23/6 21 ff.; May 1584.

I/23/7 41 ff. bound in a copy of the will of John Colpys of Stoughton, 1584; 1586.

I/23/8 52 ff.
ff.1–41, Easter 1621–Michaelmas 1626; f.42, Easter 1628; ff.43–52, Easter 1664–1670.

I/23/9 3 ff.; 1678.

I/23/10 2 ff.; n.d. [*post* 1682].

Ep.I/24 PARISH REGISTER TRANSCRIPTS, 1567–1936

By a Canterbury provincial constitution (25 Oct. 1596; royal approval 1598), churchwardens were directed to send to the diocesan registry every year within a month of Easter (from 1603, within a month of Lady Day) a transcript of the parish register entries for the preceding year. Rose's Act (52 Geo. III c.146; in force 1 Jan. 1813) transferred the obligation to the incumbent, who was to return the transcripts, written on parchment, within two months of the end of each year. By the late 19th century many incumbents had stopped this practice, and the registry did not continue to demand the transcripts. For a few parishes transcripts were made and returned until the early 20th century, the last of all being Broadwater, where the series ends in 1936.

Even in earlier years transcripts were not always made and returned as directed, but a list of them, giving the years represented for each parish, is given as an Appendix to this book. The documents are bundled according to parishes, not years.

Ep.I/24A PAPERS FOUND WITH THE TRANSCRIPTS, 1573–1863

(7). During the listing of Ep.I/24 many loose papers were found in the bundles; most were churchwardens' presentments, which have been transferred to their respective classes, and these are the remainder. The seven are lists of transcripts not returned on time, of extant parish registers, c.1812, letters, and a list of communicants (by name) at Trotton in 1573.

Ep.I/25 CHURCH TERRIERS, 1572–1692

A typescript calendar of these terriers is available in the Diocesan Record Office (Ep.I/88/1).

I/25/1 (49); Arundel deanery.

1572	1	1635	18	1664	1	1687	1
1615	18	1663	8	1673	1	1689	1

and a copy made in 1801 of the Barnham terrier, with two papers (1809) relating to land tax assessment.

I/25/2 (66); Midhurst deanery.

1615	27	1636	1	1686	3
1635	31	1663	3		

and photostat copy of *Calendar of Inquisitiones Nonarum* (1807), pp. 364–5, showing terriers (1341) of 12 parishes in the Boxgrove and Midhurst deaneries.

I/25/3 (85); Storrington deanery.

See *Sussex Archaeological Collections*, vol. 41, pp. 132–3, for abstracts of the Itchingfield terriers, 1615, 1635 (misprinted 1625) and 1663.

1615	26	1635	31	1663	23	1675	1
1616	1	1637	1	1664	1	1692	1

I/25/4 Microfilm of E. H. W. Dunkin's transcript of these terriers (BM. Add. MS. 39467).

Ep.I/26 CHURCH INSPECTION BOOKS, 1602–1724

Four inspections (1602, 1636, 1687, 1724) are represented. I/26/1 and 2 contain churchwardens' reports of dilapidations; I/26/3 contains tabulated answers to questions on parish charities, population, services and the value of the living, as well as on the fabric of the church. I/26/1 and 2 do not include every parish in the archdeaconry. A transcript index (by parishes) to all volumes is available in the Diocesan Record Office (Ep.I/88/1).

I/26/1 34 ff. ff.1–18, inspections, 1602–3; ff.20–33, court proceedings on these inspections, May 1603–Jan. 1603/4.

I/26/2 37 ff. ff.1–37, inspections, Nov. 1636.

I/26/2a (1); the original return for the Midhurst deanery, Mar. 1686/7.

I/26/3 46 ff. repaired and rebound at the Public Record Office in 1936; known as Bishop Bowers's Visitation Book. See N. Caplan, 'Visitation of the Diocese of Chichester in 1724' in *Sussex Notes and Queries*, vol. 15, pp. 289–295.

flyleaf, contemporary index to deaneries; f.1, copy of the episcopal commission and questions to be answered; ff.1v.–46, inspection of the whole diocese (except Peculiars) arranged by deaneries, 1724. (The Lewes portion is also in Ep.II/18/2.)

I/26/4 (28); the original returns for the Arundel deanery, 1724.

PROBATE RECORDS

Some of the probate records are stored in the West Sussex Record Office, and have been given the following catalogue marks, but as a matter of convenience have been included in this catalogue:

STC   Sussex Testamentary [Records, Archdeaconry of] Chichester.

STD   Sussex Testamentary [Records], Dean [of Chichester's Peculiar].

STA   Sussex Testamentary [Records], Archbishop [of Canterbury's Peculiar (Deanery of Pagham and Tarring)].

STM   Sussex Testamentary Modern [Records].

A more detailed catalogue of the above records is available in the Diocesan Record Office (Ep.I/88/2).

Ep.I/27 TESTAMENTS AND WILLS, 16th century – 1842

Three boxes of testaments and wills, letters of administration and related documents, most of which are registered in British Record Society, vols. 49 and 64. A few documents belong to other jurisdictions; almost all are in bad condition. The *post* 1800 documents consist of:

1802	1	1815	1	1828	1	1836	2
1811	2	1817	1	1830	1	1837	1
1812	2	1825	1	1834	1	1838	1
1814	1	1826	2	1835	1	1842	1

The main series of original testaments and wills for the archdeaconry of Chichester, 1534–1857, is STC II.[1]

The registers of wills, 1479–1858 (indexed to 1800 by the British Record Society, vol. 49), are STC I, as follows:

STC I/1 1479–1553 (not in chronological order; very few probates).

STC I/2 1479–1551 (not in chronological order; very few probates).

STC I/3 1520–1555 (includes also the Dean of Chichester's Peculiar and the Deanery of Pagham and Tarring). ff.110–125 are an ecclesiastical formulary (1547–1553), a typescript calendar of which is in Ep.I/88/1.

STC I/4 This volume relates to the archdeaconry of Lewes and was sent to the Lewes District Probate Registry in 1859.

STC I/5 Sep. 1543–June 1547.

STC I/6 Sep. 1545–Apr. 1546.

STC I/7 Jan. 1547/8–June 1552.

STC I/8 July 1552–Dec. 1557 (includes also the Dean of Chichester's Peculiar and the Deanery of Pagham and Tarring).

---

[1] This is a large group of records arranged chronologically. Readers are requested to ask for the document(s) by giving the name of the testator, the parish and the year of probate where the latter is known.

STC I/9   Dec. 1557–Sep. 1559 (includes archdeaconry of Lewes, Sep. 1567, on ff.145–146).

STC I/10   June 1560–Nov. 1571.

STC I/11   As STC I/4.

STC I/12   Oct. 1577–May 1581; Oct. 1581–1582.

STC I/13   Sep. 1582–Feb. 1585/6.

STC I/14   Mar. 1585/6–Feb. 1598/9 (includes 2 wills proved P.C.C. May 1597 and Jan. 1610/11).

STC I/15   Mar. 1599–Mar. 1605/6; Mar. 1607–Dec. 1610.

STC I/16   Sep. 1617–Apr. 1620.

STC I/17   Mar. 1626–Apr. 1629.

STC I/18   Apr. 1630–May 1635.

STC I/19   Mar. 1636–Jan. 1637/8; May 1637 and Jan. 1644/5.

STC I/20   Apr. 1638–Apr. 1639.

STC I/21   July 1640–Jan. 1652/3.

STC I/21b   This is a collection of various documents copied by Richard Bragge and formerly known as vol. 22A. For details of entries other than wills see Ep.I/88/2.

ff.1–85, wills, P.C.C., Feb. 1651/2–May 1668; f.131, loose copy of part of will of James Sawyer of Horsham, n.d.; ff.170–161, miscellaneous Commonwealth probate papers; f.171, list of wills proved P.C.C. 1616–1633; ff.175–172, miscellaneous Commonwealth papers (probate and civil).

STC I/22b   Sep. 1660–Mar. 1661/2.

STC I/23   Apr. 1662–Nov. 1668.

STC I/24   Nov. 1668–Jan. 1670/1.

STC I/25   Mar. 1671–Mar. 1674/5.

STC I/26   Aug. 1674–Jan. 1677/8, and wills without probates, 1651–1677.

STC I/27   Apr. 1678–May 1684.

STC I/28   June 1685–May 1688, and wills without probates, 1671–1687.

STC I/29   July 1688–Mar. 1692/3.

STC I/30   July 1693–Dec. 1706.

STC I/31	Dec. 1706–Nov. 1715.	**STC I/44**	Nov. 1782–Feb. 1794.
STC I/32	Oct. 1715–Feb. 1720/1.	**STC I/45**	Mar. 1794–Mar. 1801.
STC I/33	Feb. 1720/1–Sep. 1725.	**STC I/46**	Mar. 1801–Apr. 1807.
STC I/34	Oct. 1725–Jan. 1730/1.	**STC I/47**	Apr. 1807–Mar. 1815.
STC I/35	Jan. 1730/1–Jan. 1734/5.	**STC I/48**	Apr. 1815–Aug. 1821.

STC I/36 Jan. 1734/5–July 1739.

STC I/37 July 1739–Mar. 1743.

STC I/49 Aug. 1821–Apr. 1828, and Mar. 1821 (p.526).

STC I/38 May 1743–Dec. 1751.

STC I/50 Apr. 1828–Aug. 1833.

STC I/39 Sep. 1750–Nov. 1756.

STC I/51 Aug. 1833–May 1838.

STC I/40 Aug. 1756–Jan. 1763.

STC I/52 Apr. 1838–Oct. 1843.

STC I/41 Jan. 1763–May 1768.

STC I/53 Oct. 1843–Dec. 1848.

STC I/42 May 1768–July 1774.

STC I/54 Jan. 1849–June 1854.

STC I/43 May 1774–Nov. 1782.

STC I/55 June 1854–Jan. 1858.

This series continues as STM; the following registers were transferred from Winchester in 1962:

STM/1	Jan. 1858–Feb. 1859.	**STM/13**	Jan. 1879–Dec. 1880.
STM/2	Feb. 1859–July 1860.	**STM/14**	Jan. 1881–Dec. 1882.
STM/3	July 1860–Apr. 1861.	**STM/15**	Jan. 1883–Dec. 1884.

STM/4 May 1861–Aug. 1861. [The volume immediately following this was not transferred.]

STM/16 Jan. 1885–Dec. 1886.

STM/17 Jan. 1887–Dec. 1888.

STM/5	Jan. 1863–Dec. 1864.	**STM/18**	Jan. 1889–Dec. 1890.
STM/6	Jan. 1865–Dec. 1866.	**STM/19**	Jan. 1891–Dec. 1892.
STM/7	Jan. 1867–Dec. 1868.	**STM/20**	Jan. 1893–Dec. 1894.
STM/8	Jan. 1869–Dec. 1870.	**STM/21**	Jan. 1895–Dec. 1896.
STM/9	Jan. 1871–Dec. 1872.	**STM/22**	Jan. 1897–Dec. 1898.
STM/10	Jan. 1873–Dec. 1874.	**STM/23**	Jan. 1899–Dec. 1900.
STM/11	Dec. 1874–Dec. 1876.	**STM/24**	Jan. 1901–Dec. 1902.
STM/12	Jan. 1877–Dec. 1878.	**STM/25**	Jan. 1903–Dec. 1904.

STM/26	Jan. 1905–Dec. 1906.	**STM/32**	Jan. 1917–Dec. 1918.
STM/27	Jan. 1907–Dec. 1908.	**STM/33**	Jan. 1919–Dec. 1920.
STM/28	Jan. 1909–Dec. 1910.	**STM/34**	Jan. 1921–Dec. 1922.
STM/29	Jan. 1911–Dec. 1912.	**STM/35**	Jan. 1923–Dec. 1924.
STM/30	Jan. 1913–Dec. 1914.	**STM/36**	Jan. 1925–Dec. 1926.
STM/31	Jan. 1915–Dec. 1916.	**STM/37**	Jan. 1927–Dec. 1928.

Ep.I/28 PROBATE COMMISSIONS, 17th–19th centuries

Five boxes of probate commissions; most of the wills and administrations to which they relate are indexed in British Record Society, vols. 49 and 64. A few documents belong to other jurisdictions; many are in bad condition. They include the Commonwealth period.

Ep.I/29 PROBATE INVENTORIES, 1560–1834

These are arranged in two series, called A and B. Series A (1560–1778) are those on which Dr. E. Jaffé worked (her explanation of the arrangement and index is W.S.R.O. MP363), and series B (1581–1834) are the remainder. All jurisdictions are included; card indexes of persons and parishes (both series) are in the W.S.R.O.

Ep.I/30 RENUNCIATIONS, 16th–19th centuries

Three boxes; this group includes appointment of proxies as well as instruments of renunciation of their duties by administrators and executors. Most of the wills and administrations to which they relate are indexed in British Record Society, vols. 49 and 64.

Ep.I/31 PROBATE DIARIES, 1555/6–1858

Administration acts are indexed to 1799 in British Record Society, vol. 64

STC III/A Probate and administration acts, Mar. 1555/6–Dec. 1572.

STC III/B Probate, administration and account acts, sequestrations and marriage licences, Apr. 1575–Mar. 1594/5.

STC III/Ba As in STC III/B, Mar. 1585/6–Mar. 1588/9; this volume was not indexed by British Record Society.

Ep.I/31/1 65 ff. (some entries are duplicated); probate, administration and account acts, caveats, institutions and citations, Apr. 1589–Mar. 1591/2.

STC III/C Probate, administration and account acts, sequestrations, institutions and memoranda, Oct. 1577–Feb. 1585/6.

STC III/D Probate, administration and account acts, and marriage licences, Mar. 1594/5–Mar. 1600/1.

Ep.I/31/2 59 ff. ff.1–2, receipts for rent paid by Richard Juxon, in Vicars' Close, Apr. 1597–Oct. 1600; ff.3–55, probate, administration and account acts, marriage licences, caveats and citations, Mar. 1598/9–Mar. 1601/2; f.56, debts of the curate of Meeching, 1540.

STC III/E As in STC III/B, Mar. 1600/1–Mar. 1612/3.

STC III/F As in STC III/B, Mar. 1612/3–Mar. 1624/5.

Ep.I/31/3 55 ff. probate, administration and account acts, marriage licences, caveats and memoranda, Oct. 1623–June 1626.

STC III/G Probate, administrations and account acts, Mar. 1624/5–Mar. 1634/5.

STC III/H As in STC III/B, Mar. 1634/5–Mar. 1665/6.

STC III/K As in STC III/G, July 1644–Oct. 1653.

STC III/I As in STC III/B, Mar. 1665/6–Mar. 1670/1.

STC III/L As in STC III/B, Mar. 1667/8–Apr. 1672.

Ep.I/31/4 21 ff.; this is printed in *Sussex Notes and Queries*, vol. 12, pp. 37–9.
ff.3–5, as in STC III/B, Oct. 1675–Jan. 1675/6.

Ep.I/31/5 40 ff. ff.1–30, administrations, 1679–84; this volume was not indexed by British Record Society.

Ep.I/31/6 10 ff. ff.1–7, administrations, 1679–83; this volume was not indexed by British Record Society.

STC III/M Probate, administration and account acts, and sequestrations, Mar. 1696/7–Dec. 1714.

STC III/N Probate and administration acts, and sequestrations, Dec. 1714–Mar. 1728/9.

STC III/O Mar. 1729–Sep. 1738.

STC III/P Oct. 1738–June 1749. **STC III/T** Jan. 1783–Dec. 1799.

STC III/Q June 1749–Dec. 1757. **STC III/U** Jan. 1800–Dec. 1812.

STC III/R Jan. 1758–Sep. 1768. **STC III/V** Jan. 1813–Dec. 1825.

STC III/S Sep. 1768–Dec. 1782. **STC III/W** Jan. 1826–Apr. 1840.

STC III/X Apr. 1840–July 1850.

STC III/Y Probate and administration acts, sequestrations, faculties and consecrations, visitation documents and memoranda, Aug. 1850–Jan. 1858; and, except for probate and administration acts, the same for 1858–July 1865.

Ep.I/31/7 8 ff.; stray folios from probate diaries. ff.1–2, Nov. 1551; ff.3–4, Feb. 1644/5–June 1645; ff.5–6, 1678; f.7, 1644–5; f.8, 1599–1610.

Ep.I/32 ADMINISTRATION BONDS, 1760–1858

(3,869.)

1760	63	1785	42	1810	27	1835	27
1761	80	1786	52	1811	23	1836	17
1762	68	1787	58	1812	36	1837	24
1763	88	1788	58	1813	20	1838	21
1764	64	1789	58	1814	23	1839	12
1765	55	1790	48	1815	27	1840	22
1766	73	1791	66	1816	16	1841	19
1767	79	1792	54	1817	28	1842	19
1768	84	1793	65	1818	19	1843	15
1769	90	1794	52	1819	22	1844	21
1770	68	1795	53	1820	29	1845	23
1771	75	1796	36	1821	20	1846	18
1772	76	1797	45	1822	24	1847	23
1773	65	1798	57	1823	23	1848	30
1774	62	1799	81	1824	24	1849	16
1775	52	1800	69	1825	27	1850	19
1776	83	1801	30	1826	28	1851	32
1777	57	1802	10	1827	37	1852	14
1778	76	1803	19	1828	21	1853	19
1779	54	1804	21	1829	25	1854	15
1780	51	1805	24	1830	22	1855	25
1781	81	1806	16	1831	32	1856	30
1782	75	1807	39	1832	25	1857	16
1783	82	1808	32	1833	28	1858	1
1784	48	1809	22	1834	29		

The bonds for 1605–1759 are part of the STC group mentioned on p. 47, and are subdivision V of that group.[1]

Ep.I/33 PROBATE ACCOUNTS, 16th–18th centuries

Six boxes of executors' and administrators' accounts, most of which relate to entries in British Record Society, vols. 49 and 64.

Ep.I/34 CALENDARS, 1488–1814

These indexes to the wills and administrations are now largely superseded by vols. 49 and 64 in the Index Library (British Record Society). The

---

[1] The catalogue mark for this large group of bonds must not be confused with the Probate Diary, STC III/V mentioned on p. 51. These records are arranged chronologically; readers are requested to ask for the document(s) by giving the name of the deceased person and the year of administration where the latter is known.

volume formerly numbered I/34/4, being completely unused has been destroyed.

I/34/1   24 ff.   ff.1–23, index of wills, 1488–1543.

I/34/2   24 ff.   ff.1–20, index of wills, 1801–1807.

I/34/3   24 ff.   ff.1–23, index of wills, 1807–1814.

I/34/5   40 ff.   ff.2–37, index of diaries, 1595–1670.

I/34/6   48 ff.   ff.3–45, index of diaries, 1600–1670.

I/34/7   18 ff.   ff.1–9, notes of probate, administrations and marriage licences for accounting, 1672–9; f.9a, procurations unpaid, no date; f.10v., briefs; f.11, a precedent; ff.17–12, assignations (instance), Feb. 1677/8– Oct. 1678.

I/34/8   42 ff.   ff.1–21, index of wills, 1671–1675; ff.23–42, index of marriage licences by parishes, 1671–1675.

Other indexes, compiled at different times by officers of the courts, are in STC VIII, as follows (1–4, 7–9 are now superseded by British Record Society, vols. 49 and 64):

STC VIII/1   Wills, 1518–1574 (contemporary).

STC VIII/2   Wills, 1575–1613 (contemporary).

STC VIII/3   Wills, 1613–1670 (contemporary).

STC VIII/4   Late 19th cent. index to STC I/1–3, 5–10, compiled by E. H. W. Dunkin.

STC VIII/5   Late 19th cent. index to STC I/21–55, STD I/6–10 and STA I/10–15, wills, 1644–1857, A–J.

STC VIII/6   As STC VIII/5, K–Z.

STC VIII/7   Late 19th cent. index to STC I/4 and 11.

STC VIII/8   Administrations, 1577–1599 (contemporary).

STC VIII/9   Administrations, 1600–1609 (contemporary).

STC VIII/10   19th cent. calendar of administrations, giving name, parish, date and total of inventory, 1595–1618, 1697–1857.

STC VIII/11   19th cent. calendar of administrations, giving name, parish and date, 1556–1568, 1595–1618, 1597–1839, and index to STC I/1 and 3.

STC VIII/12   19th cent. calendar of administrations, giving name, parish and date, 1595–1857.

Ep.I/35 STAMP OFFICE ACCOUNTS, 1811–1858

These relate to the stamp duty payable on grants of probate and administration made in the Bishop's, Dean's and Archbishop's consistory courts at Chichester.

I/35/1 (28); copies of annual returns to the Stamp Office, and letters, 1811–1826. By the Act 42 Geo. III c.99 s.3 (1802) registrars were bound to "furnish such Accounts and particulars of Wills as the Commissioners of Stamps may require".

I/35/2 (7); "List of Grants of Probate and Administration, upon which the Stamps have been rectified under the provisions of the 40th and 41st Sections of the 55 Geo. III, c.184 [1815]", 1848–1853. Section 42 required the Commissioners to send these lists (which give the name of the testator or intestate, date of probate or administration, and value of the estate) to the courts concerned at least once a year.

I/35/3 128 ff. ff.12*v*.–31, accounts for sending copies of wills to the Stamp Office, 1852–1858. From 1811 copies of wills, rather than extracts, were sent to the Stamp Commissioners who paid the registrars according to a fixed rate (see circular dated 1811 in I/35/1).

Ep.I/36 PROBATE ACT PAPERS, 1834–1857

46 items, a typescript calendar of which is available in the Diocesan Record Office [Ep.I/88/1]. These are the papers of Edward William Johnson, and reflect the controversy before the passing of the Probate Act of 1857 (20 & 21 Vict. c.77), which abolished the probate jurisdiction of ecclesiastical courts. The diocesan registrars were anxious to obtain clauses in the Act to safeguard their offices. The papers include letters, newspaper cuttings, petitions, copies of speeches, pamphlets and draft bills.

Ep.I/37 RETURNS OF NONCONFORMISTS, 1577–1727

'Non-conformists' here includes recusants as well as those sought out (by order of the Privy Council) merely for refusing to go to church or receive Communion. See also the following articles in *Sussex Archaeological Collections*, 'Sussex . . . Recusants' [1584], vol. 12, pp. 199–202, 'Papists and Recusants of Sussex in 1587', vol. 2, pp. 58–62, and 'A Religious Census of Sussex in 1676', vol. 45, pp. 142–148.

I/37/1 (47); both archdeaconries, all 1580, except one list dated 1577. The documents include episcopal mandates to justices of the peace, constables, the "deane Ruralle" and incumbents to seek out nonconformists, citations to individuals to appear before the bishop, copies of the Privy Council returns, mostly arranged under rural deaneries and some with value of possessions, certificates of attendance at divine service, recognizances, and two letters from the Privy Council, one asking for more detailed information about individuals, and one concerning boys sent abroad to be educated by Papists.

I/37/2 (8); letters and lists of nonconformists for both archdeaconries, the Dean of Chichester's Peculiar and the Deanery of Pagham and Tarring, all 1593.

I/37/3 (3); incumbents' lists of popish recusants in West Grinstead, Harting and Midhurst, 1727.

Ep.I/38 CHURCHWARDENS' SUBSCRIPTION BOOKS, 1861–1894

These volumes contain the subscriptions of churchwardens, at the first visitation after their election, to the declaration to "faithfully and diligently perform the duties of the office of Churchwarden within our respective Parishes for the year ensuing". The parishes are arranged alphabetically by rural deaneries, annually from 1861 to 1894, but many churchwardens did not appear, especially in the later years.

I/38/1 119 ff.; 1861–1866.

I/38/2 141 ff.; 1867–1873.

I/38/3 137 ff.; 1874–1880.

I/38/4 143 ff.; 1881–1887.

I/38/5 146 ff.; 1888–1894.

Ep.I/39 APPOINTMENTS OF EPISCOPAL AND OTHER OFFICIALS, 1668–1929

I/39/0 4 pp. (copy); Henry King, jun.[1,3], and Philip Briscoe[1,3], Lewes archdeaconry, Dec. 1668.

I/39/1 4 pp. (copy); Thomas Briggs [4,5], Lewes archdeaconry, June 1671.

I/39/1a (2); surrogation by Thomas Briggs[4], Dean of Pagham, Tarring and South Malling and Commissary of the Dean of Chichester, Mar. 1701/2, and subscription of J. Hoper and Richard Turner, n.d. [early 18th cent.].

I/39/2 (1); Roger Pettiward[4], Nov. 1754[7].

I/39/3 (1); Roger Pettiward[4,5], Lewes archdeaconry, Nov. 1754.

[1] Registrar.
[2] Scribe of the acts.
[3] Examiner.
[4] Vicar-general and official principal.
[5] Sequestrator.
[6] Archiepiscopal seal attached.
[7] Episcopal seal attached.
[8] Chapter confirmation attached.
[9] Archidiaconal seal attached.
[10] Decanal seal attached.
[11] Chapter seal attached.

I/39/4 (2); Drake Hollingbery[4,5], Oct. 1778[7,8], to both.

I/39/4a (1); declaration of trust by Thomas Davison and Joseph Fearon indicating that they would surrender their offices[1-3], at the bishop's request, Jan. 1793.

I/39/5 (2); Henry Plimley[4], Feb. 1822[7,8], and certificate of his subscription and taking the oaths (see notes to Ep.I/3).

I/39/6 (1); Henry Plimley[4,5], Lewes archdeaconry, Feb. 1822[7,8].

I/39/7 (2); acts on admission of Thomas Robinson Welch to[4], Chichester archdeaconry and Lewes archdeaconry[4,5], Mar. 1841.

I/39/8 4 pp.; acts and oaths on admission of Robert Joseph Phillimore[4], Chichester archdeaconry, and Lewes archdeaconry[4,5], Oct. 1844.

I/39/9 (1); William Fowler and Richard Buckner[1-3], Chichester archdeaconry, June 1801[7,8].

I/39/9a (1); appointment of surrogates, Chichester archdeaconry, Sep. 1824.

I/39/10 (1); Alfred William Otter and John Romilly[1-3], Chichester archdeaconry, Mar. 1837[7,8].

I/39/11 (1); certificate on the entry of J. B. Freeland as a solicitor at the Stamp Office, Jan. 1833.

I/39/12 (1); J. B. Freeland, steward of the episcopal manors in Sussex, Sep. 1833[7,8].

I/39/13 (1); archiepiscopal faculty appointing J. B. Freeland a public notary, Oct. 1833[6].

I/39/14 (1); J. B. Freeland, chapter clerk and steward of the manors of the dean and chapter, Oct. 1833[11].

I/39/15 (1); J. B. Freeland[1-3], Dean of Chichester's Peculiar, May 1837[8,10].

I/39/16 4 pp., appointment by Alfred Otter and John Romilly (see I/39/10) of J. B. Freeland as deputy registrar, May 1841.

I/39/17 (1); J. B. Freeland, Chichester archidiaconal official, Mar. 1842[9].

I/39/18 (1); confirmation of I/39/17 by the dean and chapter, 1842[11].

I/39/19 4 pp.; appointment by archbishop's registrar of J. B. Freeland as his deputy, *sede vacante*, Nov. 1845.

[1-11] For key to these numbers, see p. 55.

I/39/20 (64); appointments of surrogates, their bonds, and precedents, 1666–1842.

I/39/20a (1); appointment of a rural dean, Chichester archdeaconry, Apr. 1858.

I/39/21 140 ff.; Lewes archdeaconry.
ff.1–6, commission and appointment of surrogates, Oct. 1722–Jan. 1731–2; ff.139–138, subscription of Charles Baker, schoolmaster, Feb. 1730/1.

I/39/21a (1); copy authority to deputy registrars to act as actuaries during vacancy of registrar, June 1828.

I/39/22 (1); archidiaconal commission appointing Bernard Husy Hunt and Edmund Charles Currey both [1,2], Apr. 1859.

I/39/23 (1); Richard Durnford[1-3], Chichester archdeaconry, Dec. 1874[7,8].

I/39/24 (2); appointment of chancellor and surrogates *sede vacante*, Oct. 1895 and Feb. 1929.

Ep.I/40 FACULTY AND CONSECRATION PAPERS, 1577–1861

A faculty had to be obtained from the Chancellor of the Diocese before the fabric of the church (including in this context the churchyard and the parsonage house) could be altered in any way, except in the course of necessary repairs. Such alterations included the demolition and removal of, and substitutions for and additions to, the fabric of the church (most commonly its windows, galleries, screens, pews, vaults and memorials), the removal of bodies from one piece of consecrated ground to another and the sale of church land for road widening. Confirmatory faculties were sometimes issued in respect of work completed without previous authority, but many alterations must have been made without any kind of licence being granted. In some cases the application was successfully opposed, or occasionally it was not pursued beyond the initial petition. Faculties were not required for the Cathedral, except for the removal of bodies. These papers include the originals or copies of petitions for faculties, citations to lead faculties (published in the church porch and inviting objections), estimates, costs, drawings and plans of proposed alterations, public appeals and subscription lists, notices and agendas of meetings, papers relating to appeals against the Chancellor's decisions, draft and original faculties and licences, and related correspondence and memoranda. The consecration papers consist mostly of conveyances and plans of sites for additional burial grounds or new chapels. From 1707 to 1853 faculties and acts of consecration for the Archdeaconry were registered in the detection books (Ep.I/17/36–47); further information may be found in the church building papers (Ep.I/41). For details of these faculties and consecrations see Ep.I/88/3, arranged under parishes. I/40/1a and **48** relate to the Dean of Chichester's Peculiar.

[1-11] For key to these numbers, see p. 55.

I/40/1 (1); Petworth [Duncton] (1577).

I/40/1a (1); Chichester, Dean's House (1729).

I/40/2 (3); Clapham (1735).

I/40/3 (1); Stoke, South (1737).

I/40/4 (3); Ashington (1737).

I/40/5 (2); Nuthurst (1737).

I/40/6 (1); Pulborough (1737).

I/40/7 (1); Angmering (1738).

I/40/8 (5); Bignor (1743).

I/40/9 (2); Marden, East (1744).

I/40/10 (4); Stedham [and Heyshott] (1749).

I/40/11 (3); Binsted (1755).

I/40/12 (2); Yapton [and Walberton] (1757).

I/40/13 (1); Westbourne (1758).

I/40/14 (2); Storrington (1764).

I/40/15 (2); Funtington (1766).

I/40/16 (2); Storrington (1767).

I/40/17 (2); Steyning (1768).

I/40/18 (1); Westbourne (1769).

I/40/19 (2); Westbourne (1769).

I/40/20 (2); Westbourne (1780).

I/40/21 (2); Bury (1782).

I/40/22 (2); Felpham (1784).

I/40/23 (1); Tillington (1785).

I/40/24 (3); Storrington (1786).

I/40/25 (2); Littlehampton (1788).

I/40/26 (3); Petworth (1790).

I/40/27 (2); Preston, East (1791).

I/40/28 (2); Sompting (1791).

I/40/29 (4); Chiltington, West (1791).

I/40/30 (2); Steyning (1792).

I/40/31 (2); Ferring (1792).

I/40/32 (2); Felpham (1793).

I/40/33 (2); Slinfold (1795).

I/40/34 (1); Burpham (1799).

I/40/35 (2); Horsham (1801).

I/40/36 (3); Billingshurst (1802–3).

I/40/37 (3); Fittleworth (1802–4).

I/40/38 (1); Madehurst (1802).

I/40/39 (3); Lyminster (1803).

I/40/40 (3); Steyning (1804).

I/40/41 (2); Mundham, North (1805).

I/40/42 (4); Sidlesham (1805).

I/40/43 (2); Worthing (1805–12).

I/40/44 (3); Funtington (1807).

I/40/45 (2); Midhurst (1807).

I/40/46 (2); Compton (1807).

I/40/47 (6); Boxgrove (1808).

I/40/48 (1); Chichester, Rumboldswyke (1808).

I/40/49　(10); Yapton [and Walberton] (1812).

I/40/50　(4); Eartham (1812).

I/40/51　(2); Billingshurst (1813).

I/40/52　(4); Bury (1813).

I/40/53　(1); Aldingbourne (1818).

I/40/54　(1); Stoughton [Stansted] (1819).

I/40/55　(2); Findon (1820).

I/40/56　(20); Horsham (1823).

I/40/57　(12); Arundel (1823).

I/40/58　(2); Littlehampton (1824).

I/40/59　(6); Horsham (1827).

I/40/60　(25); and 1 vol. (134 ff.); Horsham (1834).

I/40/61　(2); Preston, East (1835).

I/40/62　(1); Angmering (1841).

I/40/63　(1); Arundel (1845).

I/40/64　(35); Warnham (1849).

I/40/65　(12); Compton (1849).

I/40/66　(2); Walberton (1856).

I/40/67　(2); Littlehampton (1860).

I/40/68　(1); Chichester, St. Peter the Less (1861).

I/40/69　(1); Kirdford [Plaistow] (n.d.).

1/40/70　(1); list of faculties applied for, 1725–69.

1/40/71　(1); notes on an application for a faculty, no place or date given.

I/40/72　(4); letter, draft faculties and bond on a faculty, not Chichester, probably used as precedents, 1841–55.

Ep.I/41　CHURCH BUILDING PAPERS, 1743–1935

These papers include plans and specifications for new churches, chapels and parsonage houses, and for additions to existing buildings, estimates and costs for the work, public appeals and subscription lists, copies of faculties, and related correspondence and memoranda. Further information may be found in the faculty and consecration papers (Ep.I/40).

I/41/1　(12); Aldingbourne, 1824.

I/41/1a　(1); Aldingbourne, 1853.

I/41/2　(20); Amberley, 1842.

I/41/3　(1); South Bersted, 1863.

I/41/4　(1); South Bersted, 1876.

I/41/5　(1); Bosham and Apuldram, no date.

I/41/6　(15); Bosham, 1849.

I/41/6a　(5); Bosham, 1865.

I/41/7[1] (9); architect's drawings of the reredos (1908), the tester over Bishop Story's tomb (1910) and a proposed font cover, no date [c.1913], all in Chichester cathedral.

I/41/8[1] (1); 25" O.S. map of Chichester, sheet LXI, part 7, 1912, with St. Mary's hospital and other properties coloured.

I/41/9 (1); Cocking, 1859.

I/41/10 (2); East Dean, 1801.

I/41/11 (1); West Dean, 18th cent. copy of an award (1596) "for ending disputes in the parish".

I/41/12 (6); West Dean, 1833.

I/41/13 (10); West Dean and Singleton (disunion), 1849.

I/41/14 (20); Donnington, 1834.

I/41/15 (1); Donnington, 1837.

I/41/16 (1); Eastergate, 1750.

I/41/17 (40); Eastergate, 1840.

I/41/18 (3); Elsted, 1801.

I/41/19 (1); Fernhurst, 1817.

I/41/19a (1); Findon, 1935.

I/41/20 (20); Fittleworth, 1849.

I/41/21 (2); Funtington, 1807.

I/41/22 (25); Harting, 1816.

I/41/23 (20); Horsham, 1822.

I/41/24 (15); Horsham, 1840.

I/41/25 (1); Hunston and North Mundham (union), 1851.

I/41/26 (15); Itchingfield, 1822.

I/41/27 (12); Lancing, 1817.

I/41/28 (2); Littlehampton, 1828.

I/41/29 (2); Loxwood, 1867 and 1873.

I/41/30 (6); East Marden, 1803.

I/41/31 (6); architect's plans for chancel woodwork in East Marden church, 1935.

I/41/32 (1); North Mundham, 1804 (see also I/41/25).

I/41/33 (20); North Chapel, 1825.

I/41/34 (12); Oving, 1839.

I/41/35 (1); Parham, 1847.

I/41/35a (2); Partridge Green, n.d.

I/41/36 (9); Petworth, 1819.

I/41/37 (1); Pulborough, 1852.

I/41/38 (10); Rudgwick, 1835.

I/41/39 (1); Rumboldswyke, 1883.

I/41/40 (1); Rustington, 1803.

---

[1] Although these records always seem to have been filed with the episcopal records, they relate to the Cathedral and St. Mary's Hospital, Chichester, respectively.

I/41/41   (20); Rustington, 1821.

I/41/42   (2); Sennicotts in Funtington, 1856.

I/41/43   (3); architect's plans and specification for a new porch to Slindon church, 1935.

I/41/44   (15); Slinfold, 1835–1922.

I/41/45   (10); Sompting, 1841.

I/41/45a   (1); Southwater, n.d.

I/41/46   (1); South Stoke, 1801.

I/41/47   (13); Stopham, 1841.

I/41/48   (5); Sullington, 1802.

I/41/49   (18); Sullington, 1845.

I/41/50   (1); Sutton, 1806.

I/41/51   (4); Thakeham, 1847 and 1851.

I/41/52   (5); West Thorney, 1870.

I/41/53   (9); Tillington, 1817.

I/41/54   (65); Tillington, 1840 –42.

I/41/55   (1); Walberton, 1743.

I/41/56   (1); Walberton, 1813.

I/41/57   (2); Walberton, 1813–34.

I/41/57a   (1); Walberton, 1866.

I/41/58   (7); Wiggonholt and Greatham, 1817.

I/41/59   (6); Wisborough Green, 1815.

I/41/60   (2); East Wittering, 1801.

I/41/60a   (3); West Wittering, n.d.

I/41/61   (2); architect's plan and specification of a proposed lych-gate, no date or place given.

I/41/62   (2); unidentified small plans of church buildings, n.d. [c.1800].

I/41/63   *Parishes divided and districts assigned by Her Majesty's Commissioners for building new churches, 1818–1847*, London, 1847.

I/41/64   (40); returns by incumbents of the population of their parish, church accommodation and other places of worship in the parish, 1810.

I/41/65   (20); reports by rural deans on the fabric of churches and parsonage houses in their deaneries, 1817.

I/41/66   (26); reports by rural deans on the fabric of churches and parsonage houses in their deaneries, 1821.

I/41/67   (3); "number of churches in the kingdom", n.d. [18th cent.]; copy of a House of Lords resolution to enquire into places of worship in parishes of over 1,000 persons (1810); fourth annual report of the Society for Promoting the Enlargement and Building of Churches and Chapels (1822).

I/41/68   24 ff.; returns to the Treasury by the incumbents of Battle, Brighton, Broadwater, Buxted, Chichester St. Peter the Great, Cuckfield,

East Grinstead, Hastings St. Clement and All Saints, Horsham and Rye, concerning church accommodation, 1849.

Ep.I/42 REGISTERS OF NON-RESIDENT CLERGY AND RELATED PAPERS, 1742–1885

These registers contain lists of all incumbents, and, if non-resident, the reasons for their exemption, their present residence and other benefices held, and the value of the living. I/42/2–44 are arranged alphabetically by the parishes of the Chichester and Lewes archdeaconries; I/42/2–11 list the Dean of Chichester's Peculiar separately at the end of each volume, but from I/42/12 these parishes are incorporated in the main list. After 1846 (I/42/19–44) the Peculiars of Pagham and Tarring, and South Malling, are also included. Attached to many of the registers is correspondence between the Privy Council and the Bishop of Chichester, and the Bishop's Registry and incumbents, relating to the returns. The registers were prepared under the Act 43 Geo. III c.84 and subsequent legislation, all to enforce the residence of clergy in their benefices unless exempt or excused by episcopal licence. Clause 53 of the Act 57 Geo. III c.99 provided for an annual return to be made to the Privy Council giving the information contained in these volumes, which were compiled from the original returns. These Acts were repealed by the Pluralities Act of 1838 (1 & 2 Vict. c.106) which was particularly directed against the holding of benefices in plurality, but the form of the returns (see Ep.I/42a) and these registers was unchanged. I/42/2–44 each contains 18 folios.

I/42/1 40 pp.; lists of licences issued to clergy (arranged alphabetically by incumbents' names) of the Chichester archdeaconry and Dean of Chichester's Peculiar to be non-resident, 1804–09.

I/42/2	1816	I/42/17	1844	I/42/32	1873
I/42/3	1820	I/42/18	1845	I/42/33	1874
I/42/4	1823	I/42/19	1846	I/42/34	1875
I/42/5	1824	I/42/20	1847	I/42/35	1876
I/42/6	1825	I/42/21	1849	I/42/36	1877
I/42/7	1826	I/42/22	1850	I/42/37	1878
I/42/8	1829	I/42/23	1852	I/42/38	1879
I/42/9	1835	I/42/24	1853	I/42/39	1880
I/42/10	1836	I/42/25	1854	I/42/40	1881
I/42/11	1837	I/42/26	1856	I/42/41	1882
I/42/12	1838	I/42/27	1857	I/42/42	1883
I/42/13	1839	I/42/28	1869	I/42/43	1884
I/42/14	1841	I/42/29	1870	I/42/44	1885
I/42/15	1842	I/42/30	1871		
I/42/16	1843	I/42/31	1872		

I/42/45 (14); certificate of distance for a licence of non-residence (1742); lists of clergy licensed and exempt from residence (1803–1805); printed abstracts of the returns of non-resident clergy in the diocese (1809) and in England (1808); letters and memoranda about legislation against non-residence (1800–1818); copies of a questionnaire to incumbents by the bishop (1810); copy licence of non-residence from the archbishop (1840); draft return to Parliament (1849) giving details of non-resident clergy from 1838.

Ep.I/42A CLERGY RESIDENCE RETURNS, 1824–1921

Original returns (each 4 pp.) sent by incumbents to enable the registers (see Ep.I/42) to be compiled. The series continues until 1921, and from 1871 (34 & 35 Vict. c.43, s.55) questions on insurance are included. Each year is represented by one parcel of papers, and although these have not been minutely checked they appear to contain every parish in the diocese, including Peculiars. There is one return for 1824 [Northiam], which is with I/42A/1.

I/42A/1	1829	I/42A/27	1869	I/42A/53	1895
I/42A/2	1840	I/42A/28	1870	I/42A/54	1896
I/42A/3	1844	I/42A/29	1871	I/42A/55	1897
I/42A/4	1845	I/42A/30	1872	I/42A/56	1898
I/42A/5	1846	I/42A/31	1873	I/42A/57	1899
I/42A/6	1847	I/42A/32	1874	I/42A/58	1900
I/42A/7	1848	I/42A/33	1875	I/42A/59	1901
I/42A/8	1849	I/42A/34	1876	I/42A/60	1902
I/42A/9	1850	I/42A/35	1877	I/42A/61	1903
I/42A/10	1851	I/42A/36	1878	I/42A/62	1904
I/42A/11	1852	I/42A/37	1879	I/42A/63	1905
I/42A/12	1853	I/42A/38	1880	I/42A/64	1906
I/42A/13	1854	I/42A/39	1881	I/42A/65	1907
I/42A/14	1855	I/42A/40	1882	I/42A/66	1908
I/42A/15	1856	I/42A/41	1883	I/42A/67	1909
I/42A/16	1857	I/42A/42	1884	I/42A/68	1911
I/42A/17	1858	I/42A/43	1885	I/42A/69	1912
I/42A/17A	1859	I/42A/44	1886	I/42A/70	1913
I/42A/18	1860	I/42A/45	1887	I/42A/71	1914
I/42A/19	1861	I/42A/46	1888	I/42A/72	1915
I/42A/20	1862	I/42A/47	1889	I/42A/73	1916
I/42A/21	1863	I/42A/48	1890	I/42A/74	1917
I/42A/22	1864	I/42A/49	1891	I/42A/75	1918
I/42A/23	1865	I/42A/50	1892	I/42A/76	1919
I/42A/24	1866	I/42A/51	1893	I/42A/77	1920
I/42A/25	1867	I/42A/52	1894	I/42A/78	1921
I/42A/26	1868				

Ep.I/43 OFFICE ACCOUNT BOOKS, 1615–1933

These were sometimes known as Day Books. They are accounts of fees received by, or of fees due to, the bishop's officials on the issue of documents (licences, citations, mandates, letters of orders, institution, sequestration and administration, grants of probate, faculties and many others). Usually the names of the parties concerned are given, and often parishes and other detail. The volumes cover both archdeaconries and the Dean of Chichester's Peculiar.

I/43/1 26 ff. bound in contemporary interrogatories. ff.2–18, June 1615–Dec. 1617; ff.25–20, receipts of chapter clerk, Feb. 1615/6–Oct. 1619.

I/43/2 45 ff.; the two outer sheets were found among consistory court papers. ff.1A–21, Jan. 1623/4–Mar. 1626/7.

I/43/3 30 ff. ff.1–30, Mar. 1638–June 1642.

I/43/4 51 ff. bound in part of a medieval manuscript. ff.1–51, Sep. 1660–Sep. 1668.

I/43/5 12 ff. bound in part of a medieval manuscript. ff.1–12, June 1669–Mar. 1672.

I/43/6 46 ff. ff.1–46, June 1685–Dec. 1701.

I/43/7 14 ff. ff.2–14, Dec. 1697–Sep. 1698.

I/43/8 16 ff. f.1v., memoranda; ff.2–16, Dec. 1698–Sep. 1700.

I/43/9 40 pp. pp.1–38, Dec. 1707–Aug. 1710.

I/43/10 23 ff. bound in part of a contemporary deed. ff.1–19, Dec. 1709–July 1711.

I/43/11 19 ff. ff.1v.–18, Nov. 1711–Feb. 1712/3.

I/43/12 16 ff. ff.1v.–16, June 1713–Feb. 1714/5.

I/43/13 34 ff. ff.1–34, July 1715–Sep. 1718.

I/43/14 28 ff. f.1, memoranda; ff.1v.–26, Apr. 1718–Apr. 1720; f.28v., n.d.; one loose paper [bond, Oct. 1716], receipts, Nov. 1719.

I/43/14a 16 ff. ff.1–16, Oct. 1759–June 1762.

I/43/15 22 ff. ff.1–22, Sep. 1764–Nov. 1767.

I/43/16 28 ff. ff.1–28, Nov. 1767–Nov. 1773.

I/43/17 54 ff. ff.1–12, Dec. 1831–Sep. 1833.

I/43/18 58 ff. ff.1–39, July 1871–May 1874.

I/43/19 233 ff.; 1909–1933. The marriage licence entries give the names of the parties and the surrogate concerned, consecrations and sequestrations the name of the parish, and faculties the parish and description of the work. Entries cover both archdeaconries, unless otherwise indicated.
ff.1–21, marriage licences, Oct. 1909–Nov. 1916; ff.21v.–44, faculties, Oct. 1909–Jan. 1929; ff.44v.–49, consecrations, Oct. 1909–Aug. 1931; ff.49v.–51, faculties, Feb. 1927–Jan. 1929; f.52, marriage licences, Jan.–Feb. 1916; ff.53–54, Lewes faculties, Feb. 1929–Apr. 1930; ff.54v.–58, sequestrations, Oct. 1909; ff.58v.–61, faculties, Feb. 1929–Apr. 1932; ff.61v.–87, Lewes marriage licences, July 1915–Oct. 1917; ff.88v.–116, Chichester marriage licences, Nov. 1916–June 1933; ff.121v.–182, Lewes marriage licences, Oct. 1917–June 1933; f.199v., consecrations, Sep. 1931–Sep. 1932; ff.204v.–206, faculties, Apr. 1930–June 1933.

I/44/1   3 ff.; valor of episcopal possessions at the death of Bishop Curteys, 1582.

I/44/2   6 ff.; 'A booke of Tenthes for the Whole dioces', n.d. [late 16th cent.].

I/44/3   24 pp.; valor of the cathedral, Chichester archdeaconry and the Chichester, Pagham and Tarring Peculiars, n.d. [*c*.1625], giving names of incumbents and patrons, and lists of livings in the bishop's gift.

I/44/4   36 ff.; n.d. [*c*.1745].

f.1, fees payable to the bishop's secretary and steward; ff.2–22, valor of the diocese, with names of incumbents and patrons; ff.22*v*.–25, lists of curacies and donatives, unions of benefices and livings in the bishop's gift; ff.25*v*.–32, valor of the cathedral; ff.32*v*.–33, list of augmented livings.

I/44/5   44 ff.

ff.1–10, list of livings in the archdeaconry, giving names of incumbents (with dates of admission) and curates in 1796 and *c*.1810, details of residence, services held and number of communicants in 1724 and 1796, and the value of the livings (and augmentation) and glebe in 1724 and 1796; f.11, list of incumbents in the Chichester, Pagham and Tarring Peculiars, 1796; ff.42–38, parochial charities in the archdeaconry, 1724.

I/44/6   8 ff.; valor of the diocese, n.d. [*post* 1811].

I/44/7   22 ff.; early 19th cent. copy of a valor (14 May 1550) of the cathedral and diocese.

Ep.I/45   CONVOCATION PAPERS, 1557–1919

Under the Submission of Clergy Act, 1533 (25 Hen. VIII *c*.19, s.1), convocation could only be assembled by royal writ directed to the archbishop. This was followed by the latter's mandate to the provincial dean, reciting the royal writ and ordering him to summon diocesan representatives, which process is illustrated by these documents. There are copies of episcopal mandates in many of the registers (Ep.I/1). For the purposes of convocation elections the Peculiars were included in the appropriate archdeaconry; earlier elections in Lewes are in Ep.II/10–11. "Clergy" here refers only to incumbents, since unbeneficed clergy were not entitled to vote. On the death or resignation of a proctor, the archbishop issued through the dean of the province another mandate to elect a successor, which was followed by a reissue of the relevant citations and election papers within the chapter or archdeaconry concerned.

[1] "Diocese" in this section includes Peculiar jurisdictions.

I/45/1 (1); [1], 1557.

I/45/1a (1); [1], 1570.

I/45/2 (1); [1], 1592.

I/45/3 (1); [13], 1597.

I/45/4 (1); [8], 1625.

I/45/5 (3); [8,13,22] (to the Bishop of London), 1679.

I/45/6 (3); [1,8,13], 1681.

I/45/6a (1); [1], 1685.

I/45/7 (7); [1,8], 1689–90 (Canterbury *sede vacante*).

I/45/8 (2); [13,19], 1695.

I/45/9 (1); [13], 1698.

I/45/10 (1); [13], 1700.

I/45/11 (4); [1,8,13,16], 1701.

I/45/12 (2); [8,13], 1702.

[1] Mandate from the dean of the province (the Bishop of London, or if vacant, the Bishop of Winchester) to the bishop to cite the dean and archdeacons of Chichester and Lewes to appear in convocation personally and the cathedral chapter and the clergy of the diocese to appear through their elected proctors.

[2] Bishop's mandate to the dean to appear personally, and the chapter through an elected proctor.

[3] Bishop's mandate to the archdeacon of Chichester to appear in convocation.

[4] Bishop's mandate to the archdeacon of Lewes to appear in convocation.

[5] Bishop's mandate to the chancellor to cite the Chichester clergy to elect a proctor.

[6] Bishop's mandate to the chancellor to cite the Lewes clergy to elect a proctor, and/or chancellor's process to the clergy.

[7] Bishop's mandate to the chancellor to cite the clergy of the whole diocese to elect proctors (used until the late 18th cent.).

[8] Bishop's mandate to apparitors in the four Chichester deaneries to cite their clergy to elect a proctor (used until the late 18th cent.).

[9] Circulars and citations of individual clergy to attend at Chichester cathedral or St. Mary, Lewes, for the proctorial elections (19th and 20th cents.).

[10] Signed acknowledgements on printed forms of the receipt of the circulars as in previous note by all Chichester incumbents.

[11] Citations of members of the chapter to meet to elect a proctor.

[12] List of Chichester clergy cited to elect a proctor.

[13] Act of election of the Chichester proctor, which sometimes includes list of clergy as above.

[14] Certificate of election of the Lewes proctor.

[15] Certificate of election of the Chichester proctor.

[16] Chancellor's return to the bishop of the name of the Chichester proctor.

[17] Chancellor's return to the bishop of the name of the Lewes proctor.

[18] Dean and Chapter's return to the bishop of the name of their proctor.

[19] Dean and Chapter's monition to their proctor to appear in convocation.

[20] Chancellor's monition to the Chichester proctor to appear in convocation.

[21] Chancellor's monition to the Lewes proctor to appear in convocation.

[22] Bishop's return to the archbishop of names of the proctors for the diocese.

[23] Letters of apology for absence from elections, and nominations of candidates, mostly for Chichester.

[24] Agendas of the election meetings at Chichester and Lewes.

[25] Newspaper cuttings relating to the business of convocation and to election meetings at Chichester and Lewes.

I/45/13   (3); [2,7,13], 1705.

I/45/14   (5); [1,7,8,13], 1710.

I/45/15   (10); [1] (London *sede vacante*), [8,13], 1713.

I/45/16   (3); [7,8,13], 1722.

I/45/17   (2); [1,13], 1727.

I/45/18   (11); [1-3,7,8,16,18,22], 1734.

I/45/19   (3); [2,12,22], 1737.

I/45/20   (5); [7,8,13], 1741. See Ep.I/1/11, f.42*v*., for a list of proctors for the diocese.

I/45/21   (11); [1,2,7,8,13,18,22], 1747.

I/45/22   (9); [1,7,8,13,18], 1754.

I/45/23   (7); [1-3,8] (from the Chancellor) [13], 1761.

I/45/24   (11); [1,5,8,13,20,22], 1768.

I/45/25   (6); [1,13,18], 1774.

I/45/26   (3); [1,18], 1780. See Ep.I/45/27.

I/45/27   8 ff.; [13], 1780, 1784, 1790, 1796.

I/45/28   (3); [1,18], 1790. See Ep.I/45/27.

I/45/29   (7); [1-3,5,16,18], 1796. See Ep.I/45/27.

I/45/30   (10); [1-5,12-14,18,19], 1802.

I/45/31   (10); [1,2,5,8] (from the Chancellor) [13,16,18], 1806.

I/45/32   (1); [1], 1807.

I/45/33   (8); [1,13,14,16,18,23], 1812.

I/45/34   (3); [13,23], 1818.

I/45/35   (15); [1,2,5,9,13,14,18,20,23], 1820.

I/45/36   (5); [1,5,18,20], and a list of fees, 1826.

I/45/37   (8); [1,2,5,9,13,14,22], 1830.

[1-25] For key to these numbers, see p. 66.

I/45/38 (2); [1,15], 1831.

I/45/39 (8); [1,3,12–15], 1833.

I/45/40 (8); [1–3,5,13,17,18,23], 1835.

I/45/41 (6); [1,13,14,18,20,22], 1837.

I/45/42 (6); [1,2,5,13,14,18], 1841.

I/45/43 (15); [1,3,5,9,13,16–18,21], 1847. This session was adjourned on the death of Archbishop Howley.

I/45/44 (5); [1,2,22,23], 1848.

I/45/45 (19); [1,2,5,11,13,16–18,20,22–24], and a protest by stipendiary curates claiming a vote at proctorial elections, 1852.

I/45/46 (26+)*; [1–3,5,6,9–11,14,16–23], 1857.

I/45/47 (32+)*; [1–6,9,10–13,16–23], 1859.

I/45/48 (2); [1,23], 1863.

I/45/49 (19); [1–6,9,11,13,16,17,21–23], 1865.

I/45/50 (28+)*; [1–6,11,16–24], 1868 (Canterbury *sede vacante*).

I/45/51 (38); [1,6,9,14,17,21,22,23], and advertisements, 1869, caused by the resignation of Robert Shuttleworth Sutton, proctor for Lewes.

I/45/52 (17+)*; [1,5,10,11,13,16,22–24], 1871.

I/45/53 (32); [1–6,13,14,16–20,22–24], 1874.

I/45/54 (17); [1,5,11,13,16,20,22–24], 1875.

I/45/55 (36); [1–5,11,13,14,16–20,22–24], 1880.

I/45/56 (8); [1,2,18,19,22,23], 1883, caused by the resignation of Charles Anthony Swainson as proctor for the Chapter.

I/45/57 (40); [1–6,11,13,16–20,22,23], 1885.

I/45/58 (40); [1–6,11,13,16–20,22–24], 1886.

I/45/59 (11); [1,6,17,22,23], 1888, caused by the death of Charles Heathcote Campion, proctor for Lewes.

[1–25] For key to these numbers, see p. 66.

* Where the documents in [9–11] are a complete series, representing all the clergy concerned, they have not been counted.

I/45/60 (10); [1, 2, 11, 18, 19, 22, 23], 1889, caused by the death of Thomas Francis Crosse, proctor for the Chapter.

I/45/61 (45); [1-6, 11, 13, 14, 16-23], 1892.

I/45/62 (45); [1-6, 11, 13, 14, 16-24], 1895.

I/45/63 (1); a list of the cathedral clergy, n.d. [1899].

I/45/64 (65+)*; [1-6, 11, 13, 17-24], 1900.

I/45/65 (9); [1, 6, 17, 22, 23], 1902, caused by the appointment of John Julius Hannah, formerly proctor for Lewes, as Dean.

I/45/66 (83+)*; [1-6, 9, 11, 13, 14, 16-24], 1906.

I/45/67 (31); [9, 13, 14, 16-24], 1910.

I/45/68 (85+)*; [1-3, 5, 6, 9, 11-14, 16-18, 23, 24], a list of Lewes clergy and voting papers returned in both archdeaconries, 1911.

I/45/69 Voting papers returned in all three archdeaconries, 1919; Hastings and Lewes together elected a single proctor.

Ep.I/46 PARLIAMENTARY AND OTHER RETURNS, 1803–1908.

During the 19th century royal commissions were set up to enquire into ecclesiastical matters, and copies of many of the returns have survived. See also Ep.I/56/6. "Chichester courts" here includes the episcopal consistory courts and the Peculiar courts of the Dean of Chichester and the Archbishop of Canterbury (Deanery of Pagham and Tarring). Attached to many of the returns are the circular letters requesting them.

I/46/1 728 pp.; *Abstract of the Answers and Returns made pursuant to an Act for procuring Returns relative to the Expence and Maintenance of the Poor in England* (43 Geo. III c.144), 1804.

I/46/1a (1); copy of the Act 43 Geo. III c.144 (1803).

I/46/2 (34); draft calculations and annual returns, 1845–57, of the fees, allowances, etc., received by officers of the Chichester courts in each of the five years preceding the return: 7 & 8 Vict. c.68, s.2 (1844).

I/46/3 428 ff.; draft returns from the whole diocese to the bishop's enquiry about parish rooms and parochial and ecclesiastical charities likely to be transferred to the control of Parish Councils in 1893 (56 & 57 Vict. c.73).

[1-25] For key to these numbers, see p. 66.

* Where the documents in [9-11] are a complete series, representing all the clergy concerned, they have not been counted.

I/46/4 (1); letter, Feb. 1813, from the Privy Council office to the bishop about a return of dignities and benefices: Order in Council, 23 Aug. 1813.

I/46/5 (1); copy return to Secretary of State of the names and fees of officers in the Chichester courts, Mar. 1843.

I/46/6 (50); copy returns to the Registrar General, 1848–1907, of chapels in the Lewes archdeaconry, and one return (1854) for the Chichester archdeanconry, where marriages may be lawfully solemnized: 6 & 7 Will. IV c.85, s.34 (1836).

I/46/7 3 copies of a letter from the Home Office about unspecified returns, 1849.

I/46/8 (7); draft returns of fees received in Chichester courts: House of Commons Resolution, 3 Aug. 1848.

I/46/9 (2); draft return to the Episcopal and Capitular Revenues Commission about Chapter expenditure, 22 Jan. 1849.

I/46/10 (1); letter relating to a House of Commons resolution, 3 May 1850, requiring a return of preferments held by cathedral dignitaries.

I/46/11 (3); draft return of sinecure benefices in the diocese: House of Commons resolution, 27 May 1850.

I/46/12 (3); remarks on the proposed scheme of the Ecclesiastical Commissioners for the bishop's income, May 1851.

I/46/13 (5); draft return of the names, ages and income of officers of the Chichester courts: House of Commons resolution, 7 Aug. 1851.

I/46/14 (3); copy return made Apr. 1853, to the Ecclesiastical Courts Commissioners of wills proved and administrations granted in Chichester courts in the years 1850–52, giving the names, parishes, occupations and value of the estate of testators and intestates.

I/46/15 (2); draft return of fees payable on the consecration of burial grounds in the diocese (no names given): House of Commons resolution, 20 May 1853.

I/46/16 (2); draft return, made June 1854, of all churches in the Chichester archdeaconry erected 1822–1853, or for which burial grounds were provided.

I/46/17 8 ff.; draft return of the number of persons baptized in each parish in the diocese in 1851: House of Commons resolution, 11 June 1855. See Ep.I/60 and II/39 for the original returns.

I/46/18 (1); draft return made Nov. 1855, to House of Lords of "Expences attending the Consecration of Burial Ground".

I/46/19 (4); papers relating to a return of the fees received by officers in ecclesiastical courts since the alterations of diocesan boundaries under the Act 6 & 7 Will. IV c.77 (1836): House of Commons resolution 7 Apr. 1859. Chichester was not affected, and therefore there is no return.

I/46/20 (56); draft annual returns, 1860–1908, to the Home Secretary, of judicial proceedings commenced or pending in the Lewes archdeaconry court. Until 1874 there was nothing to report,[1] but from 1875 onwards full details are given of all faculty proceedings.

I/46/21 (3); draft return from Lewes archdeaconry of the name and details of appointment of the registrar and deputy registrar, and total fees received in the courts: House of Commons resolution, 1 Aug. 1861.

I/46/22 (2); draft return from Lewes archdeaconry of all augmentations of poor vicarages and curacies under the Acts 29 Chas. II c.8 (1676) and 1 & 2 Will. IV c.45 (1831): House of Commons resolution, 21 July 1865.

I/46/23 (2); draft return to (and letter from) the Registrar General of ecclesiastical districts formed in the archdeaconry between 1861 and 1871.

I/46/24 (4); draft returns for 1875, 1876, 1878 and 1908, of the fees and allowances received by the officers of Lewes court: 7 & 8 Vict. c.68, s.2 (1844) and 38 & 39 Vict. c.76 preamble par. 1 and s.4 (1875).

I/46/25 (3); copy return of burial grounds consecrated in the archdeaconry of Lewes, 1863–77: House of Commons resolution, 26 July 1877.

I/46/26 (2); copy return of fees received at Lewes for the inspection and copying of tithe commutation maps and apportionments, 1891–93: House of Commons resolution, 12 Feb. 1895.

I/46/27 (5); draft revised return of fees received by the officers of the Lewes court, 1897–99 under the Act 7 & 8 Vict. c.68, s.2 (1844): House of Commons resolution, 2 Aug. 1900.

Ep.I/47 EDUCATION PAPERS, 1823–1882

I/47/1 2 unused copies of George IV's letter on behalf of the Incorporated National Society for the Education of the Poor, 1823.

I/47/1a 10 ff.; parishes arranged by rural deaneries, giving value of the benefice, population, and number of day and Sunday schools, 1838.

I/47/2 10 ff.; rough copy of I/47/1a.

I/47/3 4 ff.; parishes arranged alphabetically giving the number of children attending day and Sunday schools and an account of endowments, n.d. [c.1845].

---

[1] Each return is endorsed "The Court is rarely called upon to exercise its Functions".

I/47/4 24 ff.; parishes arranged alphabetically, giving the number of children and average attendance at national schools, averages of income and expenditure, if under government inspection and when last inspected, if any Government apprentices, and details of other schools in the parish, 1855, abstracted from the diocesan inspectors' reports (I/47/7).

I/47/5 24 ff.; copy of I/47/4.

I/47/6 (9); conveyance of a site for Iping School (1844), letters and papers relating to the inspection of schools and the training and examination of teachers (1848–82), reports on education by the London Union on Church Matters (1849–52) and Horsham ruridecanal chapter minutes (1852).

I/47/7 (126); diocesan inspectors' reports on national schools (abstracted in I/47/4), giving some additional information and criticism under the heading of "General Remarks", 1855.

I/47/8 8 gatherings; diocesan inspectors' reports on schools, 1855–68, arranged by deaneries, consisting mostly of the degrees of proficiency attained by each class in each subject at the inspector's examination, and some general remarks and criticisms. Fishbourne, 1855–6; Horsham, 1855–7; Iping and Lodsworth, 1857, 1861, 1863; Selsey and Funtington, 1868; South Bersted, West Itchenor and Boxgrove, 1855–7, 1859.

I/47/9 2 unused forms from I/47/8.

Ep.I/48 CAUSE PAPERS, 18th century – 1877

Most of these causes came under the scope of the Church Discipline Act (3 & 4 Vict. c.85, 1840); with the decay of the regular courts and the withdrawal of secular causes in the early 19th century the bishop and archdeacon took a greater part in matters of clergy discipline. Some of these causes never came into open court.

I/48/1 6 ff. ff.1–3, petition of William Prescott, schoolmaster, to the bishop of Chichester, answering charges about the conduct of his school, n.d. [late 18th cent.].

I/48/1a 2 letters, 1822, between Archdeacon Raynes, Richard Constable (vicar of Cowfold, 1801–39) and the churchwardens of Cowfold, concerning the presentment of the Rev. John Hurst of Horsham. See also I/48/2.

I/48/1b (8); a petition (1821) for a licence of non-residence, and a petition and letters (1823) between Bishop Buckner, Godfrey Gilbert Cooper (rector of Ewhurst, 1803–25), Col. J. G. Cooper (his brother), parishioners and Mr. Spedding (sequestrator) concerning Godfrey Cooper. See also I/48/10.

I/48/1c (23); proceedings and letters, 1831–2, between Bishop Maltby, Thomas Pitman (vicar of Eastbourne St. Mary, 1828–90) and the churchwardens and parishioners concerned in a dispute over the occupancy of one pew in the church.

I/48/1d (11); letters, 1832–3, between Bishop Maltby, J. B. Freeland, Peter Wood (rector of Broadwater, 1797–1835) and the parties concerned in a dispute over Wood's refusal to build an additional pew in Broadwater church for a tenant of Mr. J. B. Daubuz.

I/48/2 335 documents, 2 bundles of receipts and 1 volume of evidence (170 pp.); an induction mandate, 1834, a newspaper, proceedings, bills and letters, 1840–9, between Bishop Gilbert, Archdeacon Webber, Archdeacon Manning, Walter John Trower (rector of Wiston, 1839–50, rural dean; later Bishop of Glasgow and Galloway), John Hurst (rector of Thakeham, 1834–81), his wife, William Bradford (rector of Storrington, 1811–57), William Barlee (rector of West Chiltington, 1830–50), John Austin (rector of Pulborough, 1822–57), Henry Hamilton Hamilton (curate of Thakeham), J. B. Freeland, Joseph Butler (sequestrator), William Botting and Edward Fuller Upperton, in Trower *v.* Hurst in the Court of Arches, 1844 and 1847. In 1844 Hurst was suspended until 1847, when he refused to pay the tithe commutation rent charge. See also I/48/1a, and Lambeth Palace Library, Arches records, Eee 31.

I/48/3 461 ff.; copy correspondence, 1842–8, and one letter, 1853, between Bishop Gilbert, Archdeacon Hare, Robert Allen (rector of Barcombe, 1826–77), his curates and churchwardens, concerning Allen's non-residence, his disputes with successive curates, chiefly about their stipends and his proposals for a second church and a new school. See also I/48/9.

I/48/4 (13); petitions and correspondence, 1845, between Archdeacon Manning, J. B. Freeland and the churchwardens of Pulborough, relating to the alleged habitual intoxication of James Overington, the parish clerk.

I/48/5 (12); a newspaper, sermon, depositions and correspondence, 1847, between Bishop Gilbert and solicitors, relating to the alleged Puseyism of William Wheeler (vicar of New Shoreham, 1843–56).

I/48/6 (123); newspapers, pamphlets and correspondence, concerning disputes in East Grinstead and the Forest Row chapelry, 1842–6. The letters are chiefly between Bishop Gilbert, Chancellor Phillimore, J. B. Freeland, Christopher Nevill (vicar of East Grinstead, 1835–47), Henry Ramus Du Pré (curate-in-charge of Forest Row, 1841–8), his father and brother, Christopher Wordsworth (rector of Buxted, 1820–46), William Lovegrove and C. R. Duplex (churchwardens of East Grinstead), George Hoper (magistrate) and the Rev. Daniel Henry Haigh, and relate chiefly to Bishop Gilbert's refusal to licence the schoolmaster, 1842, Nevill's refusal to pay Du Pré's stipend and the latter's suit to recover it, 1843–4, Du Pré's alleged neglect of his duties, 1843, numerous personal quarrels between them, 1843–6, and the bishop's proposal to assign a separate ecclesiastical district to Forest Row Chapel, 1846. There are occasional references to these matters in I/48/7.

I/48/7 (327); newspapers, pamphlets and correspondence concerning the Rev. J. M. Neale and Sackville College Chapel, East Grinstead, 1847–53. The letters are chiefly between Bishop Gilbert, Richard Whately (Archbishop of Dublin, 1831–63), Samuel Wilberforce (Bishop of Oxford, 1845–69), Charles James Blomfield (Bishop of London, 1828–56), Henry

Philpotts (Bishop of Exeter, 1831–69), the 5th Earl and Countess De La Warr, John Mason Neale (warden of Sackville College, 1847–66), his wife, John Netherton Harward (vicar of East Grinstead, 1848–63), Thomas Palmer Hutton (perpetual curate of Lingfield, 1846–55), Henry Garrett Newland (vicar of Westbourne, 1834–56). Benjamin Webb (curate of Christ Church, St. Pancras, London, 1847–9, and co-founder with Neale of the Cambridge Camden Society), Joseph Adkins Beckett (vicar of Forest Row, 1849–73), William Russell (rector of Shepperton, Middlesex, and Neale's guardian) and William Nourse (rector of Clapham, 1821–71). The documents relate to the numerous personal disputes between Harward and Neale, to popular demonstrations against Neale in East Grinstead, to Neale's inhibition by Bishop Gilbert in 1847, to the case Freeland v. Neale in the Court of Arches, 1848, because of Neale's defiance of the inhibition, and intercessions to the bishop on Neale's behalf, especially by Lord De La Warr and Bishop Wilberforce, for removal of the inhibition, which was not formally withdrawn until 1863.[1] The correspondence of 1847 includes references to matters in I/48/6.

I/48/8 42 documents and one shorthand notebook (46 ff.); proceedings, bills and letters, 1848, in Office v. Moss John Moss (vicar of Aldingbourne, 1819–52).

I/48/9 (39); proceedings and letters, 1849–50, in Dowson v. Allen, 1850. Henry Dowson (curate of Barcombe, 1846–50) sued Robert Allen (rector of Barcombe, 1826–77) for the recovery of his stipend; see also I/48/3.

I/48/9a (65); newspapers, pamphlets and letters, 1851–4, chiefly between Bishop Gilbert, John Fisher Hodgson (vicar of Horsham, 1840–84) and John Turner Rawlison, relating to the "Horsham Pew Case", Rawlison v. Medwin and Hurst, 1852. This case, instituted at Bishop Gilbert's suggestion, was to try the churchwardens' claim to treat pews as being attached to certain houses and allowing them to be bought and sold. J. T. Rawlison had been prevented from using the pew he wished, and Pilfold Medwin and Robert Henry Hurst, jun., defended the case on the churchwardens' behalf. It was followed with interest throughout the country, and there are many letters from incumbents in other dioceses requesting copies of the proceedings and the bishop's letter to Horsham parishioners after the case had been found against Medwin and Hurst; pamphlets relating to similar cases in other English and Scottish parishes.

I/48/10 (45); 1859 visitation return, and letters, 1858–60, between Bishop Gilbert, Archdeacon Otter, Richard Holmes Tuck (curate of Ewhurst, 1849–61), the churchwardens and Lewes registry, relating to the illegal appointment of a minister's churchwarden, and the non-residence of Robert Bacon (rector of Ewhurst, 1854–63). See also I/48/1b.

I/48/11 (37); proceedings and letters, 1859–60, in Johnson v. Friend and Ballard, 1860. E. W. Johnson, the Bishop's secretary, prosecuted James Friend and Richard Ballard of Patcham for burying an unbaptized infant

---

[1] For expositions of Neale's case, see E. A. Towle, *John Mason Neale, D.D., A Memoir* (1906), Mary Sackville Lawson (ed.), *Letters of John Mason Neale* (1910), and A. G. Lough, *The Influence of John Mason Neale* (1962).

in Patcham churchyard in defiance of the incumbent, Henry Allen (vicar, 1844–65).

I/48/12 (9); letters, 1860, between Bishop Gilbert, Chancellor Phillimore and Edmund Currey concerning a dispute about pews built without the necessary faculty in the chancel of Seaford church.

I/48/13 3 letters, 1861, between Bishop Gilbert, D. Tucker (rector of Sanden, Hertfordshire) and Edmund Currey concerning the alleged Romanistic practices of Randolph Payne (curate of St. Paul's, Brighton).

I/48/14 (8); letters, 1863–4, between Bishop Gilbert, E. W. Johnson and William Groome Holmes (vicar of Littlehampton, 1855–64) concerning his voluntary resignation.

I/48/15 (34); proceedings and letters, 1861 and 1864, between the 5th Earl De La Warr, Edward Polehampton (rector of Hartfield, 1859–91), the churchwardens and Edmund Currey, concerning Lord De La Warr's claim to allot certain pews in Hartfield church to his tenants. In 1861 this claim was disputed by William Wallis, a tenant, and in 1864 by the churchwardens.

I/48/16 (13); letters, 1865, between Henry B. W. Churton (vicar of Icklesham, 1844–91), Chancellor Phillimore, Edmund Currey and the churchwardens concerning the disputed election of a churchwarden at Icklesham.

I/48/17 (88); newspapers and letters, 1867, chiefly between Bishop Gilbert, Chancellor Wintle, Capt. H. H. Woodhead, Henry Beaumont, D.D. (perpetual curate of St. Andrew's Hove, 1866–8) and Edmund Currey, relating to Dr. Beaumont.

I/48/18 (23); the 1868 visitation return for Udimore, proceedings and letters, 1868, between Archdeacon Otter, William Brocklebank (perpetual curate of Udimore, 1841–69), Matthew Parrington (on behalf of Bishop Gilbert), Augustus A. Aylward (rector of Brede, 1851–86), Edmund Currey and George Jenner (churchwarden), relating to the presentment of the incumbent for alleged intoxication at a funeral.

I/48/19 4 letters, 1869, concerning the unlawful digging of a grave in the churchyard of Huggate, Pocklington, Yorkshire. The letters are between the incumbent, E. Curtis, and London solicitors; they contain no reference to the Chichester diocese, but the case is entered in the schedule of Edmund Currey's office papers, Ep.II/36/1.

I/48/20 9 letters, 1874, concerning the inaccurate recording of banns of marriage by the parish clerk of Northiam, from whom the parties concerned claimed damages.

I/48/21 (51); a newspaper, an advertisement, proceedings and letters, 1876–7, between Archdeacon Hannah, Thomas W. Adam (rector of Hollington, 1875–1906), Eversfield Botry-Pigott (unlicensed curate, 1875–6), William Lutenar Langridge (parish clerk and sexton), the churchwardens and Edmund Currey in Adam *v.* Langridge, 1877.

Ep.I/49 CORRESPONDENCE AND PETITIONS, 1617–1928

See also W.S.R.O. Add. MSS. 1867–1869 for letters written by Bishop Gilbert to Archdeacon Hare, Feb. 1842–Jan. 1855.

I/49/1 (2); letter, 9 July 1617, from Moyses Briant to [John] Swayne, at Chichester Consistory Court, mentioning William Tye (vicar of West Tarring, 1612–21), and letter from William Geering to Walter Piper about the probate of John Carter's will, n.d. [17th cent.].

I/49/2 (5); miscellaneous 18th cent. letters and petitions, from Thomas Ball [later Dean], 1749, John Steele of Chichester, 1778, Archdeacon Courtail, 1782, and Richard Lloyd (vicar of Midhurst, 1796–1834).

I/49/3 (44); correspondence, 1799–1821, mostly from William Fowler (Bishop's registrar), to Bishop Buckner relating to episcopal business, and one letter, 2 Nov. 1799, from Joseph Hinde, written on behalf of the [11th] Duke of Norfolk.

I/49/4 (4); letters and papers, 1835–36, relating to sinecure prebends.

I/49/5 (10); correspondence, 1843–44, between Bishop Gilbert, Charles Bradford (vicar of Arlington, 1839–43) and Robert Belaney (vicar of Arlington, 1843–52) in a dispute over the cost of building Arlington vicarage.

I/49/6 6 ff.; copy correspondence between Archdeacon Garbett and Thomas Vogan (vicar of Walberton, 1843–75) about ruridecanal chapters.

I/49/7 (12); correspondence, 1846, between Archdeacon Hare, George Henry Cussans Scott (vicar of Ifield, 1842–50) and T. Lewin (patron) concerning repairs and alterations to Ifield church.

I/49/8 (4); correspondence, 1851, between Bishop Gilbert, Sir Henry Thompson, bt. (rector of Frant, 1844–68) and Henry Foster (vicar of Selmeston, 1847–63) relating to national schools.

I/49/9 (12); correspondence, 1851 and 1853, between Bishop Gilbert, Edward Miller (perpetual curate of Bognor, 1838–77) and William Peace of Bognor concerning Miller's alleged Romanistic practices in Bognor church.

I/49/10 (3); letter and papers, 1852, from Nathaniel Woodard (provost of Lancing, 1850–91) to Bishop Gilbert relating to St. John's school, Hurstpierpoint.

I/49/11 (7); letters, 1853–4, to Bishop Gilbert from Archbishop [Sumner] of Canterbury, Bishop [Blomfield] of London, the [13th] Duke of Norfolk, Charles Swainson, William Willis (rector of Elsted, 1841–72) and Thomas Sewell of Twineham, about a proposed bill concerning union of benefices and a new school at Twineham.

I/49/12 (7); papers and correspondence, 1855, between Bishop Gilbert, Robert Gream (rector of Rotherfield, 1836–56) and Miss Sarah Ann

Gream concerning the proposed "Institution for supplying the Clergy of Central Sussex and South Surrey with Nurses trained for assistance on the sick poor".

I/49/13 (8); correspondence, 1863, between Bishop Gilbert, John Cooke (rector of East Wittering, 1860–80) and his wife, concerning Mrs. Cooke's allegations of her husband's misconduct.

I/49/14 (200); correspondence, 1865–69, between Bishop Gilbert and many others relating to the ill-health of John Scobell (rector of Lewes All Saints and St. John Southover, 1821–68) and the holding of the two benefices in plurality by his successors.

I/49/15 (9); correspondence, 1871–99, between Bishops Durnford, Wilberforce and Ridgeway, and Messrs. Moore and Currey (Lewes Registrars) relating to the bishops' attitude to the remarriage of divorced persons.

I/49/16 (3); correspondence, 1881, between Bishop Durnford and Edmund Currey relating to the cost of faculties.

I/49/17 (17); single letters to and from Bishop Gilbert on minor diocesan affairs, often endorsed with the date of receipt and nature of reply. The correspondents include Archdeacons Otter and Garbett, and Chichester incumbents.

I/49/18 (15); miscellaneous 19th cent. letters and a petition, mostly on ecclesiastical subjects, between diocesan clergy.

I/49/19 (6); letters, papers and precedents, 1909–28, relating to the appointment of the bishops of Lewes.

Ep.I/50 INVENTORIES OF CHURCH PLATE, 1889

These manuscript volumes, which are alphabetically arranged by parishes and cover the whole diocese, were compiled by Carey Hampton Borrer (rector of Hurstpierpoint, 1841–98; cathedral treasurer, 1879–98); additional information and drawings supplied by incumbents are loose.

I/50/1 215 ff.; vol. I, A to HOO.

I/50/2 215 ff.; vol. II, HOR–Y.

Ep.I/51 ECCLESIASTICAL FORMULARIES AND TREATISES,
16th–19th centuries

"London courts" here refers to those meeting in London (Admiralty, Arches, Audience and Episcopal). A photostat copy of an ecclesiastical formulary (Chichester courts) now in the Cambridge University Library is W.S.R.O. Add. MS. 2967; 5 precedent and other notebooks of a Chichester solicitor (1705–1828) are W.S.R.O. Add. MSS. 5499–5503.

I/51/1 188 ff., but other folios are missing. ff.1–13, Canterbury Audience and Arches courts, mid 16th cent.; ff.14–44, Canterbury diocesan and neighbouring courts, late 16th cent.; ff.45–107, mixed southern courts, late 16th cent.; f.118, *modus procedendi in Curia*, late 16th cent.; ff.119*v.*–128, Chichester courts, early 17th cent.; ff.128*v.*–155, Chichester courts, 1684–1748; f.159, form of sequestration; ff.179–182, index, 18th cent.

I/51/2 84 ff. ff.1–64, Canterbury Audience and Arches courts, and Chichester courts, *c.*1585; ff.65–83, Oxford and Berkshire courts, late 16th cent.

I/51/3 225 ff. ff.i–ii, part of a late 16th cent. treatise (see I/51/4); ff.1–8, 20–37, Chichester courts, early 17th cent.; ff.40–48, conditions of bonds (civil), early 17th cent.; ff.59–64, 70–76, 80–110, Chichester courts, early 17th cent.; ff.149–161, civil formulae, early 17th cent.; ff.200–205, synodals and bishop's rental, 1600 and 1610; ff.206–207, chapter fees; ff.208–221, contemporary index.

I/51/4 252 pp. pp.i–xxii, Practica Curiae, late 16th cent. (see I/51/3); pp.1–43, judicial commissions, London courts, late 16th cent.; pp.43–101, Canterbury Audience and other courts, late 16th cent.; pp.169–203, civil formulae (including ship money), 18th cent.; pp.225–229, part of Practica Curiae.

I/51/5 68 ff. bound in part of a contemporary deed. ff.i–ii, contemporary list of contents; ff.1–53, archiepiscopal and Chichester courts, early 17th cent.; ff.54–68, royal and civil formulae, early 17th cent.

I/51/6 374 pp. pp. i–iv, memoranda; pp.1–222, Francis Clerke,[1] *Praxis*, but without dedication and title page; pp.225–239, contemporary index; pp.241–243, Francis Clerke, *Praxis in Curia Admirallitatis Angliae*; pp.245–253, Lewes courts, late 17th cent.; pp.368–266, London courts, early 17th cent.

I/51/7 58 pp. pp.1–33, Chichester presentations, formulae of 1664 and 1665; pp.56–58, inductions in the Chichester archdeaconry, June 1677–May 1679.

I/51/8 94 ff., this book belonged to John Nicholl in 1721. ff.1–91, Lewes and Arches courts, late 17th cent.; ff.92–94, contemporary list of contents.

I/51/9 53 ff. ff.1–37, excommunications in Lewes courts, late 17th cent.; ff.50–53, the oaths of allegiance and supremacy.

I/51/10 139 ff. f.i, memoranda; ff.1–83, civil formulae, early 17th cent., and Lewes courts, late 17th cent.; ff.105–107, Lewes courts, late 17th cent.; ff.131–132, part of a contemporary index; ff.138–136, civil formulae, late 17th cent.; f.139, memoranda.

---

[1] Francis Clerke (fl.1594), practised at Doctors Commons, 1559, and wrote Latin manuals of the admiralty and ecclesiastical courts. *Praxis* was printed in Dublin in 1666.

I/51/11 234 pp. pp.1–232, Lewes courts, late 17th cent.; pp. 232–233, contemporary index.

I/51/12 92 ff. ff.1–74, Lewes courts, late 17th–early 18th cents.

I/51/13 82 pp. pp.1–75, Chichester courts, late 17th cent.; pp.80–82, civil formulae, late 17th cent.

I/51/14 29 ff. ff.1–29, Lewes courts, late 17th cent.

I/51/15 179 ff. ff.10–81, London and other courts, late 17th cent.; ff.82–121, Lewes courts, late 17th and early 18th cent.; ff.160–173, contemporary index.

I/51/16 70 ff. ff.1–16, Lewes courts, late 17th cent.; ff.17–64, Lewes courts, late 17th cent.; f.68, contemporary index to ff.1–16.

I/51/17 212 pp. pp.1–80, London and Chichester courts, 17th cent.

I/51/18 22 ff. ff.1–20, Chichester courts, early 18th cent.

I/51/18a 24 ff. pp.1–12, Chichester courts (benefices), early 18th cent.

I/51/19 204 pp. pp.1–131, Chichester courts, mid 18th cent.; pp.197–204, contemporary lists of contents.

I/51/20 116 pp. pp.1–101, Chichester and other courts, and chapter formulae, 18th cent.; pp.112–116, ecclesiastical formulae, 18th cent.

I/51/21 118 ff. ff.7–30, Lewes courts, 18th cent.

I/51/22 (411); 18th and 19th cent. documents used as precedents in the bishop's registry. Most were extracted from original series (now in the Episcopal and Capitular archives) and relate to all aspects of diocesan administration, including the ordination, appointment and conduct of clergy, church building, faculties and consecrations, visitation, confirmations, testamentary business, St. Mary's hospital, Chichester, Amberley manor, and some civil and extra-diocesan papers. There is also a copy of *A Sermon preached in the Cathedral Church of Chichester on the occasion of publicly receiving into the Church a convert from the Church of Rome* (15 Oct. 1843) by Dean Chandler (22 pp.).

Ep.I/52 FREELAND'S PAPERS, 19th century

James Bennett Freeland was deputy diocesan registrar from 1841 to 1852, and a local antiquary. His papers were transferred to the Cathedral muniment room in 1947.

I/52/1 461 ff. ff.1–433, abstract of institutions in episcopal registers and subscription books, 1397–1844; ff.447v.–461, index of benefices.

I/52/2 228 ff. ff.1–196, abstract of installations of cathedral clergy arranged by offices (compiled from I/52/1); ff.225v.–228, memoranda.

I/52/3 and 3a 198 ff. and 153 ff. flyleaf, index of benefices; ff.1–198, abstract of institutions in the Chichester archdeaconry arranged by benefices (compiled from I/52/1).

I/52/4 292 ff. flyleaf, index of benefices; ff.1–285, abstract of institutions in the Lewes archdeaconry arranged by benefices (compiled from I/52/1).

I/52/5 (34); printed forms for the above extracts, with some entries.

I/52/6 22 ff.; notes on episcopal registers.

I/52/7 182 ff. flyleaves, index of names; ff.1–157, transcripts of documents in the British Museum relating to the diocese of Chichester.

I/52/8 156 ff. ff.1–74, transcripts of charters relating to Chichester, 1249–1524.

I/52/9 (250); transcripts of documents in the bishop's registry.

I/52/10 (2); a copy of the statutes of the Prebendal School (1550) and a list of dedications of Sussex churches.

I/52/11 (8); miscellaneous papers relating to a projected biography of St. Wilfrid (1841); Stoughton parsonage house (1844) and the advowson of Itchingfield (1844); to William Hayden of Chichester (1877 and 1897); lists of bishops of Chichester, including those made freemen of Chichester from 1685 to 1741 (1741 and 1840).

Ep.I/53 MISCELLANEA, 1626–1856

These documents appear to have nothing to do with the episcopal records but have strayed into the collection.

I/53/1 (1); title page and part of dedication of a MS. entitled "The Fore Runner of t[he] Reuenge Uppon the Duke of Buckingham for the poysoning of the most potent Kinge James of happy memory King of greate Brittane and the Lord Marquis Hambleton and others of the Nobilitie" [originally published at Frankfürt, 1626], taken from the cathedral library by a fire-watcher during the last war, and returned 1961. Bound in manilla.

I/53/2 144 pp. *A list of the Existing Nominees appointed by the Lords Commissioners of His Majesty's Treasury to hold shares on the part of the public in the Tontine of the year 1789* (London, 1809); see also 30 Geo. III c.45.

I/53/3 92 pp. Herman Heinfetter, *A Literal Translation of the Gospel according to St. John*, part II (London, 1849).

I/53/4 (3); parts of the *Supplement to the Times* (14 and 24 Jan. 1853) and *The Times* (5 Dec. 1859), probably used as wrappers for bundles of documents.

I/53/5 8 pp.; printed Circular of the Metropolitan Sanitary Association, Apr. 1853.

I/53/6 (1); abstract of a bequest of trust estates by William Charles Newland, 1854.

I/53/7 8 pp.; *Memorial Church at Constantinople*, including a list of subscriptions, May 1856.

I/53/8 (1); *Specimens of 67 Types of Oriental and other Languages* (n.d.).

Ep.I/54 TITHE COMMUTATION PAPERS, 1829–1855

In the compulsory commutation of tithe (6 & 7 Will. IV c.71; 1836), J. B. Freeland (deputy diocesan registrar, 1841–52) acted for the bishop, dean and chapter, local incumbents and tithe owners, and these are his papers. They include letters, newspapers, accounts, memoranda, legal opinions, tithe accounts and draft apportionments, notices and minutes of meetings of tithe owners, copies of documents—mainly terriers, abstracts and copies of leases and acts of parliament, powers of attorney and draft bills. The diocesan copies of the awards and maps are in the Diocesan Record Offices at Chichester and Lewes and are described in F. W. Steer (ed.), *A Catalogue of Sussex Estate and Tithe Award Maps* (Sussex Record Society, vol. 61, 1962), pp. 175–208. I/54/67–72 concern parishes in which the bishop or dean and chapter were tithe owners. (The number I/54/23 has not been allocated).

I/54/1 (50); Alciston, 1837–1845.

I/54/2 (67); Aldingbourne, 1838–1853.

I/54/3 (60); Amberley, 1838–1853.

I/54/4 (1); Ashington *cum* Buncton, 1848.

I/54/5 (1); Barnham, 1846.

I/54/6 (3); Beddingham and West Firle, 1841–1844.

I/54/7 (4); Bepton, 1838–1842.

I/54/8 (4); Bexhill, 1839–1840.

I/54/9 (1); Bignor, 1844.

I/54/10 (38); Birdham, 1838–1853.

I/54/11 (62); Bishopstone, 1838–1853.

I/54/12 (1); West Blatchington, 1838.

I/54/13 (1); Boxgrove, 1838.

I/54/14 (23); Bury, 1838–1853.

I/54/15 (7); Chichester St. Bartholomew, 1846–1853.

I/54/16 (1); Chichester St. Peter the Great, 1846. (See Ep.I/16/3 for a tithe book, 1766–1780.)

I/54/17 (51); Chidham, 1838–1853.

I/54/18 (21); West Chiltington, 1832–1838.

I/54/19 (1); Climping, 1842.

I/54/20 (3); West Dean (East Sussex), 1839.

I/54/21 (28); Binderton, Chilgrove and West Dean, 1838–1851.

I/54/22 (3); Didling, 1842.

I/54/24 (8); Ditchling, 1838–1841.

I/54/25 (3); Duncton, 1838–1839.

I/54/26 (11); Earnley, 1838–1844.

I/54/27 (5); Eartham, 1838.

I/54/28 (1); Eastbourne, 1841.

I/54/29 (42); Eastergate, 1838–1855.

I/54/30 (7); Felpham, 1838–1843.

I/54/31 (14); Ferring, 1838–1839.

I/54/32 (14); Funtington, 1837–1838.

I/54/33 (1); Hamsey, 1841.

I/54/34 (2); Hardham, 1847–1848.

I/54/35 (29); Heathfield, 1833–1841.

I/54/36 (8); Henfield, 1838–1853.

I/54/37 (7); Heyshott, 1842.

I/54/38 (11); Hunston and North Mundham, 1846–1853.

I/54/39 (6); Kingston and East Preston, 1839–1840.

I/54/40 (31); Icklesham, 1843–1844. (See Ep.I/16/4 for a tithe book, 1818–1824.)

I/54/41 (15); Litlington, 1838–1842.

I/54/42 (26); Littlehampton, 1838–1853.

I/54/43 (1); Madehurst, n.d. (copy of 1663 terrier).

I/54/44 (1); Merston, 1838.

I/54/45 (4); Oving, 1839–1841.

I/54/46 (2); Pagham, 1853. (See Ep.I/16/5 for a parish survey, 1825, and I/16/10 for a tithe book, 1807–1819.)

I/54/47 (52); Pulborough, 1829–1842. (See Ep.I/16/6–9 for documents relating to tithes, 1844–1857.)

I/54/48 (4); Rackham, 1840–1841.

I/54/49 (1); Rodmell, 1838.

I/54/50 (3); Rudgwick, 1838–1840.

I/54/51 (14); Selmeston, 1838–1840.

I/54/52 (25); Selsey, 1838–1853.

I/54/53 (57); Sidlesham, 1838–1853.

I/54/54 (28); Singleton, 1838–1847.

I/54/55 (64); Slinfold, 1837–1844.

I/54/56 (15); West Stoke, 1838–1846.

I/54/57 (18); Storrington, 1838.

I/54/58 (13); Stoughton, 1838–1840.

I/54/59 (18); Sullington, 1838.

I/54/60 (1); Sutton with Seaford, 1837.

I/54/61 (25); Trotton (Dumpford), 1838–1839.

I/54/62 (11); Walberton, 1846–1853.

I/54/63 (63); Willingdon, 1838–1842.

I/54/64 (47); Wisborough Green, 1838–1853.

I/54/65 (1); East Wittering, 1851.

I/54/66 (8); Yapton, 1840.

I/54/67 (2); Amport (Hants), 1838.

I/54/68 (2); Appleshaw (Hants), 1838.

I/54/69 (8); Bapchild (Kent), 1838–1839.

I/54/70 (1); Freshwater (Isle of Wight), n.d. [*c*.1838].

I/54/71 (17); Mendlesham (Suffolk), 1839–1841.

I/54/72 (1); High Wycombe (Bucks), 1848.

I/54/73 (12); letters of attorney to J. B. Freeland, 1837–1842.

I/54/74 13 ff. unbound; index to tithe commutation letter books not in the Diocesan Record Office. n.d.

I/54/75 (8); lists of tithe meetings, accounts, legal papers and memoranda, 1838–1844.

I/54/76 (21); draft bills for Alciston, Appledram, Beddingham, Birdham, Bosham, Burpham, Chichester St. Peter the Great, Chidham, East Dean (East Sussex) (2), West Dean (with Binderton and Chilgrove), Funtington, Lullington, Oving, Rumboldswyke, Singleton, Stoughton, Trotton, Willingdon, Yapton, Bapchild (Kent) and Mendlesham (Suffolk), all 1850.

I/54/77 132 ff.; index of tithe commutation bills (not comprehensive), 1839–1851.
ff.1–13, index of parishes; ff.14–55, copies of bills.

Ep.I/55 SUSSEX VICE-ADMIRALTY COURT PAPERS, 1638–1688
276 documents, of which a typescript calendar, with introduction, is available in the Diocesan Record Office (Ep.I/88/1).

Ep.I/56 CIVIL FORMULARIES AND TREATISES, 17th–19th
centuries
These volumes, almost all containing civil documents only, were probably the result of the diocesan registrars' private practices. 5 precedent and other notebooks of a Chichester solicitor (1705–1828) are W.S.R.O. Add. MSS. 5499–5503.

I/56/1 94 ff. ff.1–92, copies of deeds, early 17th cent.

I/56/2 178 pp. pp.i–xii, part of a contemporary index; pp.1–166, common law cases, early 18th cent.

I/56/3 72 pp. pp.1–72, common law cases, 1729–1738.

I/56/4 78 ff. ff.1–70, common law court formulae, 1734–1763; ff.72–76, memoranda and part of a contemporary index.

I/56/5 276 pp. pp.ii–v, contemporary list of contents; pp.vii–268, copies of deeds, late 18th cent.

I/56/6 358 pp. pp.i–iii, contemporary list of contents; pp.1–210, copies of deeds, early 19th cent.; pp.211–302, ecclesiastical formulae, early 19th cent., including, on pp.262–265, parliamentary return of applications to build churches and chapels in the Lewes archdeaconry, 1800–1837, with details of presentation (1837), on pp.266–267, a list of chapels consecrated in the Lewes archdeaconry, 1803–1839 (1843), and on pp. 295–297, list of churches and chapels consecrated in the Chichester archdeaconry, 1812–1847; pp.346, 351, 352, accounts and memoranda, 1808–1823.

Ep.I/57 CIVIL MISCELLANEA

This group formerly consisted mainly of documents transferred with the ecclesiastical records, but having nothing to do with them. Some are now in the W.S.R.O. Add. MSS. class; others have been transferred to the archives of the city of Chichester and to those belonging to the Goodwood estate. Such of these miscellaneous records as related to the bishop and/or the dean and chapter have been merged in their proper classes and so this catalogue reference, I/57, is no longer used.

Ep.I/58 PROBATE REGISTRY FEE LISTS, 1870–1908

28 annual bundles of copies of the District Probate Registry's weekly return of fees remitted to the Principal Registry, 1870–1889, 1894–5 and 1903–1908. The District Registry was in the same office as the Diocesan Registry.

Ep.I/59 SEAL MATRICES, 1841–1934

I/59/1 Thomas Robinson Welch, Chancellor of the Diocese, 1841–44.

I/59/2 George Kennedy Allen Bell, Bishop, 1929–58.

I/59/3 Charles Philip Stewart Clarke, Archdeacon, 1934–45.

Ep.I/60 BAPTISMAL RETURNS, 1851

1 bundle of incumbents' returns of the number of persons baptized in each parish in the archdeaconry in 1851, two circulars to incumbents requesting the information (in pursuance of a House of Commons resolution dated 11 June 1855) and letters from incumbents (of both archdeaconries) relating to the returns. See Ep.I/46/17.

Ep.I/61 STATISTICAL RETURNS, 1906–1928

These returns of church work and finance for the whole diocese were prepared by the Statistical Returns department of the Central Board of Finance, and give full details (for each parish) of the numbers of baptisms, confirmations, communicants and weekly services, of church accommodation, church schools and lay help, and of parochial finances. The parishes are arranged by deaneries, prefaced by a digest of the diocesan totals; each volume contains 144 pages.

I/61/1	1906/07		I/61/9	1922
I/61/2	1907/08		I/61/10	1923
I/61/3	1912–13		I/61/11	1924
I/61/4	1914–15		I/61/12	1925
I/61/5	1915–16		I/61/13	1926
I/61/6	1916–17		I/61/14	1927
I/61/7	1918		I/61/15	1928
I/61/8	1921			

Ep.I/62 CONFIRMATION BOOKS AND PAPERS, 1798–1918

I/62/1 (3); circulars from Bishop Buckner of confirmations to be held in 1798 and 1820, and a list of candidates for the latter from Angmering (with ages).

I/62/2 89 ff. ff.1–89, numbers of persons confirmed in the diocese, 1847–1862, arranged by date of confirmation, with numbers, age and sex for each parish (no personal names).

I/62/3 54 ff. ff.1–54, numbers of persons confirmed in the diocese, arranged by date of confirmation, with numbers, age and sex for each parish (no personal names), Apr.–May, no year.

I/62/4 (55); lists of persons confirmed in the diocese, by parishes, with names and ages. Most of the documents are undated but include confirmations from 1847–1863.

I/62/5 (4); letters, 1864–65, relating to confirmations.

I/62/6 (8); printed and manuscript forms of presentation of confirmation candidates, and a confirmation poem.

I/62/7 (10); printed orders of (confirmation) service, including Frant (1862), Brighton St. Mark (1862 and 1863) and Pulborough, and a list of confirmations in the diocese, 1862.

I/62/8 (31); lists of confirmation candidates presented at Hove, 1918, and of soldiers and nurses confirmed in the diocese, 1918, all giving names and ages, and in the latter case units and home addresses.

Ep.I/63 QUEEN ANNE'S BOUNTY PAPERS, 1715–1908

The corporation of the Governors of Queen Anne's Bounty was created by the Act 2 & 3 Anne c.20 [sometimes quoted as c.11] (1703) to apply and distribute the revenues of first fruits and tenths, benefactions and part of the profits of livings sequestered for non-residence, to the relief of poor clergy and the permanent augmentation of smaller livings. Part of such augmentation was often appropriated to providing a suitable parsonage house to encourage residence.

I/63/1 (6); lists of livings in the diocese augmented, augmentable and discharged, 1715–1798. By the Act 5 Anne c.24 (1706) small livings (not exceeding £50 at augmentation) were discharged from payment of first fruits and tenths.

I/63/2 9 Mar. 1798. Counterpart lease for 14 years from previous Christmas at annual rent of £14.

Thomas Durnford, clerk, minister of All Saints Chichester, and Thomas Newman, clerk, minister of St. Peter the Less in the same city, to Griffith Richards of Farlington, co. Hants, clerk.

Meadow (5a.) in Farlington, now in the tenure of Richards and lately purchased by the Governors of Q.A.B. for the benefit of the minister for the time being of All Saints in the Pallant and St. Peter the Less, Chichester.

I/63/3 (4); letter (1799) from the secretary to Q.A.B. about the augmentation of Chichester St. Bartholomew, two copies of a resolution on curates' stipends (n.d.) and an account of the management of the income of Q.A.B. (n.d.).

I/63/4 (6); printed bills, minutes and legal opinions relating to augmentations and church buildings and lands (early 19th cent.).

I/63/5 (2); letter from the bishop's secretary to [an incumbent] about augmentation (1821) and an order to surrender the profits of Dallington rectory to Q.A.B. (1836).

I/63/6 14 ff.; *Summary of Annexations of Land etc. to Poor Benefices by the Governors of Queen Anne's Bounty to the year ending 1838.* Chichester diocese.

I/63/7 20 Apr. 1871. Counterpart mortgage. Consideration £1,000. The Bishop of Chichester to the Governors of Queen Anne's Bounty, in pursuance of the Acts 6 & 7 Will. IV c.77 and 5 & 6 Vict. c.26 empowering Q.A.B. to lend money on mortgage to improve episcopal houses of residence.

I/63/8 15 Feb. 1872. Counterpart mortgage. Consideration £1,000. The Bishop of Chichester to John Burder, in trust for the Governors of Queen Anne's Bounty, for further improvements to the episcopal house of residence (see I/63/7).

I/63/9 (4); returns by the Governors of purchases, sales and gifts of real estate for benefices in the diocese of Chichester (under 2 & 3 Vict. c.49), 1903, 1904, 1906, 1908.

Ep.I/64 THE PAPERS OF BISHOP BURROWS, 1912–1928

Papers of Bishop Burrows, mostly relating to Chichester diocesan affairs, but including some from his episcopate at Truro. 1 vol., 1912–19.

Ep.I/65 BISHOP BELL'S ENQUIRY, 1957

Answers to a questionnaire (2 pp.) sent by Bishop Bell to all clergy in the diocese, 30 Oct. 1957, relating to the numbers of sons of the clergy seeking ordination and the reasons influencing the sons of laymen. There is also correspondence on this subject between Bishop Bell and Arnold Cecil Powell (prebendary of Highleigh, 1947–1963), with the latter's tabulated summary of the returns and a list of diocesan clergy used as an index to the printed forms, drawing attention to specially detailed replies.

Ep.I/66 LETTERS TESTIMONIAL, 1570–1841

(47); these testimonials were all written on behalf of candidates for ordination, benefices and the office of schoolmaster, and were signed by three or more clergymen, usually neighbouring incumbents or members of the candidate's college. Some of the documents for 1742 have certificates of age and nominations to stipendiary curacies annexed. A typescript calendar is available in the Diocesan Record Office (Ep.I/88/1); other letters testimonial are attached to documents in Ep.I/6, 6A, 6C/2, 68/3 and 72/2.

1570	1	1677	1	1737	2	1841	1
1615	1	1691	7	1739	2		
1670	1	1692	17	1742	6		
1676	2	1693	2	1745	2		

and 2 undated [late 17th cent.].

Ep.I/67 ORDINATION PAPERS, 1663–1829

(49); a typescript calendar of these papers is available in the Diocesan Record Office (Ep.I/88/1).

I/67/1 Letters dimissory, 1663–1687, mostly from the Archbishop of Canterbury. A candidate for holy orders was required to be ordained by the bishop of the diocese in which he had his title, and if he wished to be ordained in any other place he had to produce letters dimissory from his own bishop to the ordaining or any other bishop.

1663	4	1667	5	1676	1	1686	3
1664	11	1668	2	1677	1	1687	4
1665	8	1674	1	1679	2		
1666	4	1675	1	1682	1		

and one undated document.

I/67/2 (7); letters of orders, 1667–1829, issued by the ordaining bishop as a record of the candidate's ordination and usually required to be produced at visitations.

1667, 2; 1768, 2; 1770, 1; 1776, 1; 1829, 1.

I/67/3 (1); certificate of title, 1705.

Ep.I/68 PAPERS RELATING TO STIPENDIARY CURACIES, 1692–1845

Stipendiary curates were licensed by the bishop to assist an incumbent at a fixed stipend, either in the parish church or in a dependent chapel of ease. Their appointment and stipend were regulated by the Acts 12 Anne Stat. 2 c.2 (1713), 36 Geo. III c.83 (1795), 53 Geo. III c.149 (1813), 57 Geo. III c.99, ss.48–70 (1817) and 1 & 2 Vict. c.106, ss.75–102 (1838). A typescript calendar of these papers is available in the Diocesan Record Office (Ep.I/88/1).

I/68/1 (15); incumbents' nominations to stipendiary curacies, 1692–1799. Other nominations are annexed to documents in Ep.I/6, 66, 68/2 and 68/3.
1692, 1; 1738, 1; 1742, 1; 1798, 2; 1799, 10.

I/68/2 (4); licences to stipendiary curacies, 1816–1826, one with a nomination and letter attached.
1816, 1; 1825, 1; 1826, 2.

I/68/3 (34); commissions for licensing stipendiary curates, 1819–1845, some with nominations and letters testimonial attached. The reverse of the commission was invariably used for the curate's subscriptions.

1819	1	1834	4	1840	4	1843	5
1832	1	1835	3	1841	3	1844	1
1833	1	1836	1	1842	1	1845	9

I/68/4 (2); notes on licences and institutions (1723–1761) and list of licences to perpetual and stipendiary curacies and to the mastership of Rye Grammar School (issued 1799–1814), n.d. and 1814.

I/68/5 2 unused licences to stipendiary curacies, 19th cent.

Ep.I/69 INSTITUTION AND COLLATION PAPERS, 1570–1934

After presentation (by the patron) and admission (the bishop's acceptance of the candidate) the rector or vicar was given possession of the spiritualities of the benefice by institution by the ordinary. If the bishop himself was patron, in full right or by lapse, he instituted without previous presentation, which act was called collation. In the case of a perpetual curacy the bishop's licence admitted the clerk to both spiritualities and temporalities without institution or induction. A typescript calendar of these papers is available in the Diocesan Record Office (Ep.I/88/1).

I/69/1 (20); letters of institution and collation, including those by commission, and licences to perpetual curacies, 1674–1918, giving details of vacancy and patronage.

1674	1	1769	1	1785	1	1806	1
1679	1	1771	1	1790	1	1808	1
1697	1	1776	1	1792	1	1918	1
1739	2	1783	1	1795	1		
1768	1	1784	1	1798	2		

I/69/2 (31); institution bonds, 1570–1746. Other bonds are annexed to presentations in Ep.I/6.

1570	6	1577	1	1728	1	1744	3
1571	9	1676	2	1742	1	1746	2
1573	1	1677	2	1743	3		

I/69/3 (6); episcopal commissions to institute, collate and license, 1615–1841, giving details of vacancy and patronage. The reverse of the 1841 commissions was used for clerk's subscriptions.

1615, 1; 1749, 1; 1768, 1; 1770, 1; 1841, 2.

I/69/4 (44); notices to churchwardens of the bishop's intention to institute or collate, 1909–1934, posted on the church door for one month (61 & 62 Vict. c.48, s.2; 1898). Other notices are annexed to presentations in Ep.I/6.

1909	1	1923	2	1927	5	1932	1
1912	1	1924	5	1929	1	1933	4
1920	1	1925	7	1930	3	1934	1
1922	1	1926	9	1931	2		

I/69/5 (8); petitions to the bishop from patrons in holy orders for their own institution or licensing, 1789–1830.

1789	2	1816	1	1823	1	1830	1
1798	1	1819	1	1827	1		

I/69/6 5 bundles of letters and papers relating to institutions to Fairwarp, Bexhill St. Mark, Bexhill St. Peter and Worthing St. Paul [all 1933], and Itchingfield [1934].

I/69/7 2 lists of institutions and licensings "since 5 May 1874", no date [*c*.1876].

I/69/8 (1); licence to Andrew Smith to the cure of souls within the diocese, Mar. 1607/8.

I/69/9 (3); sentence of suspension of Peter Smith (vicar of Alciston) by Court of High Commission, public notice, and order to bishop to appoint another minister, Nov. 1611.

Ep.I/70 RESIGNATIONS, 1563–1899

(45); these documents also include certificates of resignation by a notary public, and some are endorsed with the bishop's acceptance of the resignation. For each resignation from 1877 to 1899 there is a bundle of papers consisting mainly of correspondence and reports of the commissions of inquiry set up under the Incumbents' Resignation Acts, 1871 and 1887 (34 & 35 Vict. c.44; 50 & 51 Vict. c.23). For appointments of proctors see Ep.I/73; other resignations are annexed to presentations in Ep.I/6. A typescript calendar of these documents is available in the Diocesan Record Office (Ep.I/88/1).

1563	1	1586	1	1601	1	1617	1
1570	2	1587	1	1610	1	1618	1
1571	1	1588	1	1613	1	1619	1
1574	1	1589	1	1615	1	1673	1
1577	2	1591	3	1616	2	1679	1

1690	1	1710	2	1731	1	1877	1
1693	1	1712	1	1748	1	1878	2
1701	1	1717	1	1766	1	1898	1
1707	2	1720	1	1777	1	1899	1
1709	1						

Ep.I/71   SEQUESTRATION PAPERS, 1560–1929

A benefice was sequestrated by the ordinary on vacancy, or as a result of the neglect, misconduct or bankruptcy of the incumbent, or dispute about title, or if the profits of the living seemed in danger. The documents often give details of vacancy and patronage; a typescript calendar is available in the Diocesan Record Office (Ep.I/88/1).

I/71/1   (36); letters and relaxations of sequestration, some with correspondence and court papers attached.

1749	1	1801	1	1821	1	1843	1
1750	1	1811	1	1822	1	1846	1
1766	1	1812	1	1823	1	1849	1
1772	2	1813	2	1837	1	1929	1
1779	1	1814	2	1838	3		
1780	1	1815	4	1840	3		
1788	1	1819	1	1841	2		

I/71/2   (23); sequestration bonds.

1560	1	1811	2	1815	1	1825	1
1570	7	1814	6	1819	2	1828	2
1803	1						

I/71/3   (15); writs of *levari facias*, ordering the bishop to sequester the profits of the living to satisfy the incumbent's debts.

1737	4	1811	1	1819	2	1827	1
1738	1	1814	2	1825	1	1828	2
1803	1						

I/71/4   Letters and court papers relating to sequestrations.

I/71/4/1   (9); Felpham, 1797.

I/71/4/2   (7); Donnington, 1814.

I/71/4/3   (9); Middleton, 1828.

I/71/4/4   (2); opinions on the "doctrine of sequestration", n.d. [*post* 1782].

Ep.I/72   DISPENSATIONS FOR PLURALITY, 1840–1930

I/72/1   (6); archbishop's dispensations to hold benefices in plurality, according to the provisions of 1 & 2 Vict. c.106, s.6 (1838).
1840, 1; 1841, 1; 1844, 1; 1846, 1; 1848, 2.

I/72/2   (2); statements for dispensations, with testimonials attached, giving value of the livings, 1922, 1930.

(5); appointment of proctors for resignations, institutions and synods and visitations.

1567, 1; 1571, 1; 1580, 1; 1591, 1; 1610, 1.

Ep.I/74 FORMS OF SERVICE, 1801–1908

I/74/1 (1); a prayer for harvest thanksgiving (London, 1801).

I/74/2 16 pp.; form of service for the consecration of churches, chapels and burial grounds, adapted by the Archdeacon of Oxford [Charles Clerke], Oxford, 1836, with pencilled marginal notes.

I/74/3 18 pp.; form of service for the consecration of churches, chapels and churchyards, for use in the Winchester diocese (London, 1841).

I/74/4 16 pp.; order of service used on laying the foundation stone of the new church of St. Peter the Great, Chichester, Aug. 1848.

I/74/5 16 pp. (2 copies); form of consecration of a church or chapel, and burial ground, in the diocese of Chichester, n.d., one copy marked "Treyford 1849".

I/74/6 (2); forms of consecration of a churchyard or additional burial place, n.d. [19th cent.].

I/74/7 (11); letters and papers concerning applications for tickets for the consecration and enthronement of Bishop Ridgeway, 1908, and the orders of service for both.

Ep.I/75 PAPERS RELATING TO THE BISHOP'S PALACE, 1608–1804

The Palace was also known during the 18th and early 19th centuries as Chichester House. See Ep.I/63/7 and 8, I. C. Hannah, "Bishop's Palace, Chichester", in *S.A.C.*, vol. 52, pp.1–23, and F. W. Steer, *The Heraldic Ceiling at the Bishop's Palace, Chichester* (Chichester Paper 10; 1958). For accounts of work done annually in the Palace, 1765–1796, see Ep.VI/5.

I/75/1 (8); accounts of work done in the Palace in 1608. See F. W. Steer, "Repairs to the Bishop's Palace" in *Chichester Cathedral Journal*, 1961, pp.14–18.

I/75/2 (2); list of goods left by Bishop Bowers to the Palace, 1724, with copy of a letter (1949) about the finding of the document.

I/75/3 (1); copies of inscriptions on [Palace] walls [relating to re-building], 1727 and 1800.

I/75/4 (1); "An Inventory of Some Fixtures & Goods Belonging to Lord Bishop [Mawson] of Ely and sold to Lord Bishop [Ashburnham] of Chichester", 1754.

I/75/5 Microfilm of letters of J. Putman about the ceiling in the Bishop's Palace, 1804.

Ep.I/76 APPOINTMENTS OF CHAPLAINS AND SCHOOLMASTERS, 1736–1844

I/76/1 (1); draft appointment of John Wynne as Bishop Hare's domestic chaplain, 1736.

I/76/2 (1); letter from Joseph Hannay requesting licence as master of Hastings Charity School, 1809.

I/76/3 (1); copy licence to Anthony Nott as chaplain to Lewes House of Correction, 1825.

I/76/4 (1); letter from W. Bayly requesting licence as master of Midhurst School, 1830.

I/76/5 (2); commission for licensing John Allen as chaplain to Brighton workhouse, 1841.

I/76/6 (2); commission for licensing William Maher as chaplain to Brede union workhouse, 1841.

I/76/7 (2); copy appointments of Frederick Vincent and Henry Churton as Bishop Gilbert's chaplains, 1842.

I/76/8 (2); copy appointments of William Sergison and Henry Browne as Bishop Gilbert's chaplains, 1843.

I/76/9 (2); certificate of appointment of Alexander Bridges as chaplain to Horsham union, and letter, 1844.

Ep.I/77 GENEALOGICAL PAPERS, 1796–1847

I/77/1 (24); "Clarke's pedigree": notes of genealogical searches made to find the heirs of Richard Clarke, d.1796 or 1797.

I/77/2 22 pp.; J.D., *The Genealogy of the House of Tolquhon*, Edinburgh, 1839.

I/77/3 (7); "Barber Pedigree": notes of genealogical searches made 1846–7.

Ep.I/78 PAPERS RELATING TO CHARITIES, 17th century – 1858

I/78/1 (1); bond on a benefaction to the poor of Slinfold, n.d. [*temp.* James I].

I/78/2 (1); list of "Charitable Donations for the Benefit of poor Persons in the Parish of Brighton", 1617–1771, n.d. [*post* 1796].

I/78/3 (1); petition to the bishop from Thomas R[enward] about "charitey lands", July 1801; mentions Wittersham [Kent] and Hastings (All Saints and St. Clement).

I/78/4 (1); unused petition for Mrs. Ann Cam's [clergy] benefaction, n.d.

I/78/5 (6); papers and letters relating to Mr. Betton's [schools] charity, including a list of Sussex applicants, 1847.

I/78/6 (3); letters relating to Dr. Richards' [clergy] charity, 1852 [founded 1837].

I/78/7 (4); two copies of the statement of funds of a society for the relief of clergy widows and orphans, Lewes, 1827 (16 pp.), and annual statements of the society for 1857 and 1858 (each 16 pp.). See Ep.II/35/4.

Ep.I/79 CONVOCATION RETURNS, 1881

Returns from every incumbent in the diocese to a questionnaire (26 Aug. 1881) on the buildings licensed and used for worship in each parish and the numbers of persons baptized and confirmed in 1880; the information was required for a "Statistical Return for the use of Convocation". There are also a few letters from incumbents.

Ep.I/80 S.P.C.K. AND S.P.G. PAPERS, 1799–1858

I/80/1 (1); certificate of title of a prospective missionary of the S.P.G., June 1799.

I/80/2 (1); report of a general meeting of the S.P.C.K., London, June 1810.

I/80/3 (1); third report of the Chichester Diocesan Committee of the S.P.C.K., 1817.

I/80/4 (2); abstract of the proceedings of the Hastings Rape Committee of the S.P.C.K., Feb. 1821 and Apr. 1823.

I/80/5 24 pp.; *Summary Account of the Society for the Propagation of the Gospel in Foreign Parts* (London, 1858).

Ep.I/81 BISHOP GILBERT'S OXFORD PAPERS, 19th century

Bishop Gilbert was Principal of Brasenose College, Oxford, from 1822 to 1842, and these papers undoubtedly belong to this period, although most are undated. All are manuscript, and I/81/1 and 6–9 are in Gilbert's hand.

I/81/1 (36 ff.); notes and papers on the status and visitatorial powers of Oxford colleges, n.d.

I/81/2 30 ff. ff.1–20, report, addressed to "the Board of Heads of Houses and Proctors", of a committee appointed to enquire into "the defects and evils attributed to the operation of the present Examination Statute", n.d.

I/81/3 20 ff. ff.1–14, "The concurring Causes which assisted the Promulgation of the Religion of Mahommed", by Piers Calveley Claughton, Fellow of University College, n.d. A facsimile of "a Horoscope set on the Nativity of Milton the Poet by John Gadbury the Astrologer (Ashmolean MS. 436, f.119)" (1837), is attached.

I/81/4 18 ff. ff.1*v*.–9, Latin poem entitled "Delphi", n.d.

I/81/5 44 pp.; Chancellor's Prize Speech given in the Sheldonian Theatre, 1840: "Miles Romanus quando primum et quibus de causis coeperit Libertati Civium obesse".

I/81/6 12 ff.; notes on "The subjects of human knowledge, or investigation", n.d.

I/81/7 27 ff.; "Attempt at A new mode of Metaphysical Enquiry, Illustrated as here employed upon Perception by the Author of A few Pages on the Book of Job", 1816 [Pages confused].

I/81/8 5 notebooks (14 and 16 ff.); continuations of [?I/81/7] or parts of essays on similar subjects. n.d.

I/81/9 28 pp.; continuation and conclusion of [?I/81/7], or part of an essay on a similar subject, n.d.

Ep.I/82 DISSENTERS' MEETING HOUSE CERTIFICATES, 1804

I/82/1 (1); Steyning, Aug. 1804.

I/82/2 (1); Worthing, Aug. 1804.

Ep.I/83 PARISH PAPERS, [1549]–1856

Miscellaneous papers relating to parishes in the Chichester archdeaconry.

I/83/1 (1); clause of the will of Thomas Sherlock [Dean of Chichester, 1715–28; Bishop of London, 1748–61] *quoad* Aldingbourne parsonage, 1761.

I/83/2 7 ff.; [18th cent.?] copy of Ep.I/1/6, ff.71–73, on the re-endowment of Bury vicarage, Nov. 1549.

I/83/3 (1); note on a nomination to the curacy of Felpham, Jan. 1820.

I/83/4 (1); note of Mr. Denham's admission to Iping, n.d. [?1695].

I/83/5 19 ff. relating to the suicide of Harriet Frogley, of Lodsworth, 1856.

I/83/6 (2); "An Acct. of N. Chapel Church, how it came to be Parochial", copied from a parish register, 1718, and appointment of the parish clerk of North Chapel, 1847.

I/83/7 5 June 1712   Lease for 8 years at an annual rent of £60. William Brett of Lewes, apothecary, to Daniel Newell of North Stoke, yeoman.

> The Rectory or Parsonage of North Stoke, with all houses, barns, stables, stalls, closes and glebe lands belonging . . . now in the occupation of Richard Pannett of North Stoke.

I/83/8 (1); note on the perpetual curacy of North Stoke, n.d. [early 19th cent.].

I/83/9 (1); document, partly illegible, relating to Rusper, *temp.* Elizabeth I.

I/83/10 (1); list of parishes in the archdeaconry, with post towns, n.d. [18th cent.].

I/83/11 (1); alphabetical list of clergy in the archdeaconry, with their benefices, and list of curates, n.d. [*c.*1750].

I/83/12 (1); list of parishes and rural deans, n.d. [19th cent.].

Ep.I/84 MISCELLANEOUS ACCOUNTS AND RECEIPTS, 1814–1863

I/84/1 (5); stock receipts of Andrew Bowles, 1814–1817.

I/84/2 35 ff.; bank pass book, Dendy Comper with C. Ewens, 1829–1843.

I/84/3 Account book (12 ff.), Capt. Berkeley with J. C. H. Biffin (timber merchant), 1831–1835, and two copies of the valuation of leasehold tithes of Fishbourne Farm, 1835.

I/84/4 (20); miscellaneous receipts, and notice of assignment of an insurance policy, 1848–1863.

I/84/5 (2); income tax return, schedule A and B, 1856, by John Austin (rector of Pulborough, 1822–1857), and a letter from Henry Comper to Mr. Holmes about the assessment.

Ep.I/85 EPISCOPAL ACCOUNTS AND RECEIPTS, 1754–1863

I/85/1 (2); domestic bills and receipts of Bishop Ashburnham, 1754.

I/85/2 (20); domestic bills and receipts of Bishop Buckner, 1797–8.

I/85/3 (5); Bishop Carr's account with the *Sussex Advertiser*, Lewes, 1828.

I/85/4 (3); Messrs. G. & T. Hoper's account with Bishop Carr, 1828.

I/85/5 (3); Messrs. Hunt and Currey's account with Bishop Gilbert, 1859.

I/85/6 (6); receipts of Bishop Gilbert, gas rate, poor rate and for printing, 1863.

Ep.I/86 DIOCESAN PAPERS, 1571–1909

Miscellaneous papers relating to individual bishops and to the diocese as a whole.

I/86/1 (1); writ of summons of Bishop Curteys to Parliament, Feb. 1570/1.

I/86/2 (1); memorandum on distribution of fast books and proclamations sent to Chichester from London, Apr. 1679.

I/86/2a (1); declaration of Bishop Lake on his deathbed, Aug. 1689 [printed].

I/86/3 (3); notes, 1725 and 19th cent., on the history of Sussex and of the bishops of Selsey.

I/86/4 (3); writs of restitution of temporalities in Sussex, Surrey and Middlesex to Bishop Ashburnham, 1754.

I/86/5 (2); papers relating to the sale of timber belonging to Bishop Ashburnham, 1784.

I/86/5a (1); mandate to induct John Buckner into the rectory of St. Giles-in-the-Fields, Middlesex, 1788.

I/86/6 (1); note, Sep. 1798, referring to episcopal records.

I/86/7 (30); letters, memoranda, and other papers of William Leeves (formerly Fowler), registrar, 1800–1830.

I/86/8 (2); notes on payment of stipends in named parishes, and list of clergy, both for the diocese, n.d. [early 19th cent.].

I/86/9 (25); septennial returns of the revenue of the see, 1836, 1844, 1851, 1858.

I/86/10 (10); documents relating to episcopal patronage in England and Wales, 1845–49, including copies of the report of the lay sub-committee of Ecclesiastical Commissioners.

I/86/11 84 pp.; "Memorandums about matters of an Ecclesiastical nature", 1845–49, containing notes of licences, institutions and other business of the Bishop's Registry, concerning the whole diocese. There is a modern typescript index of surnames attached to the flyleaf.

I/86/12 15 ff. unbound; minutes of a meeting of Bishop and diocesan clergy, Oct. 1847.

I/86/13 2 copies of a circular, Feb. 1852, from the bishop to the archdeacons and rural deans summoning them to a meeting.

I/86/14 pp.1–18, "Memoranda of Entries of Acts as a Notary Public" made by E. W. Johnson, 1855–73, and loose papers attached.

I/86/15 38 ff. ff.1–19, minutes of a meeting of archdeacons and rural deans called by Bishop Gilbert, Nov. 1859, to discuss questions to be considered at a later assembly of bishops convened by the Archbishop of Canterbury.

I/86/16 (2); abstract of Chichester Diocesan Returns (of clergy residence, curates and church services), 1871.

I/86/17 52 ff. ff.1–9, list of Court Act Books, Chichester archdeaconry (including Peculiars); ff.33–50, return of the Deputy Registrar of the Lewes archdeaconry of records in his keeping, copied from the *Report of the Commissioners on the Public Records* (1837), p. 279.

I/86/18 (2); lists of Easter offerings, and details of church finance and dilapidations, 1906–7, probably abstracted from visitation returns.

I/86/19 (3); card containing the oath used by witnesses in Chichester consistory court, n.d. [late 19th cent.], and two copies of the "suggested Mode of Administering the New Oath" in the Chichester probate registry (Oaths Act, 1909; 9 Edw. VII c.39).

Ep.I/87 EXTRA-DIOCESAN PAPERS, 1707–1834

Miscellaneous papers apparently unconnected with the diocese, though some may have been used as precedents.

I/87/1 (1); fragment of a nomination to the benefice of Astley, dio. Lichfield, 1707.

I/87/2 (1); blank form of letters of sequestration, dio. St. David's, 18th cent.

I/87/3 (1); printed list of Peculiar benefices in the diocese of Bath and Wells, 1810.

I/87/4 52 ff.; rough entry book ["no. 13"] of testamentary business, John and J. Heseltine Bayford, Doctors Commons, May–Nov. 1833.

I/87/5 44 ff.; similar to preceding, June 1833–Feb. 1834.

I/87/6 (1); account of a case concerning church building in Lingfield, Surrey, n.d.

Ep.I/88 HANDLISTS OF, AND FILES RELATING TO, EPISCOPAL RECORDS

I/88/1 191 ff.; bound volume of typescript calendars of episcopal records referred to in this catalogue, with manuscript index.

I/88/2 34 ff.; "The Probate Records of West Sussex" (1950). This typescript list is now superseded by the entries in Ep.I/27–34, but gives greater detail.

I/88/3 42 ff.; "Index of Consecrations and Faculties in the Diocese of Chichester before 1850" [1577–1908]. This typescript volume was published as *Lists and Indexes, No. 3* (1956); this copy has been annotated and corrected.

I/88/4 25 ff.; typescript calendar of Ep.II/21/1 and II/29/1.

I/88/5 147 ff.; typescript calendar (incomplete) of episcopal leases of Sussex estates (Ep.VI/56).

I/88/6 178 ff.; temporary typescript catalogue of the episcopal records in use in the Diocesan Record Office immediately before this catalogue, with manuscript index.

I/88/7 43 ff.; typescript calendar of deposition books (Ep.III/5/2, 3, IV/3/1, 2, V/1/5 and V/5/1), with manuscript index.

I/88/8 119 ff.; various typescript papers of small value (bound) relating (a) to Sussex ecclesiastical records; (b) to Dr. Hilda Johnstone's custody of the bishops' records; with manuscript index.

I/88/9 179 ff.; lists of episcopal, capitular and Ecclesiastical Commissioners' records transferred to the Diocesan Record Office, Chichester, with manuscript index. This list was prepared by the Ecclesiastical Commissioners.

I/88/10 396 ff.; correspondence relating to the establishment of the Diocesan Record Office at Chichester and the transfer to it of the archives of the Bishop and the Dean and Chapter.

NOTE. Ep.I/88/8–10 inclusive are not available to the public.

THE ARCHDEACONRY OF LEWES

Ep.II/1   GENERAL SUBSCRIPTION BOOK, 1604–1751

For other Lewes subscriptions and for an explanation of the oaths and declarations see notes to Ep.I/3 (p. 6).

II/1/1   97 ff.   f.3[1]; f.4[3]; ff.4v.–43, incumbents, curates, schoolmasters and apothecaries[3], Oct. 1604–May 1641; ff.43–47, incumbents, curates and apothecaries[3, 6], Oct. 1662–July 1714; ff.48–78, curates, proctors, schoolmasters and apothecaries[3, 6–8, 12, 13], Oct. 1714–May 1751 (these oaths are written out in full in each case).

Ep.II/2   MARRIAGE LICENCE REGISTERS, 1586–1902

See notes to Ep.I/8 (p. 13).

II/2/1   128 ff.   ff.1–128, marriage licences, licences to curates, schoolmasters and apothecaries, and sequestrations of benefices, July 1586–Mar. 1613.

II/2/2   215 ff.   This is made up of three separate volumes sewn together all of which contain marriage licences, licences to curates, schoolmasters and apothecaries, and sequestrations of benefices. ff.1–48 (bound in part of a contemporary will), Apr. 1613–Mar. 1620/1; ff.49–156 (bound in part of a contemporary deed), Mar. 1621–Mar. 1635/6; ff.158–213, Mar. 1636–Mar. 1642/3.

II/2/3   85 ff.   ff.1–77, marriage licences, licences to curates, schoolmasters and apothecaries, sequestrations of benefices, caveats and probate commissions, Aug. 1670–Mar. 1681/2; f.84v., sequestrations of benefices, Oct.–Dec. 1679; f.85v., memoranda, Sep. 1681.

II/2/4   39 ff.   ff.2–37, marriage licences, Mar. 1682–Apr. 1688.

II/2/5   78 ff.   ff.2–77, marriage licences, May 1688–Mar. 1701/2.

II/2/6   281 ff.   ff.1–43, marriage licences, Mar. 1702–Mar. 1728/9.

II/2/7   232 ff.   ff.2–232, marriage licences, Jan. 1827–Dec. 1902.

Ep.II/2A   MARRIAGE LICENCES, 1784–1825

8 licences and special licences, five of which relate to marriages in Eastbourne church.

| 1784 | 2 | 1810 | 1 | 1814 | 1 | 1825 | 1 |
| 1807 | 1 | 1811 | 1 | 1823 | 1 | | |

[1–13] For key to these numbers, see p. 6.

Ep.II/3 MARRIAGE LICENCE BONDS AND AFFIDAVITS, 1780–1936

(4,384); the documents for 1908–1914 are filed in one binder with those for Hastings (Ep.VII/7). Marriages have been calendared in *Sussex Record* Society, vols. 1 (1586–1643), 6 (1670–1729), 25 and 26 (1772–1837), but only the following documents have reached the Diocesan Record Office. See notes on Ep.I/9 (p. 14).

1780	16	1912	64	1921	134	1930	74
1783	1	1913	48	1922	136	1931	73
1784	9	1914	107	1923	92	1932	61
1798	61	1915	417	1924	89	1933	56
1815	65	1916	327	1925	101	1934	63
1908	3	1917	538	1926	78	1935	68
1909	83	1918	650	1927	75	1936	48
1910	83	1919	412	1928	81		
1911	69	1920	187	1929	72		

Ep.II/4 INSTANCE BOOKS, 1581–1825

See notes to Ep.I/15 (p. 20). Until 1700 these volumes contain instance causes only, but between 1700 and 1720 several attempts were made to combine the instance and detection books and after 1721 the few detection causes are in this series. Where earlier instance causes appear among the detection books it is generally because several volumes have been bound together; overlapping of dates is caused by the existence of both originals and fair copies.

II/4/1 280 ff. bound in leather with laced vellum bands and blind tooling. f.1, memoranda; ff.2–279, Jan. 1580/1–Apr. 1584; instance causes for Mar. 1549/50–June 1557 are in Ep.II/9/1.

II/4/2 126 ff. ff.1–125, June 1586–Mar. 1586/7.

II/4/3 278 ff. bound in leather with laced vellum bands and blind tooling. ff.1–277, June 1586–Apr. 1589.

II/4/4 123 ff. ff.1–123, Apr.–Oct. 1587.

II/4/5 283 ff. ff.2–281, May 1589–Dec. 1593.

II/4/6 291 ff. ff.1–289, May 1599–Aug. 1602.

II/4/7 294 ff. ff.2–294, Sep. 1602–July 1606.

II/4/8 16 ff. ff.1–13, July–Oct. 1606.

II/4/9 140 ff. ff.1–139, Oct. 1606–Apr. 1611; instance causes for May 1610–Feb. 1610/11 are in Ep.II/9/26.

II/4/10 56 ff. ff.1–56, Mar. 1610/11–Dec. 1611.

II/4/11 410 pp. pp.7–407, Apr. 1612–Mar. 1613/14.

II/4/12 392 pp. pp.3–392, May 1615–Dec. 1617.

II/4/13   24 ff., originally numbered pp.393–434 as a continuation of II/4/12.   ff.1–23, Dec. 1617–Apr. 1618.

II/4/14   464 pp.   pp.3–455, Apr. 1618–Mar. 1621/2.

II/4/15   246 pp.   pp.2–241, Mar. 1622–Mar. 1624/5; instance causes for Oct. 1622–Oct. 1624 are in Ep.II/9/26.

II/4/16   131 ff.   ff.1–130, Mar. 1625–Mar. 1627/8; instance causes for May 1626–Feb. 1628/9 are in Ep.II/9/26.

II/4/17   137 ff.   ff.1–136, Apr. 1628–Nov. 1630.

II/4/17a   16 ff.   ff.1–15, Dec. 1630–Mar. 1630/1.

II/4/18   178 ff.   ff.2–176, Mar. 1631–Mar. 1634/5.

II/4/19   122 ff.   ff.2–121, Mar. 1631–May 1634.

II/4/20   155 ff.   ff.3–153, Apr. 1635–Mar. 1636/7.

II/4/21   222 ff.   ff.2–216, Mar. 1637–Dec. 1639.

II/4/22   103 ff. bound in two contemporary mandates.   ff.1–79, Apr. 1640–Dec. 1641; instance causes for Mar. 1661/2–July 1670 are in Ep. II/9/18.

II/4/23   48 ff.   ff.1–48, Jan. 1670/1–Sep. 1673.

II/4/24   164 ff.   ff.2–163, Mar. 1672/3–Mar. 1679/80.

II/4/25   135 ff.   ff.2–130, Apr. 1680–Mar. 1685/6.

II/4/26   168 ff.   ff.1–167, assignations, Jan. 1682/3–Feb. 1687/8.

II/4/27   99 ff.   ff.1–98, Apr. 1686–Mar. 1690/1.

II/4/28   41 ff.   ff.1–41, assignations, May 1691–Oct. 1693.

II/4/29   87 ff.   ff.1v.–85, Apr. 1691–Sep. 1696.

II/4/30   26 ff. bound in a contemporary deed.   ff.1–24, Oct. 1693–July 1694.

II/4/31   50 ff.   ff.1–50, assignations, Jan. 1693/4–Oct. 1695.

II/4/32   63 ff. bound in part of a contemporary deed.   ff.1–44a, instance causes, Sep. 1694–July 1698; ff.62–45, assignations, Nov. 1694–May 1698.

II/4/33   42 ff.   ff.2–41, Dec. 1696–Sep. 1700.

II/4/34   84 ff.   ff.3–83, Oct. 1700–Sep. 1705.

II/4/35 67 ff. f.1, memoranda; ff.2–64, instance and detection causes, July 1698–May 1701.

II/4/36 156 ff. ff.2–156, instance and detection causes, May 1701–Aug. 1708.

II/4/37 54 ff. ff.1–20, instance causes, Sep. 1708–May 1711; ff.54–49, register of orders, n.d. [*c*.1671].

II/4/38 100 ff. ff.1–100, Sep. 1712–Dec. 1717.

II/4/39 278 ff. ff.1–90, instance and detection causes, Mar. 1721–July 1732; ff.232–254, contemporary index of persons, and parishes if the causes concerned the churchwardens.

II/4/40 75 ff. ff.1–75, Sep. 1732–Sep. 1742.

II/4/41 54 ff. ff.1–53, Nov. 1742–Apr. 1750.

II/4/42 59 ff. ff.1–58, June 1744–Aug. 1750; f.59*v*., Mar. 1742/3.

II/4/43 44 ff. ff.2–21, June 1750–Apr. 1752.

II/4/44 74 ff. ff.1–74, Apr. 1752–Nov. 1758.

II/4/45 34 ff. ff.1–33, Dec. 1758–Aug. 1764.

II/4/46 69 ff. ff.1–64, Aug. 1764–Feb. 1782.

II/4/47 90 ff. ff.1–39, June 1788–May 1825.

Ep.II/5 DEPOSITION BOOKS, 1580–1694

See notes to Ep.I/15 (p. 20). In the earlier volumes dates are rarely given, so the series may be more continuous than appears here. Extracts from II/5/1–17 are printed in *Sussex Archaeological Collections*, Vol. 56, pp.1–15.

II/5/1 158 ff. ff.1–146, Jan. 1579/80–Jan. 1580/1; f.147, memoranda.

II/5/2 239 ff. bound in leather with laced vellum bands and blind tooling. ff.2–239, Sep. 1581–May 1584.

II/5/3 96 ff. ff.1–94, July 1585–June 1586.

II/5/4 216 ff. ff.1–216, July 1586–Nov. 1587.

II/5/5 422 ff. ff.1–418, Dec. 1587–Jan. 1593/4.

II/5/6 361 ff. ff.1–360, Feb. 1593/4–May 1604.

II/5/7 159 ff. ff.1–155, May 1604–May 1607.

II/5/8 165 ff. bound in leather with laced vellum bands and blind tooling. ff.2–165, Oct. 1606–May 1611.

II/5/9 71 ff. bound in part of a contemporary deed. ff.1–71, May 1611–June 1613.

II/5/10 98 ff. ff.1–98, May 1613–July 1616.

II/5/11 207 ff. ff.2–206, July 1616–May 1621.

II/5/12 103 ff. bound in part of a contemporary deed. ff.1–103, June 1621–July 1626.

II/5/13 118 ff. ff.1–118, Apr. 1627–Oct. 1631.

II/5/14 140 ff. ff.1–139, May 1632–Apr. 1636.

II/5/15 55 ff. ff.1–55, Nov. 1636–Mar. 1636/7; depositions for Apr. 1636–Mar. 1638/9 are in Ep. II/9/18.

II/5/16 137 ff. ff.2–136, Mar. 1636/7–Feb. 1638/9.

II/5/17 108 ff. ff.1–107, Apr. 1639–July 1641.

II/5/18 102 ff. ff.8–28, exhibits of probate accounts, Oct. 1672–June 1679; ff.37–93, depositions, Jan. 1685/6–Aug. 1690; f.102*v.*, memoranda.

II/5/19 80 ff. f.1, memoranda; ff.2–76, Mar. 1690/1–May 1694.

Ep.II/6 CITATION BOOKS, 1619–1641

See notes to Ep.I/15 (p. 20). These volumes note the issue of citations, excommunications, mandates, monitions, significavits, sequestrations of benefices, probate commissions and acquittances. See also Ep.II/9/24, f.94*v.*

II/6/1 47 ff. bound in a contemporary grant of an advowson. ff.1–47, Nov. 1619–Mar. 1635/6.

II/6/2 27 ff. ff.1–15, Apr. 1636–Sep. 1641.

Ep.II/7 EXCOMMUNICATION BOOKS, 1675–1687

See notes to Ep.I/15 (p. 20). The excommunications are arranged by parishes. See also Ep.II/6 and II/9/18, ff.256–292.

II/7/1 31 ff. ff.1–26, Oct. 1675–June 1685.

II/7/2 70 ff. ff.1–60, Mar. 1685–Feb. 1686/7.

II/7/3 24 ff. ff.1–22, Oct. 1675–Nov. 1677.

Ep.II/8   MISCELLANEOUS COURT PAPERS, 1682–1882

(80); these are more probably the registrars' miscellaneous papers, as very few relate to causes. They consist mainly of sequestration papers, certificates of penance, resignation bonds, probates and letters, 1682–1882.

Ep.II/9   DETECTION BOOKS, 1550–1721

See notes to Ep.I/17 (p. 24). Between 1700 and 1721 several attempts were made to combine the instance and detection books, and after 1721 all detection causes are in Ep.II/4. Instance causes and depositions appear in the earlier volumes because the detection books were often bound with others at a later date.

II/9/1   127 ff. bound in part of a medieval treatise.

ff.1–127, instance and correction causes and probate acts, Mar. 1550–June 1557.

II/9/2   197 ff.

ff.1–197, correction and detection causes, Apr. 1580–Jan. 1585/6.

II/9/3   94 ff.   ff.1–94, July 1586–Jan. 1586/7.

II/9/4   203 ff.; originally 3 separate volumes.

ff.1–66, Sep. 1587–May 1588; ff.67–169, May–Dec. 1587; ff.170–203, Jan. 1586/7–May 1587.

II/9/5   317 ff. bound in a contemporary will.

ff.1–314, May 1588–Apr. 1591; f.316, memoranda.

II/9/6   219 ff. bound in part of a contemporary deed.

ff.1–218, May 1591–July 1593.

II/9/7   244 ff.

ff.3–244, Sep. 1593–Oct. 1595; f.244v., royal orders relating to clerical non-residence, n.d.

II/9/8   345 ff.

ff.1–342, Oct. 1595–Mar. 1599/1600; f.345v., memoranda.

II/9/9   278 ff.   ff.2–277, Apr. 1600–July 1605.

II/9/10   117 ff.   ff.2–117, July 1605–Oct. 1606.

II/9/11   281 ff.   ff.1–279, Oct. 1606–Oct. 1610.

II/9/12   157 ff. bound in a contemporary deed.

ff.1–153, Oct. 1610–Mar. 1612/3.

II/9/13 166 ff. bound in part of a contemporary deed.
ff.1–166, Apr. 1614–Dec. 1617.

II/9/14 20 ff. ff.1–20, Jan. 1617/18–June 1618.

II/9/15 25 ff. ff.1–24, July 1618–Apr. 1619.

II/9/16 92 ff. bound in a contemporary deed.
ff.1–92, June 1619–May 1622.

II/9/17 46 ff. ff.2–46, May 1622–July 1623.

II/9/18 327 ff.; originally eight separate volumes.
ff.1–69, detection causes, June 1624–May 1626; ff.71–104, depositions, Apr. 1626–Mar. 1638/9; ff.105–128, instance causes, Apr.–Sep. 1612; ff. 129–154, detection causes, Nov. 1661–May 1666; ff.155–182, detection causes, Sep. 1623–May 1624; ff.183–206, instance causes (assignations), June 1666–July 1670; ff.209–255, instance causes, Mar. 1661/2–Feb. 1665/6; ff.256–292, excommunications, May 1621–Oct. 1639; ff.293–327, detection causes, Mar–Sep. 1636.

II/9/19 65 ff. ff.1–65, May 1628–Nov. 1629.

II/9/20 142 ff. ff.1–142, Jan. 1629/30–Mar. 1632/3.

II/9/21 87 ff. ff.1–87, Apr. 1633–Nov. 1634.

II/9/22 63 ff. ff.3–62, Apr.–Dec. 1635.

II/9/23 136 ff. bound in part of a contemporary deed.
ff.1–135, Oct. 1636–June 1639.

II/9/24 94 ff. bound in part of a contemporary deed.
ff.1–65, detection causes, June 1639–July 1641; f.94v., marriage licences, probate and administration acts, and caveats (see Ep.II/6), Oct.–Feb. [?1641–42].

II/9/25 63 ff. ff.2–63, Sep. 1664–Dec. 1668.

II/9/26 255 ff.; originally four separate volumes.
ff.1–29, instance causes, Nov. 1623–Oct. 1624; ff.30–60, instance causes, Oct. 1622–Oct. 1623; ff.61–106, instance causes, May 1610–Feb. 1610/11; ff.107–153, instance causes, May 1626–July 1627; ff.154–178, instance causes, July 1627–May 1628; ff.179–207, instance causes, June 1628–Feb. 1628/9; ff.208–254, detection causes, Feb. 1658/9–Dec. 1671; f.255v., memoranda.

II/9/27 203 ff. ff.2–202, Nov. 1671–Nov. 1674.

II/9/28 169 ff. ff.1–169, Dec. 1674–June 1679.

II/9/29 112 ff. ff.1–111, July 1679–Sep. 1683.

II/9/30   123 ff.

ff.1–111, detection causes, Oct. 1683–Feb. 1686/7; f.112, an order by the royal commissioners for ecclesiastical causes about clandestine marriages, 4 Nov. 1686; ff.113–115, detection causes, Feb. 1686/7–Apr. 1687.

II/9/31   105 ff.   ff.1–104, Apr. 1687–Dec. 1694.

II/9/32   49 ff.   ff.1–49, Jan. 1694/5–Dec. 1699.

II/9/33   65 ff.

ff.2–17, Jan. 1699/1700–Aug. 1701; detection causes for May 1701–Aug. 1708 are in Ep.II/4/35 and 36.

II/9/34   51 ff.   ff.1–50, July 1704–July 1708.

II/9/35   41 ff.   ff.1–27, July 1708–July 1711.

II/9/36   92 ff.

ff.2–31, detection causes, Sep. 1716–Mar. 1720/1; ff.49–87, instance causes, Sep. 1716–Mar. 1720/1.

Ep.II/10   LIBRI CLERI, 1600–1913

Earlier libri cleri for the archdeaconry are in Ep.I/18 (see p. 26); after 1846 the Deanery of South Malling is usually included. From 1885 libri cleri were entered on printed forms, each of 8 ff., with separate forms for clergy and churchwardens and for each day of the visitation; consequently from II/10/43–67 the figure in brackets after the catalogue mark shows the number of forms that have survived for each year.

II/10/1   84 ff.

ff.1–16[2], Sep. 1600; ff.16v.–22[3], Apr. 1601; ff.23–26[3], Jan. 1601/2; ff.26v.–310[3], Jan. 1602/3; ff.32–39[2], Sep. 1603; ff.40-44[3], Jan. 1603/4; ff.45–61[1], July 1605; ff.62v.–64[3], Apr. 1604; ff.65–75[3], Apr. 1606; ff.75v.–84[3], Apr. 1607.

II/10/2   100 ff. in two separate volumes sewn together, the second bound in part of a contemporary deed.

ff.1–6[3], May 1613; ff.6v.–11[2], Sep. 1613; ff.11v.–17[3], May 1614; ff.17v.–22[3], Apr. 1615; ff.22v.–29[1], Aug. 1615; ff.29–34[3], Apr. 1616; ff.35–41[2], Sep. 1616; ff.41–46[3], May 1617; ff.46v.–50[3], Apr. 1618; ff.51–56[3], Apr. 1619; ff.57–62[2], Oct. 1619; ff.63–67[3], May 1620; ff.68–72[3], Apr. 1621; ff.72v.–77[3], May 1622; ff.77v.–82[2], Sep. 1622; ff.82–86[3], May 1623; ff.87–91[3], Apr. 1624; ff.91v.–95[3], May 1625; ff.96–100[2], Sep. 1625.

---

[1] Metropolitical visitation.

[2] Episcopal visitation.

[3] Lewes archidiaconal visitation.

II/10/3   130 ff. in two separate volumes sewn together, the first bound in a recognizance roll of 1612.

ff.1–6³, Apr. 1626; ff.7–13³, Apr. 1627; ff.13v.–18³, Apr. 1628; ff.19–23², Oct. 1628; ff.23v.–28³, Apr. 1629; ff.29–33³, Apr. 1630; ff.34–39³, Apr. 1631; ff.39–44², Sep. 1631; ff.44–49³, Apr. 1632; ff.49v.–54³, May 1633; ff.55–59³, Apr. 1634; ff.60–64², Sep. 1634; ff.64v.–69¹, July 1635; ff.69–75³, Oct. 1635; ff.75v.–80³, May 1636; ff.81–90³, Apr. 1637; ff.90–94², Sep. 1637; ff.95–101³, Apr. 1638; ff.102–107², Sep. 1638; ff.107–114³, Apr. 1639; ff.114–119³, Apr. 1640; ff.119v.–122, May 1641.

II/10/4   72 ff. bound in part of a contemporary deed.

ff.1–7², Sep. 1670; ff.7v.–12³, May 1671; ff.13–28³, May 1672; ff.29–45², Apr. 1673; ff.48–63³, May 1674; ff.65–70³, May 1677.

II/10/5   10 ff. unbound.

ff.1–10², Sep. 1675 (see II/10/6, ff.2–16).

II/10/6   134 ff.; all episcopal visitations.

f.1, memoranda; ff.2–16, Sep. 1675; ff.18–30, Sep. 1678; ff.31–36, Sep. 1679; ff.37–50, May 1682; ff.51–67, June 1686; ff.69–82, May 1689; ff.83–91, Register of Orders, 1689; ff.92–106, July 1690; ff.107v.–125, June 1692.

II/10/7   143 ff.

f.1, memoranda; ff.7–14², Sep. 1675; ff.15–23², May 1685; ff.24–33², June 1686; ff.34–45³, May 1688; ff.47–58³, May 1691; ff.59–68³, May 1693; ff.69–78³, July 1694; ff.79–87³, June 1696; ff.88–96³, May 1698; ff.97–106³, June 1699; ff.107–116³, May 1701; ff.117–126³, May 1702; f.127, election to Convocation, Aug. 1702; ff.128–137³, May 1704.

II/10/8   105 ff.

f.1, accounts; ff.1–4³, May 1678; ff.5–14², May 1678; ff.15–37², May 1679; ff.39–52³, May 1680; ff.53–65³, May 1681; ff.66–78³, May 1683; ff.79–93³, May 1684; ff.93v.–103³, Apr. 1687; f.104v., receipts, Apr. 1687.

II/10/9   16 ff.   ff.1–14², June 1686.

II/10/10   20 ff.

ff.1–2, accounts, 1692, ff.3–12², June 1695; f.13, election to Convocation, Nov. 1695; ff.14–19³, June 1696.

II/10/11   15 ff. bound in part of a contemporary deed.

ff.1–9², June 1697; ff.10–15³, May 1698.

II/10/12   39 ff.; all episcopal visitations.

f.1, memoranda; ff.1–11, June 1700; ff.12–21, June 1703; ff.22–31, June 1706.

---

¹⁻³ For key to these numbers, see p. 107.

II/10/13   34 ff. all archidiaconal visitations.

ff.1–9, May 1705; ff.10–18, May 1707; ff.19–28, Apr. 1708; f.29, election to convocation, June 1708.

II/10/14   9 ff. bound in a contemporary deed.

ff.1–9[1] (*sede vacante*), May 1709; f.9, receipts, June 1709.

II/10/15   12 ff. bound in part of a contemporary deed.

ff.1–11[2], June 1710.

II/10/16   14 ff.

ff.1–12, a copy of Ep.II/10/15; f.13, Register of Orders, 1709.

II/10/17   10 ff.   ff.1–9[?3], 1711.

II/10/18   20 ff; all archidiaconal visitations.

ff.1–11, June 1711; ff.11v.–19, May 1712.

II/10/19   16 ff.

ff.1–12[2], June 1713; ff.13v.–14, elections to convocation, Nov. 1713–Mar. 1714/5.

II/10/20   14 ff. bound in part of a contemporary deed.

ff.3–14[3], Apr. 1714; f.14v., election to convocation, 1713.

II/10/21   40 ff. bound in part of a contemporary deed; all archidiaconal visitations. An entry for 1718 was printed in *History*, vol. 31 (1946), pp. 1–8.

ff.1–13, June 1715; ff.14–26, July 1717; ff.27–37, May 1718.

II/10/22   30 ff.   ff.2–13[2], July 1716; ff.15–24[2], July 1719.

II/10/23   24 ff. bound in part of a contemporary deed.

ff.2–11[3], July 1717.

II/10/24   12 ff.   ff.1–10[3], May 1720.

II/10/25   12 ff.   ff.2–11[3], June 1721.

II/10/26   16 ff.   ff.2–12[2], July 1722.

II/10/27   12 ff.   ff.2–11[2], July 1723.

II/10/28   114 ff.; all archidiaconal visitations.

ff.1–11, May 1724; ff.12–22, May 1725; ff.23–33, May 1727; ff.33–41, May 1728; ff.42–51, May 1730; ff.51–59, May 1731; ff.60–68, May 1732.

II/10/29   22 ff.   ff.1–20[2], June 1726; f.21, receipts, June 1726.

[1-3] For key to these numbers, see p. 107.

II/10/30 20 ff. ff.1–14^2, July 1729.

II/10/31 46 ff.

ff.1–12^3, May 1785; ff.12v.–19^3, May 1786; ff.20–27^2, June 1787; ff.27v.–35^3, May 1788; ff.35v.–43^3, May 1789.

II/10/32 43 ff.; all archidiaconal visitations.

ff.1–9, May 1790; ff.10–18, May 1791; ff.19–27, May 1792; ff.28–36, May 1793.

II/10/33 78 ff.

ff.1–8^3, May 1794; ff.9–16^3, May 1795; ff.17–25^3, May 1796; ff.26–34^3, May 1797; ff.35–44^2, Aug. 1798; ff.45–53^3, May 1799; ff.54–62^3, May 1800; ff.69–78, loose memoranda, including lists of visitations and clergy.

II/10/34 90 ff.

ff.1–10^2, July 1801; ff.11–19^3, May 1802; ff.20–29^3, May 1803; ff.29v.–40^2, July 1804; ff.40v.–50^3, May 1805; ff.50v.–60^3, June 1806; ff.61–71^3, June 1807; ff.71v.–81^2, June 1808; ff.82–90^3, June 1809.

II/10/35 86 ff.

ff.1–11^3, June 1810; ff.11v.–23^2, July 1811; ff.23v.–34^3, June 1812; ff.34v.–44^3, June 1813; ff.45–56^2, July 1814; ff.56–67^3, June 1815; ff.67v.–77^3, June 1816; ff.77v.–86^2, July 1817.

II/10/36 96 ff.

ff.1–11^3, June 1818; ff.12–22^3, June 1819; ff.23–32^3, June 1820; ff.32v.–43^2, June 1821; ff.43v.–54^3, July 1822; ff.54v.–64^3, June 1823; ff.65–75^3, June 1824; ff.76–88^2, June 1825; ff.94 and 96, list of incumbents who had not preached at a visitation.

II/10/37 93 ff. ff.1–11^3, June 1826.

II/10/38 134 ff.

ff.14v.–25^3, June 1827; ff.25v.–37^2, July 1828; ff.37v.–49^3, June 1829; ff.49v.–61^3, June 1830; ff.61v.–73^2, June 1831; ff.73v.–85^3, June 1832; ff.85v.–97^3, June 1833; ff.97v.–109^2, May 1834; ff.109v.–121^3, May 1835; ff.121v.–133^3, June 1836.

II/10/39 180 ff.

ff.1v.–13^3, 1837; ff.13v.–25^2, June 1838; ff.25v.–37^3, May 1839; ff.37v.–49^3, July 1840; ff.49v.–61^3, June 1841; ff.61v.–73^3, June 1842; ff.73v.–85^3, July 1843; ff.85v.–97^2, Oct. 1844; ff.97v.–109^3, July 1845; ff.109v.–122^3, Aug. 1846; ff.122v.–135^2, July 1847; ff.135v.–148^3, July 1848; ff.148v.–161^3, July 1849; ff.161v.–174^2, Sep. 1850.

$^{1-3}$ For key to these numbers, see p. 107.

II/10/40 177 ff.

ff.1v.–14[3], Aug. 1851; ff.14v.–27[3], July 1852; ff.27v.–40[2], Oct 1853; ff.40v.–54[3], Sep. 1854; ff.54v.–71[3], July 1855; ff.71v.–87[2], Oct 1856; ff.87–105[3], July 1857; ff.105v.–123[3], June 1858; ff.123v.–141[2], July 1859; ff.141v.–142, patent of the registrar's office; ff.142v.–160[3], July 1860; ff.160v.–177[1, 3], July 1861.

II/10/41 182 ff.

ff.1v.–19[2], Oct. 1862; ff.19v.–37[3], July 1863; ff.37v.–38, appointment of surrogates, July 1863; ff.38v.–57[3], May 1864; ff.57v.–75[2], July 1865; ff. 75v.–92[3], June 1866; ff.92v.–109[3], June 1867; ff.109v.–126[2], Apr. 1868; ff.126v.–143[3], June 1869; f.143v., appointment of surrogates, July 1870; ff.144v.–161[3], July 1870; ff.161v.–178[2], Nov. 1871.

II/10/42 182 ff.

ff.1v.–18[3], Aug. 1872; ff.18v.–35[3], July 1873; ff.35v.–52[3], Aug. 1874; ff. 52v.–69[2], Oct. 1875; f.69v., appointment of surrogates, Sep. 1876; ff.70v.–87[3], Sep. 1876; ff.87v.–104[3], June 1877; ff.104v.–121[2], Oct. 1878; ff.121v.–141[3], May 1879; ff.141v.–161[3], June 1880; ff.161v.–182[2], Aug. 1881.

II/10/43 (6)[3], May 1885.

II/10/44 (6)[3], June 1886.

II/10/45 (6)[3], May 1888.

II/10/46 (6)[3], June 1889.

II/10/47 (6)[3], May 1891.

II/10/48 (6)[3], May 1892.

II/10/49 (6)[3], May 1894.

II/10/50 (6)[3], May 1895.

II/10/51 (3)[3], May 1896 (churchwardens only).

II/10/52 (3)[3], June 1897 (churchwardens only).

II/10/53 (2)[2], July 1898 (churchwardens only).

II/10/54 (7)[3], May 1899.

II/10/55 (8)[3], May 1900.

II/10/56 (5)[3], May 1901 (churchwardens only).

II/10/57 (8)[3], May 1902.

II/10/58 (2)[2], June 1903 (churchwardens only).

II/10/59 (8)[3], May 1904.

II/10/60 (8)[3], June 1905.

II/10/61 (4)[3], May 1906 (churchwardens only).

II/10/62 (8)[3], May 1907.

II/10/63 (3)[3], June 1908 (churchwardens only).

II/10/64 (6)[3], June 1910.

II/10/65 (12)[3], May 1911.

II/10/66 (12)[3], May 1912.

II/10/67 (3)[3], May 1913 (churchwardens only).

[1–3] For key to these numbers, see p. 107.

Ep.II/11   REGISTERS OF ORDERS, 1586–1798

See notes to Ep.I/19 (see p. 37); some of these volumes include curates and schoolmasters. See Ep.II/4/37, ff.54–49, for a late 17th cent. register.

II/11/1   158 ff.

ff.1–23[1], Sep. 1586; ff.24–48[1], June 1592; ff.49–72[1], Apr. 1595; ff.73–94[1], Sep. 1597; ff.95–115[1], Sep. 1600; ff.116–133[1], Sep. 1603; ff.134–154[2], July 1605.

II/11/2   90 ff. bound in boards and fragments of medieval MSS.

f.i, contemporary list of contents; ff.1–18[1], Sep. 1606; ff.18v.–32[1], July 1609; ff.33–49[1], Sep. 1610; ff.49v.–71[1], Sep. 1613; f.71v., election to convocation, Mar. 1614; ff.72–73, elections to convocation, 1640.

II/11/3   142 ff.

f.i, contemporary list of contents; ff.1–19[1], Oct. 1628; ff.19v.–41[1], Sep. 1631; ff.42–64[1], Sep. 1634; ff.65–93[2], July 1635; ff.93v.–117[1], Sep. 1637.

II/11/4   72 ff.

ff.2–33[1], Sep. 1675; f.35, election to convocation, Nov. 1679; ff.38–66[1], June 1686.

II/11/5   114 ff.; this includes lists of churchwardens.

ff.1–42[1], July 1723; ff.42v.–71, lists of parishes with no entries; ff.72–84,[1] Aug. 1733.

II/11/5a   16 ff.   ff.1a–14[1], July 1723.

II/11/6   14 ff.   ff.1–13[1], Aug. 1733 (draft).

II/11/7   12 ff.   ff.1–11[1], May 1742.

II/11/8   2 ff.   f.1[?1], May 1745 (Hastings St. Clement and Rye).

II/11/9   6 ff. unbound.

ff.1–6, a list of the clergy with dates of induction and place of residence, possibly for [1], 1798.

Ep.II/12   LETTERS OF ORDERS, 1747–1812

See notes on Ep.I/67/2 (p. 88); all but the last were exhibited at Bishop Buckner's primary visitation in 1798.

1747	1	1767	1	1780	1	1792	1
1761	1	1769	1	1784	1	1796	2
1762	1	1770	1	1786	1	1798	1
1766	1	1777	1	1787	1	1812	1

[1] Episcopal visitation.
[2] Metropolitical visitation.

Ep.II/13 PROCURATION BOOKS AND PAPERS, 1628–1901

See notes on Ep.I/21 (p. 40). No distinction has been made between episcopal and archidiaconal procurations except for the sake of clarity. All volumes are arranged in deaneries and unless otherwise stated relate only to the Lewes archdeaconry.

II/13/1 6 ff. ff.2–6, procurations, 1628.

II/13/2 63 ff. ff.1–22, procurations, 1711–1714.

II/13/3 78 ff. flyleaf, memoranda; ff.2–3, arrears of procurations, 1711–1717; f.4, receipts, 1715; ff.4v.–10, procurations, 1716; ff.12–17, procurations (South Malling Deanery), 1714–1786; f.78v., memoranda.

II/13/4 91 ff. ff.1–8, episcopal procurations, 1798–1814, and archidiaconal procurations, 1789–1796; ff.9–14, procurations, 1797–1804; ff.15–21, procurations, 1805–1812; ff.21v.–29, episcopal procurations, 1817–1825, and archidiaconal procurations, 1813–1821; ff.30–36, procurations, 1822–1826; f.91, account for dinners at visitation, 1798.

II/13/5 1 f.; procurations and account for dinners, 1798.

II/13/6 6 loose ff. Accounts for visitations, 1804–1811.

II/13/7 (72); bundles of accounts of procurations and other fees for episcopal and archidiaconal visitations in the archdeaconry, 1829–1901, and 3 undated, and 5 letters and papers relating to visitation fees. 1829–1832, 1834–1851, 1853–1859, 1861–1901.

Ep.II/14 CHURCHWARDENS' PRESENTMENTS, 1641–1917

See notes to Ep.I/22 (p. 42). From 1853 the former Peculiar jurisdictions are included.

II/14/1 841 loose presentments; calendar is available in the Diocesan Record Office (Ep.I/88/1).

1641	4	1785	1	1862	39	1915	127
1664	1	1825	40	1865	28	1915–16	122
1667	2	1828	3	1910	7	1916–17	121
1668	3	1853	162	1911	2	and 1 undated	
1670	1	1859	177	1912	1	(17th cent.)	

II/14/2 Bound volumes of presentments, presumably complete. One of the volumes dated 1883 is of financial returns by incumbents, requested by Archdeacon Hannah in 1884 as there was no archidiaconal visitation in that year.

1856	1879	1883 (2)	1888 (2)
1876	1880	1885	
1877	1882	1886	

Ep.II/14A MINISTERS' ARTICLES OF ENQUIRY, 1808–1903

See notes to Ep.I/22A (p. 44). The articles for 1856, 1875, 1898 and 1903 are bound, the last incorrectly marked 'Chichester Archdeaconry' on the spine. See Ep.V/16A for the 1875 returns from the 14 parishes formerly in the exempt Deanery of South Malling. A calendar of the loose papers is available in the Diocesan Record Office (Ep.I/88/1); many for 1853 do not give the name of the parish.

1808	130	1850	1	1859	183	1898
1825	36	1853	135	1862	30	1903
1828	2	1856		1875	2 vols.	

Ep.II/15 REGISTERS OF PRESENTMENTS, 1637–1719

See notes to Ep.I/23 (p. 44). Ep. II/15/2 is printed in *Sussex Record Society*, vol. 50.

II/15/1 100 pp.

pp.1–13, Easter 1637[2]; pp. 13–24, Mich. 1637[1]; pp.25–33, Mich. 1637[2]; pp.34–45, Easter 1638[2]; pp.46–60, Mich. 1638[1]; pp.61–69, Mich. 1638[2]; pp.70–84, Easter 1639[2].

II/15/2 107 ff. bound in part of a contemporary deed.

ff.1–19, 1674[2]; ff.19v.–20, index of parishes in ff.1–19; f.24, list of nine parishes; ff.25–43, 1675[?1]; ff.55–75, 1676[?2]; ff.77–95, 1677[?2]; ff.102–106, n.d.

II/15/3 26 ff.

ff.1–25, Easter 1675 and Mich. 1675 (not chronological).

II/15/4 100 ff. bound in part of a contemporary deed and printed letters of administration.

ff.1–15, Easter 1678[2]; ff.16–31, Mich. 1678[1]; ff.33–47, Easter 1679[2]; ff. 56–74, Mich. 1679[1]; ff.75–97, Mich. 1680[2] and Easter 1681[2].

II/15/5 78 ff.

ff.1–20, Mich. 1681[?2] and Easter 1682[2]; ff.21–43, Mich. 1682[?2] and Easter 1683[2]; ff.45–69, May 1682[1]; ff.70v.–73, list of those who did not communicate, 1684; f.78v., memoranda, Oct. 1684.

II/15/6 109 ff. bound in a printed list of the governors of the corporation for the relief of poor widows and children of clergymen, 1678.

ff.1–108, "Apparators Returnes", Nov. 1681–Mar. 1690/1.

II/15/7 67 ff.

ff.1–38, Mich. 1684, Easter and Mich. 1685, Easter and Mich. 1686, Easter and Mich. 1687, Easter and Mich. 1688 and Easter 1689, probably all [2];

---

[1] Episcopal visitation.

[2] Archidiaconal visitation.

ff.40–64, Mich. 1689, Easter and Mich. 1690, Easter and Mich. 1691, Easter 1692, Easter and Mich. 1693 and Easter 1694 (all [2]) and an episcopal visitation in 1692.

II/15/8   43 ff.

ff.1–38, Mich. 1694, Easter and Mich. 1695, Easter 1696, Easter and Mich. 1697, Easter and Mich. 1698, Easter and Mich. 1699 and Easter and Mich. 1700 (probably all [2]); ff.38*v*. and 41, memoranda.

II/15/9   43 ff.

ff.1–37, Easter and Mich. 1701, Easter and Mich. 1702, Easter and Mich. 1703, Easter and Mich. 1704 and Easter 1705 (probably all [2]).

II/15/10   46 ff.; a note of the 1709 amnesty is written on the front cover.

ff.1–36, Easter and Mich. 1709, Easter and Mich. 1710, Easter and Mich. 1711, Easter and Mich. 1712, Easter and Mich. 1713, Easter and Mich. 1714 and Easter and Mich. 1715 (probably all [2]).

II/15/11   74 ff.

f.1, memorandum; ff.2–74, Easter and Mich. 1716, Easter and Mich. 1717, Easter and Mich. 1718 and Easter and Mich. 1719 (probably all [2]).

Ep.II/16   PARISH REGISTER TRANSCRIPTS, 1592–1912

See notes to Ep.I/24 (p. 45). A list of transcripts, giving the years represented for each parish, is given as an Appendix to this book.

Ep.II/16A   PAPERS FOUND WITH THE TRANSCRIPTS, 1813–1878

(50); papers found in the bundles of transcripts when these were listed. They are mostly returns by incumbents and curates at the visitation, June 1813 (with a few later) of the number and description of their extant parish registers. There are also lists of transcripts wanting (1827), and letters from incumbents.

Ep.II/17   CHURCH TERRIERS, 1615–1728

(239); a typescript calendar of these documents is available in the Diocesan Record Office (Ep.I/88/1), and an index (made 1887) is in Ep.II/26/5, pp.69–80.

1615	20	1627	2	1675	53	1689	1
1616	8	1635	82	1676	7	1729	1
1618	1	1636	33	1678	17		

3 undateable documents and 10 later copies of some of the above.

[1–2] For key to these numbers, see p. 114.

Ep.II/18 CHURCH INSPECTION BOOKS, 1686–1724

Two inspections are represented; II/18/1 contains reports on church fabric by episcopal commissioners in each deanery, and II/18/2 also contains answers to questions about parish charities, population, services and the value of the living. A typescript calendar of both volumes and of the Lewes portion of Ep.I/26/3 is available in the Diocesan Record Office (Ep.I/88/1).

II/18/1 9 ff. ff.1–9, inspections, arranged by deaneries, 1686.

II/18/2 50 ff. f.1, copy of the episcopal commission and questions to be answered; ff.2–44, inspections, arranged by parishes, 1724, which are also included in Ep.I/26/3.

Ep.II/19 REGISTERS OF DEATHS, 1661–1732

These were compiled from parish register transcripts (Ep.II/16) for the purpose of citing executors and administrators. Unless otherwise indicated all volumes are arranged by parishes, with names only.

II/19/1 11 ff. ff.1–11, 1661–1669, giving date and place of death.

II/19/2 18 ff. ff.2–16, 1674–1675.

II/19/3 76 ff. bound in a printed marriage licence form. ff.1–75, 1676–1685, arranged by years.

II/19/4 98 ff. ff.3–93, 1685–1694, giving occasional dates; f.95*v*., memorandum.

II/19/5 14 ff. bound in part of a list of 'burials in woollen', Cuckfield, 1694. ff.1–12, 1695–1696; f.14*v*., a list of names.

II/19/6 24 ff. ff.1–22, 1697–1698.

II/19/7 58 ff. ff.1–57, 1704–1709.

II/19/8 10 ff. ff.1–10, 1710.

II/19/9 10 ff. ff.1–8, 1711.

II/19/10 12 ff. ff.1–9, 1727; f.10, Deanery of South Malling, 1727.

II/19/11 10 ff. ff.1–9, 1728.

II/19/12 12 ff. ff.1–10, 1729.

II/19/13 10 ff. ff.1–10, 1732.

Ep.II/20   PROBATE COMMISSIONS, 1720–1742

See notes to Ep.I/28 (p. 50). The writs of *levari facias* (completely unconnected with probate) which were wrongly filed with these commissions at Lewes, have been transferred to Ep.I/71/3. See also Ep.II/2/3.

1720	1	1730	1	1735	3	1741	2
1726	3	1731	3	1736	1	1742	2
1727	3	1732	1	1738	7		
1728	3	1733	3	1739	1		
1729	2	1734	1	1740	2		

Ep.II/21   PROBATE DIARY, 1645–1646

This is a stray volume from Lewes probate records and has not been indexed in British Record Society, vol. 24; a calendar of this volume is available in the Diocesan Record Office (Ep.I/88/4).

II/21/1   46 ff.   ff.1–9, probate and administration acts, and caveats, Mar. 1645–Jan. 1645/6.

Ep.II/22   ADMINISTRATORS' ACCOUNT BOOK, 1670–1684

This volume is the only one of its kind in the episcopal records; it contains the names of administrators (arranged by parishes) and the totals for which they accounted.

II/22/1   32 ff.   ff.1–22, 1670–1684; f.23, memoranda.

Ep.II/23   CAVEAT BOOK, 1671–1728

A caveat was entered in an ecclesiastical court to stop probates, administrations, licences, faculties and similar instruments being granted without the knowledge of the party entering it. In canon law a caveat nullified any such grant pending it, but in the civil court it was only accepted as information. A later volume (Mar. 1727/8–Sep. 1858) is with Lewes probate records in the East Sussex Record Office. See Ep. II/2/3.

II/23/1   66 ff. with some loose entries.   f.1, against probate and inventory, Apr. 1690; ff.3–65, against probates, administrations, marriage licences, churchwardens' oaths and licences to apothecaries, Nov. 1671–Mar. 1727/8.

Ep.II/24   RETURNS OF NONCONFORMISTS, 1603–1727

II/24/1   35 ff. unbound; the original answers, in the incumbents' own hands, from 80 parishes in the archdeaconry and from Ringmer, to Archbishop Whitgift's seven articles (20 June 1603). These articles, asking for the number of communicants, recusants and other nonconformists in each parish, details of benefices held in plurality, patrons, impropriations,

117

vicarages and curates and valuations in the King's books, were sent to each bishop; Bishop Watson apparently summoned his clergy to answer separately. The documents are printed in Sussex Record Society, vol. 4, pp. 3–17.

II/24/2 (1); "Mr. Levitt's returne of Popish Recusants 1727", Eastbourne.

Ep.II/25 MEETING HOUSE AND FACULTY REGISTERS, 1662–1852

From 1803 faculties are registered in Ep.II/26; see Ep.I/88/3. The dissenters' meeting house certificates are supplementary to the Quarter Sessions certificates and are not duplicates.

II/25/1 68 ff. ff.1–3, copy lease of Portslade rectory, 1662; ff.4–64, faculties, Mar. 1683/4–June 1734 and meeting house licences, July 1690–Feb. 1733/4, including on f.41 a midwife's licence, July 1715, ff.65–66, contemporary list of contents.

II/25/2 176 pp. pp.1–152, faculties and consecrations, Aug. 1735–Aug. 1803, including on pp. 15–81 meeting house licences, Aug. 1741 - July 1773; pp.153–156, list of contents; pp.157–161, faculty, Aug. 1802; p.176, meeting house licences, July 1736 and May 1739.

II/25/3 87 ff. ff.1–34, meeting house licences, Jan. 1809–Feb. 1852.

II/25/4 28 pp. unbound.
pp.1–28, a return of meeting houses registered from 1760 to 1808.

II/25/5 (6); a list of the number of licences granted 1809–1820, unused forms of return to the General Register Office, letters from the Office concerning the returns, and a copy of the Act, 15 & 16 Vict. c.36 (1852).

Ep.II/26 FACULTY REGISTERS AND MUNIMENT BOOKS, 1803–1905

Earlier faculties are registered in Ep.II/25/1–2.

II/26/1 172 pp. pp.1–157, faculties and consecrations, Feb. 1803–Mar. 1827; pp. 163–165, list of contents.

II/26/2 358 pp. pp.1–6, registrar's and deputy registrar's commissions, 1812 and 1827; pp.7–356, faculties, consecrations, mortgages, conveyances and exchanges of glebe, Jan. 1828–Oct. 1836; p. 357, list of contents.

II/26/3 462 pp. pp.1–456, faculties, consecrations, mortgages, conveyances and other instruments, Mar. 1837–Sep. 1849; pp.459–461, list of contents.

II/26/4   488 pp.   pp.1–481, consecrations, faculties, mortgages, grants of rent charges and citations to executors, Sep. 1849–June 1853; pp.485–488, list of contents.

II/26/5   80 pp.   flyleaf, list of contents; pp.1–16, consecrations, 1826–Oct. 1903; pp.17–27, register of documents other than those mentioned elsewhere in the volume (conveyances, exchanges of glebe, etc.); pp. 28–29, mortgages, Aug. 1829–Nov. 1902; pp.30–32 and 34, augmentation of vicarages by the Ecclesiastical Commissioners, June 1867–July 1903; p.33 accounts relating to the building of parsonage houses, Oct. 1844–Mar. 1903; p.35, instruments instituting rectories and a vicarage, June 1866–Nov. 1867; pp.36–41, Orders in Council, June 1837–Feb. 1905; pp.42–51, faculties (an index to volumes including Ep.II/25/2 and II/26/1–4), Aug. 1735–Feb. 1904; pp. 69–80, a list, made in 1887, of church terriers in the Lewes Registry (Ep.II/17).

Ep.II/27   FACULTY PAPERS, 1732–1908

For details of II/27/1–72 see Ep.I/88/3 which is arranged under parishes; II/27/73–257 were not included in this and as yet no detailed list is available.

II/27/1   (1); Bishopstone (1732).

II/27/2   (1); Rottingdean (1732).

II/27/3   (1); Jevington (1735).

II/27/4   (1); Warbleton (1733).

II/27/5   (25); Cuckfield (1735).

II/27/6   (1); Burwash (1735).

II/27/7   (1); Burwash (1737).

II/27/8   (1); Rye (1743).

II/27/9   (1); Shermanbury (1748).

II/27/10   (1); Wilmington (1751).

II/27/11   (1); Salehurst (1749).

II/27/12   (1); Rye (1761).

II/27/13   (1); Lewes (Southover) (1765).

II/27/14   (1); Hastings St. Clement (1766).

II/27/15   (3); Eastbourne St. Mary (1767).

II/27/16   (1); Maresfield (1772).

II/27/17   (1); South Heighton (1772).

II/27/18   (1); Seaford (1772).

II/27/19   (1); Berwick (1774).

II/27/20   (1); Hastings St. Clement (1781).

II/27/21   (1); Iford (1794).

II/27/22   (6); Bolney (1802).

II/27/23   (5); Plumpton (1803).

II/27/24   (1); Brighton St. Nicholas (1803).

II/27/25   (15); Lewes All Saints (1807).

II/27/26   (1); Slaugham (1810).

II/27/27   (3); Heathfield (1811).

II/27/28 (3); Brightling (1811).

II/27/29 (3); Woodmancote (1811).

II/27/30 (10); Ore (1816).

II/27/31 (1); Brighton St. Nicholas (1816).

II/27/32 (4); Hastings St. Clement (1818).

II/27/33 (8); Hastings All Saints (1818).

II/27/34 (1); Pett (1820).

II/27/35 (4); Hamsey (1821).

II/27/36 (1); Frant (1822).

II/27/37 (5); Lewes All Saints (1823).

II/27/38 (2); Slaugham (1829).

II/27/39 (4); Lewes St. Michael (1829).

II/27/40 (6); Lewes All Saints (1829).

II/27/41 (4); Ditchling (1830).

II/27/42 (1); Hastings St. Mary (1833).

II/27/43 (6); Henfield (1833).

II/27/44 (3); Brighton St. Nicholas (1833).

II/27/45 (4); Northiam (1837).

II/27/46 (7); Hastings St. Clement (1837).

II/27/47 (8); Brighton Christ Church (1838).

II/27/48 (4); Lewes St. John sub Castro (1839).

II/27/49 (10); Ore (1840).

II/27/50 (14); Fletching (1840).

II/27/51 (11); Northiam (1842).

II/27/52 (4); Shermanbury (1843).

II/27/53 (8); Fairlight (1845).

II/27/54 (19); Hurstpierpoint (1843).

II/27/55 (33); Northiam (1845).

II/27/56 (30); Hurstpierpoint (1845).

II/27/57 (12); Crawley (1845).

II/27/58 (22); Lewes (Southover) (1846).

II/27/59 (12); Frant (1848).

II/27/60 (6); East Grinstead (1850).

II/27/61 (120); Dallington (1863).

II/27/62 (150); Cuckfield (1865).

II/27/63 (80); Hastings St. Clement (1874).

II/27/64 (200); Hartfield (1874).

II/27/65 (120); Brighton St. Nicholas (1876).

II/27/66 (40); Hastings St. Leonard (1881).

II/27/67 (60); Rye (1881).

II/27/68 (15); Eastbourne St. Anne (1896).

II/27/69 (120); Southwick (1898).

II/27/70 (40); Seaford (1899).

II/27/71 (300); Hastings St. Mary (1891).

II/27/72 (3); Rotherfield (1907).

II/27/73 (3); Albourne (1852).

II/27/74 (9); Ardingly (1874).

II/27/75 (2); Ardingly (1887).

II/27/76 (1); Ardingly (1896).

II/27/77 (12); Balcombe (1872).

II/27/78 (11); Barcombe (1878).

II/27/79 (20); Barcombe (1879).

II/27/80 (2); Beckley (1884).

II/27/81 (1); Beckley (1890).

II/27/82 (4); [Upper] Beeding (1852).

II/27/83 (12); Lower Beeding (1862).

II/27/84 (2); Lower Beeding (1884).

II/27/85 (1); Lower Beeding (1888).

II/27/86 (1); Lower Beeding (1895).

II/27/87 (26); Bexhill St. Peter (1877–78).

II/27/88 (20); Bexhill St. Peter (1907).

II/27/89 (2); Bexhill St. Mark (1885).

II/27/90 (3); Bishopstone (1907).

II/27/91 (55); Bodiam (1853–4).

II/27/92 (8); Bolney (1853).

II/27/93 (3); Bolney (1905).

II/27/94 (3); Brede (1905).

II/27/95 (3); Brede (1908).

II/27/96 (6); Brighton Holy Trinity (1869).

II/27/97 (11); Brighton St. Margaret (1874).

II/27/98 (2); Brighton St. Mark (1890).

II/27/99 (2); Brighton St. Martin (1907).

II/27/100 (1); Brighton St. Mary (1897).

II/27/101 (43); Brighton St. Nicholas (1853).

II/27/102 (1); Brighton St. Peter (1889).

II/27/103 (1); Brighton St. Nicholas (1892).

II/27/104 (4); Brighton Extra Mural Cemetery (1888).

II/27/105 (8); Brighton Parochial Cemetery (1889).

II/27/106 (3); Brighton Extra Mural Cemetery (1900).

II/27/107 (2); Burgess Hill (1889).

II/27/108 (25); Buxted (1879).

II/27/109 (6); Chailey (1878).

II/27/110 (2); Chalvington (1897).

II/27/111 (2); East Chiltington (1889).

II/27/112 (2); Colgate in Lower Beeding (1891).

II/27/113 (32); Cowfold (1875).

II/27/114 (14); Cowfold (1877–8).

II/27/115 (12); Crawley (1879).

II/27/116 (30); Crawley Down (1871).

II/27/117 (2); Crawley Down (1888).

II/27/118 (1); Crawley Down (1893).

II/27/119 (20); Crowhurst (1856).

II/27/120 (50); Cuckfield (1855).

II/27/121 (4); Cuckfield (1906).

II/27/122 (1); Danehill (1893).

II/27/123 (11); West Dean (1878).

II/27/124 (2); Eastbourne Holy Trinity (1884).

II/27/125 (1); Eastbourne St. John Meads (1895).

II/27/126 (3); Eastbourne St. John Meads (1907).

II/27/127 (4); Eastbourne St. Michael (1906).

II/27/127a (2); Eastbourne St. Saviour (1896).

II/27/128 (10); Etchingham (1856).

II/27/129 (1); Etchingham (1896).

II/27/130 (4); Ewhurst (1907).

II/27/131 (15); Flimwell (1872).

II/27/132 (11); Folkington (1851).

II/27/133 (80); Forest Row (1876–7).

II/27/134 (3); Forest Row (1907).

II/27/135 (2); Framfield (1891).

II/27/136 (25); Framfield (1892).

II/27/137 (6); Framfield (1907).

II/27/138 (2); Friston (1891).

II/27/139 (25); East Grinstead (1873).

II/27/140 (1); New Groombridge (1897).

II/27/141 (4); New Groombridge (1905).

II/27/142 (2); Hammerwood [St. Peter, Holtye] (1892).

II/27/143 (6); Hartfield (1906).

II/27/144 (10); Hastings All Saints (1877).

II/27/145 (10); Hastings All Saints (1878).

II/27/146 (1); Hastings Christ Church (1897).

II/27/147 (1); Hastings Holy Trinity (1890).

II/27/148 (2); Hastings St. Clement, Halton (1888).

II/27/149 (2); Hastings St. Mary (1894).

II/27/150 (6); Hastings Cemetery (1906).

II/27/151 (3); Hellingly (1906).

II/27/152 (5); Henfield (1870).

II/27/153 (3); East Hoathly (1855).

II/27/154 (16); East Hoathly (1873).

II/27/155 (1); East Hoathly (1892).

II/27/156 (10); East Hoathly (1906).

II/27/157 (4); West Hoathly (1907).

II/27/158 (1); Hollington St. John (1893).

II/27/159 (2); Hooe (1890).

II/27/160 (25); Horsted Keynes (1885).

II/27/161 (6); Horsted Parva (1862).

II/27/162 (2); Hove All Saints (1894).

II/27/163 (6); Hove St. Barnabas (1906).

II/27/164 (1); Hove St. John (1894).

II/27/165 (3); Hove St. John (1906).

II/27/166 (2); Hove St. Patrick (1886).

II/27/167 (3); Hove St. Patrick (1906).

II/27/168 (5); Hove Cemetery (1908).

II/27/169 (1); Hurst Green (1894).

II/27/170 (2); Icklesham (1905).

II/27/171 (10); Ifield (1883).

II/27/172 (4); Iford (1907).

II/27/173 (20); Isfield (1875).

II/27/174 (20); Keymer (1865).

II/27/175 (2); Keymer (1890).

II/27/176 (2); Laughton (1868).

II/27/177 (12); Laughton (1883).

II/27/178 (18); Lewes All Saints (1882).

II/27/179 (2); Lewes St. Anne (1889).

II/27/180 (6); Lewes St. John Sub Castro (1883).

II/27/181 (20); Lewes (Southover) (1884).

II/27/182 (3); Lewes St. Michael (1877).

II/27/183 (11); Lewes St. Michael (1878).

II/27/184 (2); Lewes St. Michael (1884).

II/27/185 (1); Lewes St. Michael (1891).

II/27/186 (1); Lewes St. Michael (1897).

II/27/187 (8); Lewes St. Thomas-at-Cliffe (1869).

II/27/188 (6); Lewes St. Thomas-at-Cliffe (1877).

II/27/189 (2); Lewes St. Thomas-at-Cliffe (1885).

II/27/190 (32); Lindfield (1883).

II/27/191 (6); South Malling (1907).

II/27/192 (18); Maresfield (1878).

II/27/193 (40); Mayfield (1852).

II/27/194 (1); Mountfield (1896).

II/27/195 (2); Newick (1886).

II/27/196 (1); Newtimber (1892).

II/27/197 (2); Newtimber (1906).

II/27/198 (2); Ninfield (1885).

II/27/199 (6); Ninfield (1906).

II/27/200 (10); Northiam (1878).

II/27/201 (8); Nutley (1907).

II/27/202 (1); Ore (1868).

II/27/203 (14); Patcham (1876).

II/27/204 (1); Patcham (1897).

II/27/205 (1); Peasmarsh (1893)

II/27/206 (10); Pevensey (1877).

II/27/207 (10); Piddinghoe (1882).

II/27/208 (6); Plumpton (1867).

II/27/209 (2); Plumpton (1886).

II/27/210 (6); Portslade (1858).

II/27/211 (17); Portslade (1868).

II/27/212 (12); Prestonville (1878).

II/27/213 (2); Ringmer (1884).

II/27/214 (10); Ripe (1863).

II/27/215 (10); Rotherfield (1896).

II/27/216 (1); Rottingdean (1897).

II/27/217 (10); Burgess Hill St. John's Common (1877).

II/27/218 (10); St. Leonards Christ Church (1906).

II/27/219 (6); St. Leonards St. Leonard (1869).

II/27/220 (2); St. Leonards St. Leonard (1887).

II/27/221 (1); St. Leonards St. Leonard (1897).

II/27/222 (12); St. Leonards St. Matthew, Silverhill (1873).

II/27/223 (2); St. Leonards St. Paul (1893).

II/27/224 (2); St. Leonards St. Peter (1894).

II/27/225 (1); Upper St. Leonards (1894).

II/27/226 (1); Salehurst (1897).

II/27/227 (2); Salehurst (1905).

II/27/228 (1); Seaford (1897).

II/27/229 (2); Selmeston (1906).

II/27/230 (2); Shermanbury (1882).

II/27/231 (10); New Shoreham (1876).

II/27/232 (2); Old Shoreham (1906).

II/27/233 (12); Slaugham (1857).

II/27/234 (12); Slaugham (1879).

II/27/235 (3); Southease (1907).

II/27/236 (2); Southwick (1892).

II/27/237 (6); Streat (1854).

II/27/238 (10); Streat (1882).

II/27/239 (1); Streat (1897).

II/27/240 (4); Streat (1907).

II/27/241 (4); Telscombe (1906).

II/27/242 (12); Ticehurst (1879).

II/27/243 (1); Turners Hill (1896).

II/27/244 (3); Turners Hill (1906).

II/27/245 (1); Twineham (1893).

II/27/246 (2); Uckfield (1888).

II/27/247 (10); Waldron (1862).

II/27/248 (11); Warbleton (1882).

II/27/249 (2); Warbleton (1889).

II/27/250 (15); Westfield (1884).

II/27/251 (1); Westfield (1888).

II/27/252 (35); Wilmington (1882).

II/27/253 (20); Withyham [Crowborough] (1870).

II/27/254 (10); Withyham (1882).

II/27/255 (2); Withyham (1892).

II/27/256 (17); Wivelsfield (1868).

II/27/257 (18); Woodmancote (1868–9).

II/27/258 (2); list, prepared for the *Church of England Year Book*, of the number of consecrations and faculties in the archdeaconry, 1872–81.

Ep.II/28 REGISTER OF NON-RESIDENT CLERGY, 1804–1853

See notes to Ep.I/42 (p. 62).

II/28/1 68 ff.; an alphabetical list (by surnames) of licences and notifications of non-residence, with full details of each licence, 1804–53.

Ep.II/29 FORMULARY, 17th CENT.

See also Ep.I/51 for other Lewes formularies; a calendar of this volume is available in the Diocesan Record Office (Ep.I/88/4).

II/29/1 545 ff.; London and Welsh original court documents, early 17th cent.

Ep.II/30 INDUCTION MANDATES, 1752–1924

See notes to Ep.I/7 (p. 12).

II/30/1 (935); episcopal mandates for induction, and some by commission, 1787–1924, including some from the Bishop of Lewes, 1909–1924. These documents usually give the name of the previous incumbent and the patron, and the cause of vacancy; they are occasionally endorsed with the date of the archdeacon's mandate and a certificate of induction.

1787	1	1822	3	1857	2	1891	18
1788	3	1823	6	1858	8	1892	12
1789	4	1824	7	1859	5	1893	11
1790	5	1825	7	1860	3	1894	5
1791	5	1826	4	1861	5	1895	7
1792	8	1827	6	1862	5	1896	10
1793	6	1828	4	1863	9	1897	10
1794	7	1830	7	1864	6	1898	10
1795	7	1831	2	1865	4	1899	7
1796	8	1832	6	1866	6	1900	9
1797	3	1833	6	1867	3	1901	12
1798	5	1834	5	1868	8	1902	6
1799	2	1835	6	1869	4	1903	7
1800	5	1836	7	1870	8	1904	4
1801	6	1837	6	1871	9	1905	9
1802	4	1838	3	1872	16	1906	13
1803	6	1839	7	1873	1	1907	3
1804	3	1840	7	1874	7	1908	10
1805	9	1841	11	1875	14	1909	14
1806	4	1842	3	1876	5	1910	12
1807	8	1843	7	1877	10	1911	9
1808	2	1844	8	1878	11	1912	6
1809	5	1845	1	1879	9	1913	11
1810	4	1846	10	1880	11	1914	3
1811	2	1847	3	1881	8	1915	9
1812	6	1848	9	1882	14	1916	5
1813	4	1849	4	1883	6	1917	8
1815	7	1850	6	1884	5	1918	11
1816	3	1851	5	1885	6	1919	11
1817	3	1852	4	1886	8	1920	8
1818	4	1853	3	1887	12	1921	8
1819	3	1854	8	1888	9	1922	4
1820	3	1855	4	1889	20	1923	1
1821	10	1856	9	1890	10	1924	3

II/30/2 (8); archdeacon's general mandates to all clergy in the archdeaconry to induct on his behalf, endorsed with the date of induction, 1752–1798; all but one of these documents were exhibited at Bishop Buckner's primary visitation in 1798.

1752, 1; 1757, 1; 1772, 1; 1790, 1; 1792, 1; 1795, 1; 1798, 2.

II/30/3 (43); correspondence relating to Lewes inductions, 1920–1924.

Ep.II/31 VISITATION PAPERS, 1755–1920

See notes to Ep.I/20 (p. 38), although this series is not comparable.

II/31/1 (10); lists of clergy, parishes and visitation preachers (1755, 1798, 1821, 1856); articles of enquiry not returned (1871); church repairs recommended by churchwardens; an unused copy of the ministers' articles (1811). All relating to episcopal visitations.

II/31/2 (47); processes for archidiaconal visitations, 1860–1896, ordering all clergy and old and new churchwardens to be cited to appear. From 1860 to 1883 a separate process was sent to each rural deanery.

1860	1867	1874	1882
1861	1869	1876	1883
1863	1870	1877	1885
1864	1872	1879	1886
1866	1873	1880	1888

1889	1892	1895	1896
1891	1894		

II/31/3 (32); circulars of archidiaconal visitation proceedings, 1903–1920.

II/31/4 (18); unused churchwardens' articles of enquiry and receipts for fees, archidiaconal visitations, 1904–1917.

II/31/5 (34); processes and inhibitions for episcopal visitations, 1862–1909. From 1862 to 1893 one process was sent to the deaneries of Lewes and Pevensey, and one to Hastings and Dallington; for 1898 to 1909 there are inhibitions only.

1862	1875	1887	1903
1865	1878	1890	1909
1868	1881	1893	
1871	1884	1898	

II/31/6 (80); correspondence between Bishop Burrows (as Suffragan Bishop of Lewes), Archdeacon Churton, the archdeacon's registry, incumbents and churchwardens concerning archidiaconal visitations, 1908–1917.

II/31/7 9 books (each approx. 150 ff.) of receipts for visitation fees, by deaneries, 1911–1917. Brighton, Lewes and Hastings, 1911, 1912; Brighton and Lewes, 1915, 1916; Brighton, 1917.

Ep.II/32 CHURCHWARDENS' DECLARATIONS, 1910–1920

Signed declarations made before the archdeacon or his surrogate.

1910	222	1912	54	1917	100
1911	230	1915	50	1920	103

Ep.II/33 OFFICE ACCOUNT BOOKS, 1862–1894

Accounts of fees received by, or of fees due to, archdeaconry officials on the issue of documents (licences, citations, mandates, letters of orders, institution, faculties and many others). Usually the names of the parties concerned are given, and often parishes and other detail. The first few pages of each volume contain miscellaneous receipts ([1]) and the rest individual accounts ([2]).

II/33/1 86 pp. pp.1–23 and 78–80[1], Jan. 1862–Dec. 1864; pp.24–77 and 80–82[2], May 1862–Jan. 1865; pp.83–86, index.

II/33/2 92 pp. pp.1–25[1], Jan. 1865–Dec. 1867; pp.28–87[2], Jan. 1865–Nov. 1867; pp.89–92, index.

II/33/3 104 pp. pp.1–20[1], Jan. 1868–Dec. 1870; pp.23–100[2], Aug. 1869–Dec. 1870; pp.101–104, index.

II/33/4 112 pp. pp.1–20[1], Jan. 1871–Dec. 1873; pp.31–108[2], Jan. 1871–Aug. 1872; pp.109–112, index.

II/33/5 116 pp. pp.1–17[1], Jan. 1874–Dec. 1876; pp.29–112[2], Feb. 1874–Oct. 1876; pp.112–116, index.

II/33/6 116 pp. pp.1–16[1], Jan. 1877–Dec. 1880; pp.25–112[2], Jan. 1877–Mar. 1881; pp.113–116, index.

II/33/7 72 pp. pp.1–12[1], Jan. 1881–Dec. 1883; pp.17–68[2], Aug. 1883–Nov. 1883; pp.69–72, index.

II/33/8 116 pp. pp.1–20[1], Jan. 1884–Sep. 1890; pp.25–112[2], Mar. 1884–Nov. 1888; pp.113–116, index.

II/33/9 116 pp. pp.1–20[1], May 1889–Jan. 1894; pp.25–112[2], May 1889–Apr. 1894; pp.113–116, index.

Ep.II/34 ASSESSORS' ELECTION PAPERS, 1888–1919

(60); letters, citations to the beneficed clergy of the archdeaconry and returns to the bishop for the triennial elections of a commissioner under the Pluralities Act (48 & 49 Vict. c.54; 1885) and four assessors under the Clergy Discipline Act (55 & 56 Vict. c.32; 1892).

Ep.II/35 REGISTRARS' PRIVATE CORRESPONDENCE, 1823–1910

This is primarily the personal and private business correspondence of the firm of solicitors at 213 High Street, Lewes, who were also registrars for the archdeaconry and the South Malling Peculiar. Four bundles of letters found with these papers, relating to South Malling affairs, have been transferred to Ep.V/22. During this period the firm was known by various combinations of the names Hoper, Greene, Hunt, Husey-Hunt, Currey and Nicholson.

II/35/1 Correspondence, 1823–1872, in strict chronological order. For each of the years 1823–1830, 1832 and 1834 there is one bundle of letters to John Hoper (each approx. 120), many of which are personal. The rest of the group is business correspondence, bundled by quarter-years, each bundle containing between 150 and 300 letters. The series runs 1849–1851, 1853–1855, 1857–1860, 1864, 1866, 1868–1869, 1870 (Apr.–June only), 1871 (Jan.–Mar., July–Dec. only) and 1872.

II/35/2 (500); letters to John and George Hoper, 1828–30 and 1832–43. Many are personal, but the business correspondents include Dr. [later Bishop] Gilbert, then Principal of Brasenose College, Oxford. The letters are not necessarily related, but many are from William Campion (Danny Park, Hurstpierpoint), Frederick Ellman (Battle) and Miss Elizabeth Mead (Clapham).

II/35/3 (120); letters to George Hoper, 1833–1845, on proposed Ecclesiastical Courts Bills (Ecclesiastical Courts Act, 1844; 7 & 8 Vict. c.68).

[1–2] For key to these numbers, see note to EP.II/33, p. 127.

II/35/4 (150); letters and applications, 1837–1845, related to a clergy charity, of which the Hopers were apparently trustees. This may be the charity whose papers are in Ep.I/78/7.

II/35/5 (15); letters and papers, 1844–1849, mostly between the Poor Law Commissioners and South Malling parish officers, and a copy of *The Case of the Country Registrars* (see Ep. I/36).

II/35/6 (55); miscellaneous letters, 1848–1910, all but two relating to Lewes archdeaconry affairs. The correspondents include John Hoper, Bernard Husey Hunt, A. S. Greene, Bishop Gilbert, Chancellor Phillimore, William Sergison (rector of Slaugham, 1839–74) and Queen Anne's Bounty Office; the letters relate chiefly to faculties for Bodiam (1854), Burwash (1855), Heathfield (1855) and Slaugham (1855) churches, consecration of burial ground at Lewes St. Michael (1855), the celebration of marriages in Upper Dicker Common Chapel (1849) and the appointment of surrogates for Brighton (1855).

II/35/7 (800); four bundles of letters from solicitors at 2 New Inn, London: 1856 (Mr. Lowndes), 1857 (Lowndes and Attree) and 1861 and 1862 (Senior and Attree).

II/35/8 (10); personal letters and papers, 1869, of W.P. Moore (of Moore and Currey, Doctors Commons).

II/35/9 (4); letters and a telegram, 1884, relating to "Mrs. Rosseter's Case".

Ep.II/36 REGISTRARS' OFFICE PAPERS, 1836–1879

These were among the office papers of the registrars; see notes to Ep.II/35 (p. 128). More of the cases scheduled in II/36/1 can be found in the cause papers (Ep.I/48), correspondence (Ep.I/49) and the appropriate group of faculty or sequestration papers, etc.

II/36/1 4 ff.; "Schedule of Mr. Currey's Papers in the Office Cupboard", n.d.

II/36/2 (1); a copy of the Registration of Births, Deaths and Marriages Act (6 & 7 Will. IV c.86; 1836).

II/36/3 (5); copies of Acts relating to Stamp Duties, 13 & 14 Vict. c.97 (1850), 16 & 17 Vict. c.59 and c.63 (1853), 17 & 18 Vict. c.83 (1854) and 28 & 29 Vict. c.96 (1865).

II/36/4 (18); letters of administration and papers relating to the administration of the estate of Harriet Taylor of South Malling, 1852–4.

II/36/5 (31); letters and papers relating to the sequestration of the rectory of Beaconsfield, Bucks., 1867, and of the rectory of Rodmell, Sussex, 1854, used as a precedent.

II/36/6 (6); letters and a monition relating to the unauthorized erection of altar ornaments in St. George's, Barrow, Lancs., 1868. These papers were sent to Edmund Currey by his brother William, who was acting on behalf of the churchwardens of Barrow.

II/36/7 (37); papers and correspondence, 1874–76, chiefly between Robert Barker (rector of Chastleton, Oxon., 1874–5), Mrs. M. J. Nutting (his mother-in-law) and John Fielder Mackarness (Bishop of Oxford, 1869–88), relating to Barker's non-residence in Chastleton rectory because Mrs. Nutting refused to move out of it.

II/36/8 (20); letters and papers relating to the Clerical Disabilities Act (1870) Extension, 1877.

II/36/9 (22); letters and papers in a dispute among the archdeacons of the Ely diocese about precedence in the cathedral, 1877–79.

II/36/10 (19); papers and circular correspondence between diocesan registrars relating to ecclesiastical fees, 1889–1908.

II/36/11 (8); correspondence between Chancellor Tristram and the diocesan registrars on ecclesiastical fees, 1891–94.

Ep.II/37   REGISTRARS' MISCELLANEA, 1852–1895

Miscellaneous private and semi-official papers; see notes to Ep.II/35 (p. 128).

II/37/1 50 ff.; quitrent receipt book, Manor of Willingdon, 1852–54.

II/37/2 64 pp.; "Index of Courts of which the Records, Wills, Grants . . . and other Instruments relating . . . to Matters or Causes Testamentary, have been transmitted to the Court of Probate, pursuant to . . . 20 & 21 Vict. c.77 [s.89]; also a List of the several registries of the Court of Probate, with the Titles of the Ecclesiastical Courts, of which the Testamentary Records have been or are to be transmitted to the said Registries", March 1862.

II/37/3 (70); letters and papers relating to the will of Stephen Lowdell, and to Lewes All Saints and Cliffe Burial Board, 1866–69.

II/37/4 (2); draft affidavit about the goods of Charlotte Mary Delaney, deceased, 1868.

II/37/5 140 ff.; day book, Dec. 1868–July 1869. ff.1–3, "labour account"; ff.33v.–34, "creditor"; ff.87v.–89, "debtor".

II/37/6 (16); letters and papers relating to a claim for dilapidations to the house called Ryders Wells, South Malling, 1874.

II/37/7 (80); letters and papers relating to land requisitioned by the Lewes and East Grinstead Railway Co. in Horsted Keynes, 1878–80.

II/37/8 (2); letters relating to the benefice of St. Leonard's-on-Sea St. Paul, 1878.

II/37/9 (50); letters and papers from agents relating to testamentary business, 1894.

II/37/10 (50); letters and papers relating to the administration of the estates of Edward Scrase (d. 1 Mar. 1885) and Clara Scrase (d. 10 Dec. 1893), 1894–95.

Ep.II/38 SEAL MATRICES, 1912–1946

II/38/1 Henry Kemble Southwell, Archdeacon 1912–1930.

II/38/2 Francis Henry Dumville Smythe, Archdeacon 1930–1946.

II/38/3 James Herbert Lloyd Morrell, Archdeacon 1946–1959.

Ep.II/39 BAPTISMAL RETURNS, 1851

1 bundle of incumbents' returns of the number of persons baptized in each parish in the archdeaconry in 1851; see Ep.I/60 (p. 85).

Ep.II/40 EDUCATION PAPERS, 1823–1868

II/40/1 52 ff.; parishes, arranged alphabetically, giving the number of children and average attendance at national schools, averages of income and expenditure, if under government inspection and when last inspected, if any Government apprentices, and details of other schools in the parish, 1855.

II/40/2, 3 32 ff.; copies of II/40/1.

II/40/4 (23); application for union of Westham school to the National Society and for financial assistance (1823); West Firle ruridecanal chapter minutes (1849); notes on Buxted and Uckfield schools (n.d.); diocesan inspectors' reports on Barcombe and Brighton (St. Margaret's chapel) schools (1855); return of schools for the poor (with numbers of pupils and teachers, and details of finance) in the Westham rural deanery, mid 19th cent.

II/40/5 32 gatherings; diocesan inspectors' reports on schools, 1855–68, arranged by deaneries, consisting mostly of the degrees of proficiency attained by each class in each subject at the inspector's examination, and some general remarks and criticisms.
Balcombe, 1857, 1859–61; Bexhill and Hastings, 1855–6; Burwash, 1855, 1857–8, 1861–2, 1864; Firle, 1855–7, 1859–60; Frant, 1855, 1858; Hastings, 1861–4; Hurstpierpoint, 1857–61, 1864–5, 1868; Lewes, 1855; Ripe, 1861; Shermanbury, 1858, 1861.

II/40/6 **7** gatherings; detailed reports on schools in the Shermanbury rural deanery, 1856–7, 1862, 1864–5.

Ep.II/41 CHURCH BUILDING PAPERS, 1704–1935

Some of these papers properly belong to Ep.II/27 (faculties and consecrations) but were retained with other 'stray' papers in this group of records because of their references to the church or church land. See notes to Ep.I/41 (p. 59).

II/41/1 (1); Alciston, 1841.

II/41/2 (80); Aldrington, 1876.

II/41/3 (50); Aldrington, 1898.

II/41/4 (7); Barcombe, 1816.

II/41/5 (80); Barcombe, 1865–6.

II/41/6 (20); Beckley, 1839.

II/41/7 (1); Beckley, 1935.

II/41/8 (1); Berwick, n.d.

II/41/9 (1); Bexhill St. Barnabas, n.d.

II/41/10 (1); Bishopstone, 1908.

II/41/11 (1); Bodiam, n.d. [*post* 1931].

II/41/12 (3); Brighton and East Blatchington (union), **1706–1774**.

II/41/13 (1); Brighton Christ Church, n.d.

II/41/14 (80); Brighton Holy Trinity, 1869.

II/41/15 (1); Brighton St. Anne, n.d.

II/41/16 (2); Brighton [St. James], 1828.

II/41/17 (6); Brighton St. James, 1889.

II/41/18 (1); [Brighton St. James?], n.d.

II/41/19 (15); Brighton St. John Evangelist, 1878.

II/41/20 (1); Brighton St. Nicholas, 1873.

II/41/21 (3); Brighton St. Nicholas, 1892.

II/41/22 (1); Brighton St. Peter, 1790.

II/41/23 (1); Brighton, n.d. [early 19th cent.]. Appeal to parishioners for contributions towards a "Free Chapel . . . dependant upon the Mother Church".

II/41/24 (50); Broadwater Down, 1866.

II/41/25 (15); Burwash, 1867.

II/41/26 (3); Buxted, 1849.

II/41/27 (8); Catsfield, 1815–16.

II/41/28 (1); Clayton with Keymer, 1865.

II/41/29 (2); Crowhurst, 1863.

II/41/30 (27); Cuckfield, 1818–19.

II/41/31 (20); Danehill, 1881.

II/41/32 (1); East Dean, 1817.

II/41/33 (30); Denton, 1814.

II/41/34 (4); Ditchling, 1856.

II/41/35 (1); Ditchling, 1865.

II/41/36 (2); Ditchling, 1884.

II/41/37 (1); bond on the rebuilding of Eastbourne vicarage house, 1704.

II/41/38 (12); Eastbourne All Saints, 1928.

II/41/39 (60); Eastbourne St. John Meads, 1867.

II/41/40 (2); Eastbourne St. John Meads, 1894.

II/41/41 (55); Eastbourne St. Saviour, 1867.

II/41/42 (1); Etchingham, 1809.

II/41/43 (1); Ewhurst, 1850.

II/41/44 (3); Ewhurst, 1869.

II/41/45 (1); Ewhurst, 1907.

II/41/46 (10); Fairlight, 1824.

II/41/47 (20); West Firle and Beddingham, 1824.

II/41/48 (15); Fletching, 1813 and 1837.

II/41/49 (60); Fletching, 1882–3.

II/41/50 (6); Folkington, 1849.

II/41/51 (30); Frant, 1845.

II/41/52 (10); Frant, 1870.

II/41/53 (1); Glynde, 1878.

II/41/54 (8); East Grinstead, 1836.

II/41/55 (2); East Grinstead, 1873.

II/41/56 (4); Groombridge, 1905.

II/41/57 (10); Guestling, 1856.

II/41/58 (7); Hailsham, 1844.

II/41/59 (3); Hamsey, 1821.

II/41/60 (8); Hastings, 1835.

II/41/61 (10); Hastings, St. Clement and All Saints (disunion), 1847.

II/41/62 (1); Hastings, St. Clement Halton, n.d.

II/41/63 (5); Hellingly, 1831–5.

II/41/64 (1); Hellingly, n.d. [*post* 1927].

II/41/65 (1); Henfield, 1806.

II/41/65a (1); Henfield, n.d. [19th cent.].

II/41/66 (1); East Hoathly, 1801.

II/41/67 (10); East Hoathly, 1887.

II/41/68 (10); West Hoathly, 1837.

II/41/69 (1); West Hoathly, n.d.

II/41/70 (3); Hollington, 1856.

II/41/71 (70); Horsted Keynes, 1881.

II/41/72 (4); Hove All Saints, n.d.

II/41/73 (10); Icklesham, 1819.

II/41/74 (10); Ifield, 1845.

II/41/75 (10); Isfield, 1873.

II/41/76 (1); Isfield, 1908.

II/41/77 (10); Laughton, 1837.

II/41/78 (30); Laughton, 1892.

II/41/79 (1); Lewes All Saints, n.d. [early 19th cent.].

II/41/80 (1); Lewes St. John Baptist (Southover), 1864.

II/41/81 (1); Lewes St. John Baptist (Southover), 1869.

II/41/82 (1); [Lewes] St. John Baptist [Southover], 1906.

II/41/83 (200); Lewes St. Michael, 1877 and 1878.

II/41/84 (2); Lewes St. Michael, 1890 and 1891.

II/41/85 (3); Lewes St. Thomas-at-Cliffe, 1883.

II/41/86 (80); South Malling, 1881.

II/41/87 (2); South Malling, n.d.

II/41/88 (1); Maresfield, 1811.

II/41/89 (100); Maresfield, 1881.

II/41/90 (1); Netherfield, 1860.

II/41/91 (10); Newhaven [alias Meeching], 1819

II/41/92 (1); Newhaven, 1864.

II/41/93 (60); Newhaven, 1883.

II/41/94 (1); Newhaven, 1899.

II/41/95 (70); Newick, 1862–4.

II/41/96 (3); Northiam, 1845.

II/41/97 (50); Nutley, 1867.

II/41/98 (10); Nutley, 1884.

II/41/99 (62); Ore, 1869.

II/41/100 (1); Patcham, 1871.

II/41/101 (20); Peasmarsh, 1838.

II/41/102 (20); Pevensey, 1876.

II/41/103 (1); Portslade, 1864.

II/41/104 (3); Pyecombe, 1881.

II/41/105 (1); Pyecombe, 1884.

II/41/106 (6); Ringmer, 1849.

II/41/107 (15); Ripe, 1818.

II/41/108 (10); Rye, 1893.

II/41/109 (2); Rye, n.d.

II/41/110 (1); "St. Leonard's Chapel", n.d.

II/41/111 (6); Salehurst, 1862.

II/41/112 (1); Salehurst, 1905.

II/41/113 (2); Sedlescombe, 1804.

II/41/114 (5); Selmeston, 1835.

II/41/115 (8); Selmeston, 1866.

II/41/116 (20); Shermanbury, 1835.

II/41/117 (2); Southwick, 1815.

II/41/118 (40); Southwick, 1841.

II/41/119 (50); Southwick, 1879.

II/41/120 Act (49 Geo. III, sess. 1809, no. 109) for uniting the rectory of Stanmer with the vicarage of Falmer, and for an exchange of land.

II/41/121 (40); Stonegate, 1879.

II/41/122 (8); Streat, 1822.

II/41/123 (20); Streat, 1883.

II/41/124 (10); Telscombe, 1849.

II/41/125 (9); Telscombe and Piddinghoe (union), 1876–78.

II/41/126 (10); Ticehurst, 1853.

II/41/127 (150); Twineham, 1879–82.

II/41/128 (2); Warbleton, 1814.

II/41/129 (1); Westfield, 1827.

II/41/130 (15); Westfield, 1848.

II/41/131 (10); Westfield, 1851.

II/41/132 (2); Westfield, 1882.

II/41/133 (100); Westham, 1877–80.

II/41/134 (8); Westham, 1887.

II/41/135 (40); Westmeston, 1878–9.

II/41/136 (20); Willingdon, 1844.

II/41/137 (20); Willingdon, 1844 and 1851.

II/41/138 (1); Willingdon, 1935.

II/41/139 (12); Winchelsea, 1873–4.

II/41/140 (40); Winchelsea, 1876.

II/41/141 (80); Winchelsea, 1880–3.

II/41/142 (3); Worth, 1872.

II/41/143 (6); Orders in Council relating to the augmentation of Selmeston and Alciston, Crawley Down, Flimwell, Bolney, Icklesham and Brighton St. Nicholas, 1863–74.

II/41/144 (6); Instruments constituting Uckfield (Holy Cross), Bexhill (SS. Peter and Paul and St. Mark, Little Common), Hollington and Bodle Street Green rectories, and Lower Beeding a vicarage, 1866–7.

II/41/145 (4); Reports by rural deans on the fabric of churches and parsonage houses in the deaneries, 1813, 1818, 1822 and 1823.

II/41/146 (2); Lists of chapels consecrated in the archdeaconry, 1803–39.

II/41/147 (1); Letter from Queen Anne's Bounty Office to Lewes Registry covering papers on mortgages, Oct. 1844.

Ep.II/42 PARISH PAPERS, 1586–1854

Miscellaneous papers relating to parishes in the archdeaconry.

II/42/1 (1); Crown certificate of the receipt of Chapter confirmation that the rector of Balcombe [William Selhurst] had paid his Queen's tenths, 1 Aug. 1586.

II/42/2 (1); petition to Bishop Buckner from the parishioners of Bolney about the conduct of John Taylor, parish clerk, 24 June 1808.

II/42/3 4 ff.; "A Catalogue of the Parochial Library given by the late Mr. Richard Wilkin to the Use of the residing Ministers of Heathfield, for ever, and now in the possession of William Preston Vicar of that Parish 1745".

II/42/4 (2); letter and appeal, 1854, for subscriptions for a proposed memorial to Robert Leighton [Archbishop of Glasgow, 1669–1674] in Horsted Keynes church where he was buried.

II/42/5 (5); papers, 1839, relating to a proposed exchange of lands in Jevington between the 2nd Earl of Burlington and Henry Thomas Grace (rector of Jevington, 1812–1872).

II/42/6 4 ff.; minutes of Lewes [Southover] ruridecanal chapter, 1850.

II/42/7 (1); petition to the Bishop of Chichester from parishioners of Rye against the holding of political and judicial office by John Myers (vicar of Rye, 1793–1834), n.d.

II/42/8 (4); list of parishes in the archdeaconry [with value?], no date, and lists of rural deans and their deaneries, n.d. [all early 19th cent.].

Ep.II/43 APPOINTMENTS OF OFFICIALS, 1782–1922

II/43/1 (1); John Fisher of Lewes, yeoman, to be apparitor for the archdeaconry, 1782.

II/43/2 (1); instructions for surrogates in the archdeaconry, 1787.

II/43/3 (1); notarial faculty; George Hoper to be deputy registrar of the South Malling deanery, 1810.

II/43/4 (1); notarial faculty; George Hoper to be joint deputy registrar of the archdeaconry, 1827.

II/43/5 (8); letters and papers, 1921–22, concerning the appointment of surrogates to act during Archdeacon Upcott's illness.

THE DEAN OF CHICHESTER'S PECULIAR

Ep.III/1 GENERAL SUBSCRIPTION BOOK AND PAPERS, 1739–1840

Other subscriptions for the deanery are in Ep.1/3; see Ep.I/3 (p. 6) for an explanation of the oaths and declarations.

III/1/1 6 ff. ff.1v.–2[2, 7–10]; f.3, subscription of Robert Sandham[3, 5, 6], Nov. 1739.

III/1/2 (10); loose subscription papers[3, 5–8], 1746–1840, mostly giving the names of the previous incumbent, and patron of the living, and the cause of vacancy.

Ep.III/2 PRESENTATIONS AND NOMINATIONS, 1590–1833

Presentations made to the bishop during the vacancy of the deanery are included in Ep.I/6.

1578	1	1637	1	1713	1	1771	1
1590	1	1662	1	1728	1	1774	2
1614	1	1663	1	1746	1	1792	1
1627	1	1704	1	1758	1	1833	1
1629	2	1707	2	1766	1		
1636	1	1709	1	1768	1		

Ep.III/2A GRANT OF NEXT PRESENTATION, 1578

See notes to Ep.I/6A (p. 11); grant of next presentation to the rectory of St. Pancras by Agnes Carpenter to John Rhodes, 28 Feb. 1577/8.

Ep.III/3 MARRIAGE LICENCE BONDS AND AFFIDAVITS, 1666–1908

(3,072); see notes to Ep.I/9 (p. 14). Bonds from 1590 to 1665 are in STD V; bonds and affidavits are here counted as two documents until 1770 and onwards, when they were folded together and are therefore counted as one. There are no copies of baptismal entries or marriage licences attached to any of the documents. Marriages for 1582/3 to 1730 have been calendared in Sussex Record Society, vol. 12.

1666	18	1679	6	1690	7	1700	3
1667	2	1680	6	1691	25	1701	4
1669	7	1681	2	1692	9	1702	17
1670	3	1682	2	1693	20	1703	4
1671	21	1683	7	1694	24	1704	10
1672	2	1684	11	1695	9	1705	11
1675	1	1685	15	1696	24	1706	19
1676	12	1686	6	1697	23	1707	42
1677	4	1687	1	1698	11	1708	24
1678	5	1689	16	1699	9	1709	16

[1–10] For key to these numbers, see p. 6.

Year	No.	Year	No.	Year	No.	Year	No.
1710	18	1769	20	1815	9	1861	8
1711	27	1770	9	1816	21	1862	14
1712	15	1771	15	1817	5	1863	13
1713	32	1772	16	1818	14	1864	12
1714	16	1773	28	1819	13	1865	5
1715	20	1774	25	1820	13	1866	5
1716	10	1775	15	1821	11	1867	3
1717	23	1776	12	1822	10	1868	9
1718	24	1777	12	1823	17	1869	10
1719	15	1778	24	1824	18	1870	8
1720	23	1779	15	1825	13	1871	3
1721	14	1780	26	1826	20	1872	7
1722	11	1781	23	1827	18	1873	5
1723	15	1782	21	1828	9	1874	3
1724	18	1783	11	1829	19	1875	7
1725	13	1784	26	1830	17	1876	4
1726	10	1785	18	1831	15	1877	5
1727	12	1786	27	1832	12	1878	5
1728	22	1787	16	1833	9	1879	7
1729	15	1788	20	1834	8	1880	7
1730	26	1789	31	1835	18	1881	7
1731	13	1790	12	1836	15	1882	2
1732	20	1791	19	1837	17	1883	6
1733	11	1792	15	1838	10	1884	7
1734	12	1793	30	1839	15	1885	6
1735	20	1794	16	1840	9	1886	6
1736	21	1795	16	1841	20	1887	7
1737	9	1796	14	1842	12	1890	5
1738	27	1797	23	1843	8	1891	5
1739	20	1798	18	1844	9	1892	2
1740	8	1799	23	1845	10	1893	2
1741	18	1800	17	1846	17	1894	3
1742	4	1801	11	1847	19	1895	2
1743	25	1802	19	1848	11	1896	1
1744	17	1803	28	1849	18	1897	5
1755	2	1804	23	1850	13	1898	10
1759	29	1805	19	1851	12	1899	4
1760	41	1806	14	1852	14	1900	2
1761	32	1807	21	1853	18	1901	2
1762	15	1808	14	1854	14	1902	4
1763	28	1809	15	1855	17	1903	1
1764	41	1810	18	1856	9	1904	3
1765	20	1811	13	1857	13	1905	2
1766	34	1812	18	1858	9	1906	2
1767	29	1813	26	1859	8	1908	1
1768	15	1814	6	1860	12		

Ep.III/4   ACT BOOKS, 1484–1853

These general act books contained at different periods:

[1] instance causes		[7] wills	
[2] depositions		[8] marriage licences	
[3] correction causes		[9] caveats	
[4] detection causes		[10] admissions to benefices	
[5] libri cleri		[11] faculties	
[6] probate acts			

III/4/1   119 ff. bound in two 15th cent. papal bulls.   ff.1–119[1, 3, 4, 6, 7], May 1484–Jan. 1503/4 (greatly confused and not chronological). The wills are printed in *Sussex Archaeological Collections*, vol. 87, pp. 1–27; instance causes and wills for Jan. 1523/4–Apr. 1525 are in Ep.I/10/3.

III/4/2 14 ff. bound in interrogatories. ff.1–12[1, 3, 4, 6, 7, 10], July 1554–Aug. 1564.

III/4/3 50 ff. ff.1–50[1, 2, 4, 10], July 1571–Mar. 1575/6.

III/4/4 82 ff. in two books, one bound in part of a medieval service book and the other in parchment. ff.1–41[1, 4, 5], Dec. 1577–Mar. 1580/1; ff.42–82[1, 4–6, 8], Oct. 1582–Feb. 1586/7.

III/4/5 141 ff. ff.1–140[1, 4–6, 8], Jan. 1590/1–July 1601.

III/4/6 73 ff. f.i, schoolmasters' subscriptions to the three articles (see notes to Ep.I/3, p. 6), Sep. 1604 and Jan. 1604/5; ff.1–70[1, 4, 6, 8], June 1601–Oct. 1605.

III/4/7 107 ff. ff.1–107[1, 2, 4, 6, 8–10], Oct. 1605–Mar. 1609/10.

III/4/8 93 ff. ff.1–92[1, 4–6, 8], Mar. 1609/10–June 1614.

III/4/9 168 ff. ff.1–168[1, 4–6, 8–10], Apr. 1614–Apr. 1619.

III/4/10 187 ff. ff.1–186[1, 4–6, 8, 9], Apr. 1619–Oct. 1622.

III/4/11 249 ff. ff.1–247[1, 4–6, 8, 9], Oct. 1622–June 1629.

III/4/12 274 ff. ff.1–274[1, 4–6, 8, 9], June 1629–Oct. 1637.

III/4/13 352 ff. ff.3–114[1, 4, 5, 8, 10], Nov. 1637–Apr. 1643; ff.115–346[1, 4, 5, 9, 10], May 1661–Dec. 1699, including on f.345 a commissary's commission, 1686.

III/4/14 186 ff. ff.1–186[1, 4, 5, 10], June 1717–June 1752.

III/4/15 180 ff. ff.1–139[1, 4, 5, 11], Sep. 1752–Nov. 1853.

Ep.III/5 DEPOSITION BOOKS, 1607–1677

Other depositions are in Ep.III/4 and 6. See notes to Ep.I/15 (pp. 20, 21). A typescript calendar of III/5/2, 3 is available in the Diocesan Record Office (Ep.I/88/7).

III/5/1 103 ff. bound in part of a papal document. ff.1–103, Mar. 1606/7–June 1623.

III/5/2 215 ff. ff.1–214, July 1623–Mar. 1633/4.

III/5/3 56 ff. ff.5–39; Nov. 1634–Nov. 1640; ff.40–56, July 1662–Nov. 1677.

[1–11] For key to these numbers, see p. 139.

Ep.III/6 MISCELLANEOUS COURT PAPERS, 16th–19th centuries

5 boxes of papers similar to those in Ep.I/15 (pp. 20, 21), but relating to the peculiar court of the Dean of Chichester.

Ep.III/7 CHURCHWARDENS' PRESENTMENTS, 1621–1828

(265); as the Peculiar was not subject to archidiaconal visitation most of these presentments are for episcopal visitations. The documents have been bundled according to parishes. See notes to Ep.I/22 (pp. 42, 43).

III/7/1 (32); Chichester St. Andrew, 1621–1772.

III/7/2 (19); Chichester St. Bartholomew, 1621–1772.

III/7/3 (34); Chichester St. Martin, 1621–1773.

III/7/4 (26); Chichester St. Olave, 1621–1773.

III/7/5 (26); Chichester St. Pancras, 1621-1773.

III/7/6 (24); Chichester St. Peter the Great, 1629–1828.

III/7/7 (27); Chichester St. Peter the Less, 1628–1777.

III/7/8 (43); New Fishbourne, 1621–1772.

III/7/9 (34); Rumboldswyke, 1621–1792.

Ep.III/7A MINISTERS' ARTICLES OF ENQUIRY, 1825–1828

See note to Ep.I/22A (p. 44). 1825, 1; 1828, 10.

Ep.III/8 PARISH REGISTER TRANSCRIPTS, 1591–1912

See notes to Ep.I/24 (p. 45). Burials for the Chichester Friends' Meeting House, 1890, are in Ep.I/24/23. A list of transcripts, giving the years represented for each parish, is given as an Appendix to this book.

Ep.III/9 PROBATE PAPERS, 1608–1739

The inventories found in this group have been transferred to the main collection (Ep.I/29, series B). See notes to probate papers (p. 47).

III/9/1 Administrators' accounts.

1608	1	1620	1	1640	3	1669	3
1610	2	1621	2	1641	1	1678	3
1613	3	1622	1	1662	1	1679	1
1616	4	1627	2	1664	2	1694	1
1617	1	1628	3	1665	1	1701	1
1618	1	1638	1	1667	1		
1619	5	1639	1	1668	2		

III/9/2 Certificates of oaths of administration, one with bond attached.
1662, 1; 1667, 1; 1739, 1.

III/9/3 Renunciations of letters of administration.

| 1671 | 1 | 1679 | 1 | 1705 | 1 | 1736 | 1 |
| 1678 | 1 | 1681 | 1 | 1732 | 1 | 1738 | 1 |

III/9/4 Proxy for the recovery of debts, **1732.**

Ep.III/10   ADMINISTRATION BONDS, 1666–1857

(1,248); see notes to Ep.I/32 (p. 52). Bonds from 1584 to 1665 are part of the STD group mentioned on p. 47, and are subdivision V of that group.

1666	9	1712	18	1771	9	1813	4
1667	1	1713	16	1772	5	1814	1
1669	8	1714	12	1773	11	1815	2
1670	10	1715	7	1774	11	1817	1
1671	21	1716	4	1775	4	1818	3
1672	4	1717	7	1776	15	1819	3
1675	8	1718	8	1777	11	1820	3
1676	17	1719	9	1778	13	1821	3
1677	11	1720	8	1779	6	1822	7
1678	14	1721	23	1780	9	1823	3
1679	13	1722	11	1781	14	1824	2
1680	8	1723	13	1782	8	1825	2
1681	8	1724	11	1783	2	1826	5
1682	15	1725	8	1784	14	1827	4
1683	2	1726	15	1785	9	1828	7
1684	10	1727	15	1786	9	1829	1
1685	8	1728	11	1787	6	1830	3
1686	5	1729	18	1788	16	1832	2
1687	2	1730	20	1789	14	1833	2
1688	5	1731	16	1790	5	1834	3
1689	8	1732	10	1791	5	1835	5
1690	13	1733	5	1792	8	1836	3
1691	3	1734	10	1793	9	1837	2
1692	7	1735	2	1794	7	1838	3
1693	17	1736	13	1795	11	1839	1
1694	21	1737	7	1796	3	1840	1
1695	5	1738	15	1797	3	1842	4
1696	9	1739	10	1798	8	1843	1
1697	6	1740	12	1799	11	1844	2
1698	4	1741	21	1800	9	1845	3
1700	2	1742	7	1801	4	1846	1
1701	6	1743	14	1802	1	1847	2
1702	7	1744	5	1803	6	1848	2
1703	6	1760	4	1804	2	1849	3
1704	9	1761	8	1805	3	1851	2
1705	14	1762	7	1806	2	1853	1
1706	10	1763	6	1807	3	1854	3
1707	10	1764	12	1808	1	1855	3
1708	11	1765	11	1809	1	1856	1
1709	14	1766	8	1810	7	1857	4
1710	10	1767	13	1811	3		
1711	5	1770	13	1812	3		

TESTAMENTS AND WILLS, 1536–1857

Wills and administrations for the Peculiar, 1553–1800, are indexed in *British Record Society*, vol. 64. The original testaments and wills, 1558–1857, are STD II.[1]

The registers of wills, 1536–1857, are STD I, as follows (the numbers STD I/1, 4 and 5 were not allocated):

STD I/2 Aug. 1554–May 1570 (not chronological), with one for May 1536.

STD I/3 Feb. 1577/8–Jan. 1642/3.   **STD I/8** Aug. 1766–Mar. 1793.

STD I/6 Oct. 1704–Jan. 1731/2.   **STD I/9** May 1793–Oct. 1830.

STD I/7 June 1732–July 1766.   **STD I/10** Jan. 1831–Apr. 1857.

PROBATE DAIRIES, 1577/8–1857

The Probate Diaries are STD III, as follows (vols. 2, 3, 6 and 7 have not been indexed by the British Record Society):

STD III/1 Probate, administration and account acts, marriage licences, licences to schoolmasters, institutions and sequestrations, Feb. 1577/8–Sep. 1626.

STD III/2 27 ff., apparently duplicating STD III/1, Feb. 1577/8–June 1597.

STD III/3 Probate, administration and account acts, Nov. 1626–Mar. 1667/8; marriage licences are also included from Nov. 1660.

STD III/4 Probate, administration and account acts, and marriage licences, Oct. 1660–Apr. 1672.

STD III/5 Probate and administration acts, marriage licences and sequestrations, Aug. 1689–July 1768.

STD III/6 Probate fee accounts, administration acts and marriage licences, Jan. 1770–Dec. 1781.

STD III/7 Probate and administration acts, marriage licences and sequestrations, Jan. 1781–Aug. 1857, and marriage licences, Sep. 1857–Feb. 1862.

There are also the following:

STD IV/1 Caveat book for the Dean of Chichester's Peculiar and for the Deanery of Pagham and Tarring, Feb. 1747/8–Jan. 1784, and for the bishop's consistory court *sede vacante*, Mar. 1754.

---

[1] For an explanation of the ST series p. 47.

STD VIII/14.[1] Contemporary index of probates and administrations in STD III/1 and 2; the index of administrations is from A to G only.

Ep.III/11   APPOINTMENTS OF OFFICIALS, 1642–1792
Other appointments for the Peculiar are in Ep.I/39.

III/11/1   (1); commission appointing John Halsey and Wakeford Bridger, writers of the acts, principal registrars and examiners, 26 Feb. 1727/8, with chapter seal and confirmation attached.

III/11/2   (1); commission appointing William Wakeford, writer of the acts, principal registrar and examiner, 19 Jan. 1738/9, with chapter seal and confirmation attached.

III/11/2A   (9); appointments of surrogates, 1642, 1661, 1665, 1669, 1670, 1715, 1736, 1739, and one undated.

III/11/3   (33); appointments of surrogates, with their bonds, 1736–1792, drafts of these documents written in 1754 on the backs of letters dated 1717 and 1718, and the appointment of a deputy steward of the Dean's manorial court, 1718.

Ep.III/12   OFFICE ACCOUNT BOOKS, 1678–1862
These volumes are related to the probate diaries in STD III.

III/12/1   10 ff. bound in part of a contemporary deed.   ff.1–10, fees, Oct. 1678–Oct. 1685.

III/12/2   13 ff.   ff.1–12, fees, Mar. 1718–Dec. 1728.

III/12/3   40 ff.   ff.1–40, fees (and the Deanery of Pagham and Tarring), Sep. 1731–Mar. 1742.

III/12/4   48 ff.   ff.1–48, fees (and the Deanery of Pagham and Tarring), Mar. 1742–July 1756.

III/12/5   48 ff.   ff.1–47, fees (and the Deanery of Pagham and Tarring), July 1756–Dec. 1769.

III/12/6   (16); fee accounts, 1840–1862.

Ep.III/13   FACULTY PAPERS, 1805–1847
For details of these faculties see Ep.I/88/3, arranged under parishes. See also notes to Ep.I/40 (p. 57).

[1] The series of indexes was originally numbered 1–14 and the references STC VIII, STD VIII or STA VIII added later according to the volumes to which they referred. Consequently the series runs: STC VIII/1–12, STA VIII/13 and STD VIII/14.

III/13/1 (3); Chichester St. Pancras (1805).

III/13/2 (2); Chichester St. Martin (1829).

III/13/3 (1); Chichester Cathedral (1835).

III/13/4 (30); Chichester St. Bartholomew (1846).

III/13/5 (20); New Fishbourne (1847).

Ep.III/14 INSTITUTION PAPERS, 1642–1801
See notes to Ep.I/69 (p. 89).

III/14/1 (4); appointment of proxies to receive the resignation of John Payne (vicar of St. Peter the Great) and to admit William Payne; certificate by notary public of John Payne's resignation (both Jan. 1641/2); presentation of William Payne to the vicarage (Feb. 1641/2) and draft of Ep.III/4/13, ff.110*v.*–111.

III/14/2 Letters of institution, 1679–1784, and memoranda about Roger Collins' institution.

1679	1	1709	1	1767	1
1707	1	1746	1	1784	1

III/14/3 (1); Letter requesting the withdrawal of a caveat and the admission of [William] Lamerton to the rectory of New Fishbourne, 1706.

III/14/4 (2); decanal commissions to institute, 1792 and 1799.

III/14/5 (1); licence to Samuel Joliffe Tufnell to the perpetual curacy of Chichester St. Bartholomew, Feb. 1801.

Ep.III/15 RESIGNATIONS, 1571–1713
1571, 1; 1627, 1; 1655, 1; 1713, 1.

Ep.III/16 SEQUESTRATION PAPERS, 1768–1834
Letters and relaxations of sequestration, some with registrar's notes attached, and notes of later sequestrations. See notes to Ep.I/71 (p. 91).

1768	1	1792	1	1817	1
1771	1	1805	1	1834	1

Ep.III/17 DISPENSATION FOR PLURALITY, 1784
Archbishop's dispensation to Richard Tireman to hold the vicarage of St. Peter the Great and the rectory of Rodmell in plurality, 18 June 1784, with Crown confirmation attached (19 June).

THE EXEMPT DEANERY OF PAGHAM AND TARRING

Ep.IV/1 MARRIAGE LICENCE BONDS AND AFFIDAVITS, 1692–1907

(1,534); bonds and affidavits are here counted as two documents until 1780 and onwards, when they were folded together and are counted as one. There are no copies of baptismal entries or marriage licences attached to any of the documents. Marriages from 1579/80 to 1730 have been calendared in Sussex Record Society, vol. 12. See notes to Ep.I/9 (p. 14).

Year	No.	Year	No.	Year	No.	Year	No.	Year	No.
1692	1	1740	8	1783	9	1826	8	1869	6
1693	3	1741	7	1784	6	1827	8	1870	6
1694	4	1742	9	1785	5	1828	12	1871	5
1695	5	1743	7	1786	7	1829	4	1872	4
1696	17	1744	5	1787	6	1830	7	1873	7
1697	3	1745	5	1788	8	1831	4	1874	2
1698	4	1746	7	1789	8	1832	8	1875	4
1699	8	1747	8	1790	5	1833	7	1876	1
1700	3	1748	8	1791	12	1834	4	1877	3
1701	9	1749	6	1792	10	1835	14	1878	3
1702	2	1750	11	1793	7	1836	4	1879	3
1703	6	1751	7	1794	5	1837	6	1880	7
1704	1	1752	4	1795	6	1838	4	1881	5
1710	6	1753	5	1796	6	1839	8	1882	2
1711	3	1754	9	1797	5	1840	5	1883	5
1712	10	1755	10	1798	29	1841	11	1884	5
1713	4	1756	24	1799	20	1842	4	1885	1
1714	15	1757	13	1800	8	1843	6	1886	1
1715	4	1758	12	1801	7	1844	9	1887	1
1716	11	1759	8	1802	7	1845	2	1888	4
1717	4	1760	14	1803	10	1846	7	1889	3
1718	6	1761	10	1804	4	1847	9	1890	1
1719	7	1762	20	1805	8	1848	4	1891	3
1720	2	1763	10	1806	8	1849	10	1892	2
1721	7	1764	2	1807	10	1850	7	1893	4
1722	3	1765	24	1808	3	1851	10	1894	2
1723	5	1766	8	1809	7	1852	8	1895	4
1724	12	1767	8	1810	6	1853	3	1896	1
1725	3	1768	5	1811	3	1854	9	1897	4
1726	5	1769	14	1812	5	1855	13	1898	5
1727	7	1770	12	1813	8	1856	7	1899	3
1728	5	1771	12	1814	5	1857	9	1900	5
1729	5	1772	14	1815	9	1858	3	1901	7
1730	7	1773	19	1816	8	1859	4	1902	8
1731	7	1774	14	1817	8	1860	8	1903	3
1732	8	1775	28	1818	3	1861	8	1904	2
1733	7	1776	16	1819	6	1862	3	1905	7
1734	6	1777	14	1820	9	1863	3	1906	4
1735	10	1778	8	1821	9	1864	3	1907	3
1736	10	1779	18	1822	5	1865	6		
1737	6	1780	8	1823	10	1866	5		
1738	7	1781	13	1824	5	1867	2		
1739	9	1782	3	1825	20	1868	7		

and one undateable document.

Ep.IV/2   ACT BOOKS, 1538–1844

These general act books contained at different periods:

[1] instance causes	[7] wills
[2] depositions	[8] marriage licences
[3] correction causes	[9] caveats
[4] detection causes	[10] consecrations and faculties
[5] libri cleri	[11] dissenters' meeting house certificates
[6] probate acts	

They occasionally include diocesan business (*sede vacante*).

IV/2/1   11 ff.; [1-3, 5-7], Feb. 1537/8–Oct. 1540.

IV/2/2   12 ff., bound in part of a record of a cause on appeal (1500); ff.1–8[1, 3, 5, 6], May 1541–Sep. 1544; ff.9–12[1, 3, 5, 6], Nov. 1550–July 1553.

IV/2/3   9 ff.; [1, 4], June–Dec. 1568.
See STA III/C (p. 151) for Dec. 1568–Feb. 1575/6.

IV/2/4   16 ff.; 1–8[1, 4–6, 8], Aug. 1576–Sep. 1578; f.16*v*., memoranda.

IV/2/5   81 ff.; [1, 2, 4], June 1588–Nov. 1592.

IV/2/6   43 ff.; [1, 4, 5], Feb. 1592/3–May 1596.

IV/2/7   85 ff.; [1, 4–7], May 1596–July 1601 (bound in the will of Richard Earnle of Cackham, West Wittering).

IV/2/8   96 ff.; [1, 4–7], Sep. 1601–Mar. 1608/9.

IV/2/9   84 ff.; [1, 4–8], Mar. 1609–July 1614.

IV/2/10   16 ff.; [1, 4], July 1614–July 1615.

IV/2/11   31 ff.; [1, 4, 7], Oct. 1615–May 1616.

IV/2/12   152 ff.; [1, 4, 5], Mar. 1617/8–June 1622.

IV/2/13   288 ff.; [1, 4, 5], July 1622–Sep. 1629.

IV/2/14   228 ff. bound in part of a medieval service book. ff.1–225[1, 4, 5], Oct. 1629–July 1636; ff.227*v*.–228, memoranda.

IV/2/15   59 ff.; [1, 4, 5], Sep. 1636–Mar. 1638/9 (bound in lease, Apr. 1599, from Richard Page of Kellshams, Pet[worth], yeo., to Edward Rose of West Itchenor, yeo., of property in West Itchenor and a fishing place in "one arme of the Sea" near West Itchenor).

IV/2/16   85 ff.; [1, 4, 5], May 1639–June 1642 (bound in part of a contemporary lease of Chapter property to Edmond Southcott).

IV/2/17   46 ff.; [1, 4, 5, 9], June 1661–Apr. 1666 (bound in part of a medieval MS.).

IV/2/18 48 ff.; [1,4,5,9], May 1666–Oct. 1674 (bound in part of a medieval MS.).

IV/2/19 31 ff.; [1,4,5,9], Mar. 1674/5–Nov. 1676.

IV/2/20 48 ff.; [1,4,5], Dec. 1676–Nov. 1684, including on f.25 the union of Durrington and Tarring, 24 Jan. 1679/80.

IV/2/21 48 ff.; [1,4,5], Dec. 1684–Dec. 1699.

IV/2/22 75 ff.; [1,4,5], Jan. 1699/1700–June 1724 (bound in part of a contemporary assignment of mortgage from Richard Streetin to John Styant at the direction of William Bridger).

IV/2/23 48 ff.; [1,4,5], June 1724–Aug. 1728 (bound in part of a mortgage Dec. 1721, from Samuel Roe of Yapton, butcher, to Edward Johnson of Climping).

IV/2/24 46 ff.; [1,5], Dec. 1728–Feb. 1733/4.

IV/2/25 50 ff.; [1,5], Feb. 1733/4–Dec. 1744.

IV/2/26 44 ff.; [1,5], Jan. 1744/5–July 1754.

IV/2/27 46 ff.; [1,5,10], June 1755–May 1779.

IV/2/28 136 ff.; [1,5,10,11], July 1780–Aug. 1844, including on ff.73a–95 description of consecration of site of St. John's Chapel, Bognor (1822), and plan of the chapel, and on ff.133–135 detailed reports on the churches of East Lavant, Slindon and Tangmere (1843).

Ep.IV/3 DEPOSITION BOOKS, 1611–1661
See notes to Ep.I/15 (pp. 20, 21). A typescript calendar of these volumes is available in the Diocesan Record Office (Ep.I/88/7).

IV/3/1 47 ff.; June 1611–Mar. 1624/5 (bound in part of a lease, Jan. 1590/1, from Francis Hobbes [of Nuthurst], gent., to John Ellis of the same, tanner, of property called Alice Land in Nuthurst).

IV/3/2 84 ff., (bound in a sheet of wine merchant's accounts, 1606); ff.1–77, Mar. 1625/6–Mar. 1640/1; ff.78–83, June–Oct. 1661; f.84, memoranda.

Ep.IV/4 MISCELLANEOUS COURT PAPERS, 16th–19th centuries
Includes cause papers, citations, forms of penance and excommunication, churchwardens' presentments and letters.

IV/4/1 (200); South Bersted.   **IV/4/2** (200); Chichester All Saints.

[1–11] For key to these numbers, see p. 147.

IV/4/3 (50); Durrington. 　　　**IV/4/7** (70); Patching.

IV/4/4 (30); Heene. 　　　**IV/4/8** (15); Plaistow.

IV/4/5 (100); East Lavant. 　　**IV/4/9** (200); Slindon.

IV/4/6 (200); Pagham.

IV/4/10 (35); Tangmere (includes churchwardens' accounts, 1632).

IV/4/11 (200); West Tarring.

IV/4/12 (20); Chichester (the Headacre).

IV/4/13 (1); Chichester (the Vintry).

IV/4/14 (15); Horsham (the Bishoprick).

IV/4/15 (350); papers relating to the whole deanery, including visitation papers and letters.

IV/4/16 (250); unidentified papers.

Ep.IV/5 DETECTION BOOK AND LIBER CLERI, 1581–1591
See notes to Ep.I/15 (pp. 20, 21) and I/18 (p. 26).

IV/5/1 45 ff.; liber cleri and detection causes, Apr. 1581–May 1591.

Ep.IV/6 CHURCHWARDENS' PRESENTMENTS, 1602–1811
(86); presentments and ministers' articles of enquiry for some of these parishes for 1850, 1853 and 1868 are in Ep.I/22/1 and I/22A/2. See notes to Ep.I/22 (p. 42).

IV/6/1 South Bersted, 1662, 1668(2), 1675, 1682, 1685, 1799.

IV/6/2 Chichester All Saints, 1662, 1664(2), 1665, 1682, 1685, 1710, 1797.

IV/6/3 Durrington, 1696, 1797; see also Ep.IV/7/3 for presentments for 1684, 1685, 1687, and 1692 written on the same sheets as the transcripts.

IV/6/4 Heene, 1662, 1663, 1664(3), 1665(2), 1667(3); see also Ep.IV/7/4 for a presentment for 1685 written on the same sheet as the transcripts.

IV/6/5 East Lavant, with West Lavant, 1662, 1663, 1667, 1668(2), 1673(2), 1680, 1682, 1685, 1797.

IV/6/6 Pagham, 1662, 1664, 1665, 1668, 1673, 1684, 1685, 1687.

IV/6/7 Patching, 1662, 1668, 1673, 1674, 1797.

IV/6/8   Plaistow, 1667.

IV/6/9   Slindon, 1663, 1664, 1665, 1682, 1683, 1685, 1797, 1811.

IV/6/10   Tangmere, 1662, 1663(2), 1664, 1665, 1675, 1682, 1683, 1685, 1797.

IV/6/11   West Tarring, 1602, 1662, 1663(2), 1664(3), 1665, 1667(3), 1674(2), 1685, 1797, 1811.

Ep.IV/7   PARISH REGISTER TRANSCRIPTS, 1610–1912

See notes to Ep.I/24 (p. 45). A list of transcripts, giving the years represented for each parish, is given as an Appendix to this book.

Ep.IV/8   CHURCH TERRIERS, 1615–1665

IV/8/1–2   South Bersted, 1617 and 1625.

IV/8/3–4   Chichester All Saints, 1626/7 and 1635, the latter endorsed
with note of production in an Exchequer suit, Bartholomew Middleton *v.*
John Quantock.

IV/8/5   Durrington, 1635/6.

IV/8/6   Heene, 1635/6.

IV/8/7–10   East Lavant, 1615, 1633, 1635 and 1663.

IV/8/11–13   Pagham, 1626 and 1635 (with later copy).

IV/8/14–16   Patching, 1615, 1632 and 1635.

IV/8/17–19   Slindon, 1632, 1635 and 1665.

IV/8/20–23   Tangmere, 1615, 1626, 1633 and 1635.

IV/8/24–27   Tarring, 1615, 1626, 1636 and 1664.

TESTAMENTS AND WILLS, 1516–1858

See notes to probate papers in Ep.I (p. 47). Wills and administrations for
the Peculiar, 1520–1648, are indexed in *British Record Society*, vol. **64**.
The original testaments and wills, 1580–1858, are STA II.[1] Some of the
earlier volumes contain documents relating to the Deanery of South
Malling, and during vacancies of the see of Chichester, consistory wills are
registered here.

---

[1] For explanation of the ST series, see p. 47.

STA I/1A Oct. 1516–June 1541.

STA I/1B and **3** (bound together) Chichester archdeaconry, Apr. 1553 and Oct. 1568–Mar. 1569/70; Deanery of Pagham and Tarring, May 1561–Dec. 1563.

STA I/A June 1560–Oct. 1567, and liber cleri of the diocese for episcopal visitation, May–July 1553.

STA I/2 Wills and administration acts for Deanery of South Malling, Oct. 1560–Feb. 1567/8.

STA I/10 Sep. 1622–Apr. 1642 and May, June 1648.

STA I/11 Nov. 1678–June 1724 (including Chichester archdeaconry, 1685, 1696, 1709, 1722, 1724).

STA I/12 May 1725–Sep. 1786 (including Chichester archdeaconry, 1754).

STA I/13 Jan. 1787–Sep. 1820 (including Chichester archdeaconry, 1787, 1798).

STA I/14 June 1821–Dec. 1846 (including Chichester archdeaconry, 1824, 1836, 1842); May 1849–June 1854.

STA I/15 Jan. 1856–Jan. 1858.

STA I/9A Oct. 1614–May 1615.

STA I/4 and **5** (bound together) [1568]–Sep. 1572 (includes Deanery of South Malling); July 1576–Feb. 1578/9; act book of the Deanery of Pagham and Tarring (instance and detection causes, liber cleri, probate and administration acts and marriage licences), July 1576–Mar. 1578/9; copies of administration bonds, July–Oct. 1576.

STA I/5A Copy of part of STA I/5.

STA I/6 Mar. 1578/9–June 1592.

STA I/7 Dec. 1592–Dec. 1622; P.C.C. wills, May 1616.

STA I/9 P.C.C. wills, Jan. 1615/16–Oct. 1622.

STA I/8 P.C.C. wills, Nov. 1622–May 1639, and 1657–1670 (very confused).

PROBATE DIARIES, 1568–1858

The Probate Diaries are as follows (only vols. B–F have been indexed in *British Record Society*, vol. 64):

STA III/C Instance and detection causes, depositions, administration acts, caveats and sentences, Dec. 1568–Feb. 1575/6.

STA III/D   Probate and administration acts, Mar. 1578/9–Nov. 1592.

STA III/B   Probate, administration and account acts, and marriage licences, Dec. 1592–Nov. 1614.

STA III/E   As STA III/B, Mar. 1613/4–June 1639.

STA III/F   As STA III/B, July 1639–Mar. 1652/3, and Sep. 1660–July 1670.

STA III/G   As STA III/B, Feb. 1689/90–May 1803.

STA III/H   As STA III/B, June 1803–Jan. 1858; marriage licences, Apr. 1858–Sep. 1907.

There is also the following:

STA VIII/13[1]   Late 19th cent. calendar of administrations, giving name, parish and date: Dean of Chichester's Peculiar, 1781–1857, and Deanery of Pagham and Tarring, 1805–1857.

Ep.IV/9   ADMINISTRATION BONDS, 1694–1857

(671); bonds from 1579–1689 are in STA V. See notes to Ep.I/32 (p. 52).

Year	No.	Year	No.	Year	No.	Year	No.
1694	7	1734	11	1769	7	1807	6
1695	9	1735	6	1770	5	1808	1
1696	15	1736	7	1771	8	1809	3
1697	7	1737	5	1772	7	1811	2
1698	2	1738	11	1773	4	1812	1
1699	5	1739	6	1775	6	1813	1
1700	3	1740	7	1776	4	1815	2
1701	5	1741	2	1777	5	1819	1
1702	6	1742	11	1778	4	1820	1
1703	5	1743	16	1780	3	1822	3
1704	2	1744	10	1781	7	1824	2
1710	1	1745	2	1782	2	1825	2
1711	6	1746	3	1783	3	1828	3
1712	8	1747	1	1784	4	1834	2
1713	2	1748	9	1785	4	1835	5
1714	10	1749	1	1786	4	1836	2
1715	6	1750	5	1787	6	1837	2
1716	6	1751	7	1788	9	1838	1
1717	7	1752	4	1789	3	1840	5
1718	6	1753	3	1790	8	1841	1
1719	6	1754	9	1791	4	1842	4
1721	13	1755	7	1792	1	1843	1
1722	10	1756	6	1793	7	1844	1
1723	2	1757	4	1794	1	1845	1
1724	18	1758	3	1795	7	1846	2
1725	6	1759	9	1796	7	1849	2
1726	9	1760	5	1797	2	1850	1
1727	7	1761	4	1798	7	1851	1
1728	1	1762	3	1799	7	1852	2
1729	13	1763	6	1800	8	1853	3
1730	10	1764	8	1801	1	1854	1
1731	15	1765	2	1802	2	1855	1
1732	5	1766	6	1803	1	1856	2
1733	5	1767	4	1805	1	1857	3

[1] The series of indexes was originally numbered 1–14 and the references STC VIII, STD VIII or STA VIII added later according to the volumes to which they referred. Consequently the series runs: STC VIII/1–12, STA VIII/13 and STD VIII/14.

Ep.IV/10 ADMINISTRATORS' ACCOUNTS, 1610–1643

The probate accounts in STA VII have been transferred to this group to make the series complete according to the contemporary indexes which accompany each bundle. See notes to Ep.I/32 (p. 52) and p. 47.

IV/10/1 (64); Sep. 1610–Mar. 1630/1.

IV/10/2 (36); May 1631–May 1643.

IV/10/3 *c.*1597. Lease for 8 years from previous Michaelmas at total annual rent of £26, from Robert Harrison of Chichester St. Bartholomew, gent., and Elizabeth his wife, and Katherine Smallpage of Chichester, widow, to William Oliffe *alias* Mylles of Chichester St. Martin and Philip Phesie of Chichester St. Andrew.

Gallowes Heath (60a.), land "wherein a conditt now standeth" (18a.), two little crofts called the Hartes (3a.), one field called the Merifield (20a.), and other closes called Jaques Lands (20a.), in occupation of William Oliffe and Philip Phesie, parcel of Broyle Farm or Grange, near the City of Chichester.

Ep.IV/11 OFFICE ACCOUNT BOOK, 1718-1735

IV/11/1 10 ff.; fees, Lady Day 1718–Mar. 1734/5, includes *sede vacante* accounts; later accounts are in Ep.III/12/3–5.

Ep.IV/12 CHURCHWARDENS' SUBSCRIPTION BOOK, 1835–1846

See notes to Ep.I/38 (p. 55).

IV/12/1 Includes Chichester archdeaconry and the Dean of Chichester's Peculiar for each year.
ff.1–7, 1835; ff.8–14, 1836; ff.14*v.*–20, 1837; ff.20*v.*–26, 1838; ff.27–32, 1839; ff.33–40, 1840; ff.40*v.*–46, 1841; ff.47–53, 1842; ff.53*v.*–58, 1843; ff.59–66, 1844; ff.66*v.*–73, 1845; ff.74–80, 1846.

Ep.IV/13 FACULTY PAPERS, 1783–1855

See Ep.I/88/3 and notes to Ep.I/40 (p. 57).

IV/13/1 (4); Chichester All Saints, 1783.

IV/13/2 (3); South Bersted, 1788.

IV/13/3 (4); South Bersted, 1855.

Ep.IV/14 CHURCH BUILDING PAPERS, 1819–1828

See notes to Ep.I/41 (p. 59).

IV/14/1 (30); South Bersted, 1827.

IV/14/2 (2); Patching with Tarring, 1819–20.

IV/14/3 (30); Tangmere, 1819–28.

THE EXEMPT DEANERY OF SOUTH MALLING

Ep.V/1 MARRIAGE LICENCE REGISTERS, 1620–1732

These volumes contain other entries besides marriage licences; marriages entered in these registers have been calendared in Sussex Record Society, vol. 6. See notes to Ep.I/8 (p. 13). A typescript calendar of V/1/5 is available in the Diocesan Record Office (Ep.I/88/7).

V/1/1 97 ff.; marriage licences and probate and administration acts. ff.1–76, Apr. 1620–June 1646; ff.76–87, Dec. 1661–Mar. 1669/70; ff.88–89, citations, Dec. 1619–1624; ff.1a–8a, index of testators.

V/1/2 44 ff.; marriage licences and probate and administration acts. ff.1–39, Apr. 1679—Apr. 1682; ff.42–44, index of testators.

V/1/3 86 pp.; marriage licences and probate and administration acts. pp.1–82, Apr. 1682–Apr. 1688; pp.83–86, index of testators.

V/1/4 90 ff.; ff.1–19, marriage licences and probate and administration acts, Apr. 1688–Apr. 1692; ff.19–80, probate and administration acts, Apr. 1692–Mar. 1710/11; ff.81–90, index of testators.

V/1/5 159 pp.; pp.i–iv, index of surnames (male) appearing in this volume; pp.1–62, marriage licences, Oct. 1692–Sept. 1721; pp.153–131, depositions Mar. 1686/7–Feb. 1688/9.

V/1/6 142 ff.; marriage licences (names and parishes only). ff.1–17, Feb. 1692/3–Dec. 1732.

Ep.V/2 MARRIAGE LICENCE AFFIDAVITS, 1862–1881

(110); marriages have been calendared in Sussex Record Society, vols. 6 (1620–1732) and 25 and 26 (1772–1837), but the original documents have not reached the Diocesan Record Office. See notes to Ep.I/9 (p. 14).

1862	6	1867	4	1872	5	1877	4
1863	7	1868	5	1873	4	1878	1
1864	6	1869	10	1874	4	1879	3
1865	9	1870	6	1875	6	1880	3
1866	10	1871	7	1876	8	1881	2

Ep.V/3   ACT BOOKS, 1613-1865

Extracts from these volumes appear in *Sussex Archaeological Collections*, vol. 50, pp.41–46.

V/3/1   90 ff.; [1,2], June 1613–July 1624, bound in part of an illuminated medieval service book.

V/3/2   43 ff.; [1,2], Mar. 1624/5–June 1627, bound in part of a lease, 1612, between William Pitman and Abraham Campion of property in par. St. Olave, Southwark.

V/3/3   161 ff.; [2], Nov. 1624–Nov. 1630.

V/3/4   48 ff.; [1], June 1627–June 1632.

V/3/5   41 ff.; [1,2], Jan. 1672/3–Dec. 1675, bound in part of a contemporary conveyance of property in par. St. Mary Abchurch, London.

V/3/6   47 ff.; [1,2], Dec. 1675–Nov. 1678.

V/3/7   27 ff., bound in part of a contemporary deed relating to property in Falmer, and printed administration forms.
ff.1–24[1,2], Dec. 1678–Feb. 1681/2; ff.24v.–27, memoranda and libri cleri, Apr. 1718.

V/3/8   19 ff.; [1,2], Nov. 1682–July 1684, bound in part of a contemporary deed between Humfrey Row and Samuel Young, relating to property in Blatchington.

V/3/9   32 ff.; ff.1–28[1,2], June 1682–Jan. 1683/4; ff.32–29, register of presentments, Easter 1685.

V/3/10   122 ff.; ff.1–68 [1,2], Nov. 1683–July 1687; ff.84–98[1,2], Oct. 1694–Sep. 1696; ff.99–115[1,2], Sep. 1715–Nov. 1721.

V/3/11   113 ff.; ff.1–109[1,2], Jan. 1687/8–Feb. 1696/7; ff.113–110, memoranda, May 1688–Sep. 1695.

V/3/12   28 ff.; f.1, a list of South Malling records, n.d.; ff.4–26[1,2], Aug. 1697–Mar. 1699/1700.

V/3/13   34 ff.; ff.1–15[1,2], Mar. 1696/7–Sep. 1699; ff.33–16, libri cleri (churchwardens only), 1698–1708.

---

[1] Instance causes.

[2] Detection causes.

V/3/14   36 ff.; [1,2], Apr. 1700–Aug. 1702.

V/3/15   126 ff.; f.i, memoranda, July 1705; f.ii, list of the inhabitants of Chiltington hamlet, 1708; ff.1–120[1,2], Nov. 1702–Nov. 1713; f.124, memoranda, Sep. 1706–July 1712; ff.123v.–120v., the three articles (written twice) and three subscriptions to them and to the oath of Allegiance, 1713–1716.

V/3/16   136 pp.; see V/4/2 for the original papers of some acts entered here.

pp.1–74, appointment of surrogates, a faculty and consecrations, mortgages and other acts, June 1822–Apr. 1865; pp.135–136, list of contents.

Ep.V/4   ACTS OF COURT, 1724–1865

V/4/1   (26); 1724–1776.   **V/4/2**   (20); 1803–1865.

Ep.V/5   DEPOSITION BOOK, 1604–1621

A list of witnesses is printed in *Sussex Archaeological Collections*, vol. 56, pp.1–15. See notes to Ep.I/15 (p. 20). A typescript calendar of this volume is available in the Diocesan Record Office (Ep.I/88/7).

V/5/1   78 ff.; depositions, 1604–Apr. 1621.

Ep.V/6   EXCOMMUNICATION BOOK, 1673–1680

V/6/1   6 ff.; excommunications, July 1673–Apr. 1680. See notes to Ep.I/15.

Ep.V/7   MISCELLANEOUS COURT PAPERS, 1694–1720

V/7/1   10 docs. relating chiefly to wills, marriage licences and presentments.

Ep.V/8   LIBRI CLERI, 1606–1845

The meeting house licences are printed in *Sussex Archaeological Collections*, vol. 54, pp.273–274. See notes to Ep.I/18 (p. 26).

V/8/1   106 pp., bound in part of a contemporary deed.

pp.1–5, June 1606; pp.9–11, June 1608; pp. 12–14, June 1609; pp.15–16, May 1610; pp.17–21, Apr. 1611; pp.24–25, July 1612; pp.26–28, May

---

[1] Instance causes.

[2] Detection causes.

1613; pp.29–32, June 1614; pp.33–35, Apr. 1615; pp.39–42, Apr. 1616; pp.42–44, May 1617; pp.45–47, May 1618; pp.47–49, Apr. 1619; pp. 49–50, May 1620; pp.51–52, May 1621; pp.53–54, June 1622; pp.55–56, May 1623; pp.57–58, Apr. 1624; pp.59–61, June 1625; pp.61–64, May 1626; pp. 65–67, Apr. 1627; pp.68–70, May 1628; pp.71–74, Apr. 1629; pp.74–75, May 1630; pp.79–83, May 1630; pp.84–88, June 1631; pp.89–90, May 1633; pp. 90–91, May 1634; pp.92–95, July 1635; pp.96–97, May 1636; pp.97–98, May 1637; pp.99–100, May 1638; pp.100–101, June 1639; pp. 101–102, May 1640.

V/8/2 12 ff., bound in part of a contemporary deed relating to land in Tilgate and Worth.

ff.1–2, May 1673; ff.3–4, Apr. 1674; f.5, June 1675; f.6, Apr. 1676; f.7, Apr. 1677; ff.8–9, Apr. 1678; ff.9v.–10, May 1679; ff.10v.–11, Apr. 1680; ff.11v.–12, Apr. 1681.

V/8/3 22 ff.

ff.1–2, Apr. 1682; ff.3–5, Apr. 1683; ff.6–8, Apr. 1684; ff.9–10, June 1685; ff.11–13, Apr. 1686; ff.13v.–15, Apr. 1687; ff.15v.–17, May 1688; ff.17v.–19, May 1689; ff.19v.–21, May 1690; ff.22–23, May 1691; ff.24–25, Oct. 1692; ff.26–27, May 1693; ff.28–29, Apr. 1694.

V/8/4 68 ff.

ff.1–3, July 1695; ff.4–5, June 1696; ff.6–7, May 1697; ff.8–9, May 1698; ff.10–11, May 1699; ff.12–13, May 1700; ff.13v.–14, May 1701; ff.15–16, May 1702; ff.17–18, May 1703; ff.19–20, May 1704; ff.21–22, May 1705; ff.23–24, May 1706; ff.25–26, May 1707; ff.27–28, May 1708; ff.29–30, May 1709; ff.30v.–31, June 1710; ff.32–33, June 1711; ff.34–35, May 1712; ff. 35v.–38, June 1713; ff.39–40, Sep. 1714; ff.41–42, Sep. 1715; ff.42v.–43, June 1716; ff.68–44v., register of presentments, faculties and dissenters' meeting houses, Sep. 1685–1717.

V/8/5 94 ff.

ff.1–2, July 1717; ff.3–4, Apr. 1718; ff.4–5, May 1719; f.5, May 1720; f.6, Apr. 1721; f.7, Apr. 1722; f.8, May 1723; f.9, May 1724; f.10, July 1725; f.11, June 1726; f.12, May 1727; f.13, June 1728; f.14, May 1729; f.15, May 1730; f.16, June 1731; ff.17–18, May 1732; f.93, register of presentments, 1717.

V/8/6 54 loose ff.

f.1, June 1733; f.3, June 1734; f.5, May 1735; f.6, June 1736; f.8v., June 1737; f.10, May 1738; f.12, June 1739; f.14, June 1740; f.16, June 1741; f.18, June 1742; f.20, June 1743; f.22, June 1744; f.24, June 1745; f.26, June 1746; f.28, June 1747; f.30, June 1748; f.32, June 1749; f.34, June 1750; f.36, n.d. [1751?]; f.38, July 1752; f.40, July 1753; f.42, Oct. 1754; f.44, July 1755; f.46, June 1756; f.48, June 1757; f.49, July 1758; f.51, Sep. 1759; f.53, July 1760.

V/8/7 37 ff.

ff.1–2, Deaneries of Pagham and Tarring and of South Malling, July 1761; f.3, July 1762; f.4, July 1763; f.5, Aug. 1764; f.6, July 1765; f.7, July 1766; f.8, Oct. 1767; f.9, July 1768; f.10, Aug. 1769; f.11, July 1770; f.13, Aug. 1772; f.14, July 1773; f.15, July 1774; f.16, July 1775; f.17, July

1776; f.18, May 1777; f.19, June 1778; f.20, June 1779; f.21, June 1780; f.22, June 1781; f.23, May 1782; f.24, June 1783; f.25, May 1784; f.26, June 1785; f.27, June 1786; f.27*v*., July 1787; f.28, June 1788; f.28*v*., June 1789; f.29, Aug. 1790; f.30, July 1792; f.30*v*., Deanery of Pagham and Tarring, July 1792; f.31, June 1793; f.31*v*., June 1794; f.32, June 1795; f.32*v*., June 1796; f.33, June 1797; f.33*v*., June 1798; f.34, July 1799; f.34*v*., July 1800; f.35, Aug. 1801; f.35*v*., July 1802; f.36, July 1803; f.36*v*., July 1804; f.37, July 1805; f.37*v*., July 1806.

V/8/8 45 ff.

f.1, July 1807; f.1*v*., July 1808; f.2, July 1809; f.2*v*., July 1810; f.3, Deanery of Pagham and Tarring, July 1810; f.3*v*., July 1811; f.4, July 1812; f.4*v*., July 1813; f.5, July 1814; f.5*v*., July 1815; f.6, July 1816; f.6*v*., July 1817; f.7, July 1818; f.7*v*., July 1819; f.8, July 1820; f.8*v*., July 1821; f.9, July 1822; f.9*v*., July 1823; f.10, July 1824; f.10*v*., July 1825; f.11, July 1826; f.11*v*., Aug. 1827; f.12, Aug. 1828; f.12*v*., July 1829; f.13, June 1830; f.13*v*., July 1831; f.14, Aug. 1832; f.14*v*., Deanery of Pagham and Tarring, Aug. 1832; f.15, June 1833; f.15*v*., July 1834; f.16, July 1835; f.16*v*., May 1836; f.17, June 1837; f.17*v*., July 1838; f.18, July 1839; f.18*v*., June 1840; f.19, Sep. 1841; f.19*v*., July 1842; f.20, July 1843; f.20*v*., Sep. 1844; f.21, Aug. 1845.

V/8/9 (18); the original lists of clergy and churchwardens from which V/8/8 was compiled, 1832–1845, including the visitation of the Deanery of Pagham and Tarring, 1832.

Ep.V/9 REGISTER OF PRESENTMENTS, 1682–1719
See notes to Ep.I/23 (p. 44).

V/9/1 19 ff. ff.1–14, May 1682–Feb. 1684/5; ff.18–16, May–Sep. 1719.

Ep.V/10 PARISH REGISTER TRANSCRIPTS, 1662–1908
See notes to Ep.I/24 (p. 45). A list of the transcripts, giving the years represented for each parish, is given as an Appendix to this book.

Ep.V/11 CAVEAT BOOK, 1684–1734
See notes to Ep.II/23 (p. 117).

V/11/1 48 ff. ff.1–17, caveats, Oct. 1684–Jan. 1733/4; ff.47–36, Ringmer manor courts, Dec. 1680–Aug. 1687; f.48, oaths of allegiance and supremacy (1 Will. and Mary, c.8) and memoranda, Mar. 1689.

Ep.V/12 OFFICE ACCOUNT BOOKS, 1787–1881[1]

V/12/1 85 ff., with several loose accounts attached; office receipts, Dec. 1787–Dec. 1802.

[1] V/12/2–6 are each labelled "Deanry Debt Book".

V/12/1a 94 ff.; office receipts, Jan. 1803–Dec. 1823.

V/12/2 92 pp.; office receipts, Jan. 1824–Dec. 1833.

V/12/3 96 pp.; pp.1–92, office receipts, Jan. 1834–Dec. 1845; pp. 93–95, index of persons.

V/12/4 48 pp.; pp.1–40, office receipts, Jan.1846–Dec. 1851; pp.43–45, index of persons.

V/12/5 48 pp.; pp.1–38, office receipts, Jan. 1852–Mar. 1858; pp.43–45, index of persons.

V/12/6 32 pp.; pp.1–24, office receipts, Apr. 1858–Nov. 1881; pp.30–32, incomplete index of persons.

V/12/7 94 ff.; George Hoper's accounts in ecclesiastical business, Jan. 1804–Dec. 1845.

Ep.V/13   ACCOUNTS, 1833–1874

(20); chiefly accounts and parliamentary returns, all relating to the Chichester archdeaconry, Dean of Chichester's Peculiar and the Deanery of Pagham and Tarring, with no reference to the Deanery of South Malling.

Ep.V/14   MISCELLANEA, 1710–1881

V/14/1 20 ff., "Index of the Books in the Peculiars". f.i, County Court at Lewes, Feb. 1709/10; ff.1–3, shelf list of the Peculiar records, 18th cent.; ff.18–16, County Court at Lewes, continued from f.i.

V/14/2 (1); a list of South Malling records, 19th cent.

V/14/3 (1); copy of a licence to William Edwards to the curacy of the newly-consecrated chapel of St. Mark, Hadlow Down (Buxted parish), July 1836.

V/14/4 (1); expenses at the consecration of Stanmer church and additional burial ground, 1839.

V/14/5 (1); a list of the clergy in the deanery, c.1840.

V/14/6 (3); the appointment of parish clerks for Lewes St. Thomas-at-Cliffe, and Isfield, 1835, and the resignation of the South Malling parish clerk, 1844.

V/14/7 (1); citation against Philadelphia Simmons of Framfield to prove her husband's will, 1852.

V/14/8 (1); mortgage (Henry Kingsmill, rector of Buxted, to the governors of Queen Anne's Bounty), 1850.

V/14/9 (1); deed of covenant by Thomas Oliver Goodchild to resign the perpetual curacy of South Malling, 1832.

V/14/10 (1); instructions for applicants for probate and letters of administration, *post* 1815.

V/14/11 (10); letters, 1877–1881, relating to the abolition of peculiar jurisdiction, and an extract from the Order in Council of 8 Aug. 1845.

V/14/12 (1); list of clergy in the Deaneries of Pagham and Tarring and of South Malling, n.d. [*c*.1802].

Ep.V/15 VISITATION PAPERS, 1832–1845

V/15/1 (10); processes for the annual visitations, 1836–45.

V/15/2 (8); correspondence, accounts and receipts relating to the annual visitations, 1832–1845.

Ep.V/16 CHURCHWARDENS' DECLARATIONS, 1835–1845

(25 docs.)

Ep.V/16A MINISTERS' ARTICLES OF ENQUIRY, 1875

See notes to Ep.I/22A (p. 44).

V/16A/1 1 volume of ministers' returns at the episcopal visitation, 1875, from 14 parishes, including the 13 formerly known as the Deanery of South Malling.

Ep.V/17 DISSENTERS' MEETING HOUSE CERTIFICATES, 1773–1852

(48); original certificates for registration, all but one of which had not been registered in Ep.II/25 (p. 118). These are included in the card index of dissenters' meeting houses in the W.S.R.O.

Ep.V/18 FACULTY PAPERS, 1747–1821

See Ep.I/88/3 and notes to Ep.I/40 (p. 57).

V/18/1 (1); Framfield (1747).

V/18/2 (3); Lindfield (1747).

V/18/3 (1); Midhurst (1753).

V/18/4 (2); Lewes, St. Thomas-at-Cliffe (1753).

V/18/5 (1); Framfield (1760).

V/18/6 (1); Buxted (1762).

V/18/7 (1); Framfield (1778).

V/18/8 (6); Ringmer (1789).

V/18/9 (8); Buxted (1821).

Ep.V/19 LICENCES TO NON-RESIDENT CLERGY, 1838–1845

(21); licences and copies of licences to incumbents to be non-resident. See notes to Ep.I/42 (p. 62).

1838	5	1840	6	1842	2	1845	1
1839	1	1841	4	1843	2		

Ep.V/20 LICENCES TO STIPENDIARY CURATES, 1824–1845

(15); licences and copies of licences to stipendiary curates. See notes to Ep.I/68 (p. 89).

1824	1	1835	2	1840	2	1845	1
1833	2	1839	4	1843	2		

Ep.V/21 CHURCH BUILDING PAPERS, 1812–1835

See notes to Ep.I/41. (p. 59).

V/21/1 (20); Isfield, 1835.

V/21/2 (4); Mayfield, 1812.

Ep.V/22 REGISTRARS' CORRESPONDENCE, 1827–1856

Four bundles of letters (200 docs.) found with Ep.II/35 (p. 128), 1827–1856.

EPISCOPAL ESTATES

Ep.VI/1 CARTULARIES, 13th–16th centuries

Early charters from VI/1/6 volume have been printed by Dugdale, Kemble and Birch. Some originals of the charters which are copied here are still amongst the chapter records (Cap.I/17).

VI/1/1 LIBER A. 46 parchment folios repaired and rebound at the P.R.O. in May 1936. The contemporary title on f.3*v*. is "Liber m[agistri] Will[ielm]i Reed Ep[iscop]i Cicestr[ensis] que[m] scribi fecit p[er] Will-[ielm]um atte Hulle . . ." The early roman foliation runs from ff.i–xxxviii consecutively, but there are traces of an earlier arabic foliation which prove that the present arrangement of folios is not original; more than half the volume is missing. A number of documents in this volume has been translated in Sussex Record Society, vol. 46, pp. 219–229; a short account appears in H.M.C., Var. Coll., I, p. 179.

f.3*v*., title page; f.4, contemporary list of contents; ff.5–13, rights and customs of episcopal manors; ff.14–16, proceedings in royal courts; ff.17–18, manorial inventory; ff.23–38, charters; ff.38*v*.–39, rents and services due from the Earl of Arundel.

VI/1/2 LIBER B. 142 parchment folios repaired and rebound at the P.R.O. in May 1936. This is described on f.12*v*. as "Liber Will[ielm]i Reed Cicestr[ensis] Ep[iscop]i". This volume also has contemporary arabic and later roman foliation, neither of which shows any gaps or misplaced folios. A number of documents has been translated in Sussex Record Society, vol. 46, pp.229–257, and *Sussex Notes and Queries*, vol. 1, p. 233, and vol. 2, p. 45. An account of this volume appears in H.M.C., Var. Coll., I, p. 179.

ff.2 and 4, memoranda, including note of production in a Chancery suit, Butler, Peckham and Peckham *v*. Bishop Carleton, 1681; ff.5–10, early 16th cent. list of contents; ff.11–15, memoranda and contemporary lists of contents; ff.16–68, charters; ff.69–71, terriers and memoranda relating to Arundel; ff.73*v*.–86, charters relating to Chichester; ff.96*v*.–97, letter and deed of the Earl of Arundel; ff.98–100, charters relating to Amberley; ff.101–111, charters relating to Drungewick (Wisborough Green); ff.113–120, homages received by Bishop Robert Rede, 1396–1415; ff.120–125, memoranda; ff.126–136, list of tenants holding by military service; ff.137–140, memoranda.

VI/1/3 LIBER C. 189 folios repaired and rebound at the P.R.O. in December 1933. This volume has only one foliation in addition to the modern one, viz. the contemporary arabic foliation as noted in the descriptions of the previous volumes. The custumals printed in Sussex Record Society, vol. 31, from VI/1/5 were collated with the copies in this volume. Various charters have been translated in Sussex Record Society, vol. 46, pp. 257–274, *Sussex Archaeological Collections*, vol. 68, p. 159, and *Sussex Notes and Queries*, vol. 1, p. 115. There is a short note on the volume in H.M.C., Var. Coll., I, p. 185.

f.2*v*., memoranda; ff.3–48, rentals of episcopal manors; ff.49–52, custumals and charters; ff.53–74, custumals; ff.74*v*.–80, terriers; ff.85–166, rentals; ff.168–188, memoranda.

Liber D. Until Bishop Sherburne's episcopate (1508–1536) Libri D and E formed one volume. At that time the volume was divided so that all provincial constitutions and allied documents were in Liber D and all royal charters and diocesan documents in Liber E. Later, possibly during the Civil War, Liber D was lost and passed into the hands of Elias Ashmole, the antiquary. An account of its discovery in the Bodleian Library (Ashmole 1146) by Mr. W. D. Peckham is in *Sussex Notes and Queries*, vol. 2, p. 105, where it is noted that there is a contemporary list of contents of both volumes, and a kalendar used in Chichester cathedral; this has been partly printed by W. D. Peckham in *Sussex Notes and Queries*, vol. 2, p. 105, and C. R. Cheney, *Handbook of Dates* (1945), p. 73. See Ep.VI/1/7.

VI/1/4 LIBER E. 147 parchment folios repaired and rebound at the P.R.O. in May 1936. References in Sussex Record Society, vol. 46, pp. 275–338, to documents printed from this volume are to the contemporary arabic foliation which runs from f.137 (now f.17) to f.275 (now f.147), with several gaps. Various Chichester cathedral statutes were printed from this volume in F. G. Bennett, R. H. Codrington and C. Deedes, *Statutes and Constitutions of the Cathedral Church of Chichester* (1904), and the will of St. Richard (f.42) in *Sussex Archaeological Collections*, vol. 1, p. 164. A typescript calendar of this volume is available in the Diocesan Record Office (Ep.I/88/1). There is a late 16th cent. copy of this volume in Cap.I/12/1.

ff.4 and 6, memoranda, including note of production in a Chancery suit, Kemp *v.* Manningham, 1749; ff.6*v.*–7, composition between the archbishop of Canterbury and the bishop of London, early 16th cent.; ff.9–16, early 16th cent. list of contents; ff.17–31, royal charters of liberties; f.32*v.*, memoranda; ff.34–72, charters and other documents relating to the diocese; ff.72*v.*–112, appropriations of churches and ordinations of vicarages; ff.113–135, taxation of Pope Nicholas; ff.136–147, memoranda.

VI/1/5 LIBER P. 208 parchment folios repaired and rebound at the P.R.O. in December 1933. This volume has both arabic and roman foliation as well as modern pencil, and they are mostly in agreement. The custumals in Sussex Record Society, vol. 31, were printed from the text in this volume and collated with those in VI/1/3. Charters and similar documents from this volume have been translated in Sussex Record Society, vol. 46, pp.339–358, and two others appear in *Sussex Notes and Queries*, vol. 1, p.47, and vol. 2, p. 123.

ff.1*v.*–4, list of contents and memoranda; ff.11–18, rentals; ff.22*v.*–94, custumals; ff.95–149, rentals and terriers; ff.150–158, parliamentary and other statutes; ff.161–202, charters; ff.202*v.*–207, memoranda.

VI/1/6 LIBER Y. 249 parchment folios repaired and rebound at the P.R.O. in May 1936. The early roman foliation (to which all 19th century writers refer) begins on f.56. This volume, which is the earliest cartulary at Chichester, was used by Mr. W. D. Peckham as the basis for Sussex Record Society, vol. 46, and he gives a full account of it in his introduction to that volume. Another account is in H.M.C., Var. Coll., I, pp. 188–193, where it is referred to as a chapter cartulary. It has sometimes been known as the Muniment Book.

ff.4*v.*–43, early 16th cent. list of contents; ff.44–55, late 16th cent. notes on chapter estates; ff.56*v.*–60, charters (15th cent. copies); ff.62*v.*–71, miscellaneous charters; ff.72–144, charters relating to the diocese; ff.145*v.*–225, charters relating to the chapter; ff.226–232, charters (15th cent. copies); ff.233–249, memoranda.

VI/1/7   9 ff.; photocopy of the two parts of the former Liber D (see note after VI/1/3) which are of particular Sussex interest.

Ep.VI/2   RENTALS, 1552–1894

VI/2/1   46 ff.; Jan. 1551/2, with occasional marginal notes to 1634. Rentals and custumal, bound in part of medieval MS.

f.i, rental of property in Lewes; ff.1–6, Selsey; ff.7–12, Sidlesham; ff.12*v.*–16, Cakeham; ff.16*v.*–19, Aldingbourne; ff.19*v.*–22, Waltham; ff.22*v.*–23, Houghton; ff.23–26, Amberley; ff.26–28, Rackham; ff.28–29, Ferring and Fure; ff.30–31, Billingshurst; ff.31–36, Streatham; ff.36*v.*–39, Preston;[1] ff.39–40, Heathfield; ff.40–41, Bishopstone; ff.41*v.*–45, Bexhill; f.45*v.*, memoranda.

VI/2/2   [*c.*1700–1710] 9 parchment ff. filed at head.

f.1, Cakeham; f.2, Ferring and Fure; ff.2*v.*–4, Streatham; ff.4*v.*–5, Aldingbourne; ff.6–8, Amberley; ff.8*v.*–9, Rackham.

VI/2/3   [*post* 1727]; parchment rental of Sussex estates, sites 1–34, with details of leases.

VI/2/4   [*post* 1732]; parchment rental of Sussex estates, sites 35–50, with details of leases.

VI/2/5   Copy (parchment) of VI/2/4.

VI/2/6   [*post* 1743, with additions of 1777]; parchment rental of Sussex estates, sites 1–51, with details of leases.

VI/2/7   Parchment copy of VI/2/6, with additions to 1753; more legible, but with mistake in copying repeated in VI/2/8; site 34 is Aldingbourne Mill, and Amberley corn rents should be numbered 3, 4.

VI/2/8   1754 and 1798; 2 rentals of Sussex estates, sites 1–34.

VI/2/9   1754; parchment rental of Sussex estates, sites 1–50, with details of leases.

VI/2/10   90 ff.

f.1*v.*, memoranda; ff.2–11, Sussex rental, sites 1–50, 1754–6; ff.12*v.*–13, Bexhill and Cowfold pensions, 1754–6; ff.14–16, corn rents, 1754–6; ff.17–

---

[1] Printed (from another copy) in *Brighton and Hove Archaeologist*, vol. I (1914), p. 29.

19, quitrents, 1754–6; ff.20–31, episcopal tenths, deaneries of Boxgrove and Midhurst, 1754–6; ff.32–38, London rental, sites 1–29, 1754–8; ff. 39–48, Sussex rental, sites 1–34, 1757; ff.71v.–74, dates of Sussex leases for lives, sites 2–52, 1754–99; ff.75–78, names of lives in Sussex leases, sites 1–54, 1790–9; f.79, Sussex leases for years, sites 1–50, 1773–1803; f.82, names of lives in Sussex leases, sites 2–9, 1783; f.84v., Sussex leases for years, 1773–84; f.85, details of London leases for lives, sites 1–25, *post* 1785; f.86, details of London leases for years, sites 5–30, *post* 1783, with additions to 1794; f.87v., Sussex leases for 21 years, sites 1–50, 1733–84; ff.88–89, names of lives in Sussex leases, sites 2–49, n.d.; f.89v., names of lives in London leases, sites 1–25, n.d.; f.90, London leases for 21 years, sites 5–30, 1719–96.

VI/2/11   90 ff.; some letters and papers loosely inserted.

ff.1–54, details of fines and rents on Sussex leases, sites 1–54, 1754–1817; ff.54–82, details of fines and rents on London leases, sites 1–30, 1754–1818; ff.89–86, Bishop Buckner's notes on estates sold for land tax redemption, and repairs to "Chichester House" [the Bishop's Palace], 1799–1806.

VI/2/12   148 pp.

pp.i–iv, list of contents; pp.1–56, Sussex rental, with details of leases, sites 1–57, 1769–1838; pp.56a–56b, leases of land allotted to the bishop as lord of the manor of Amberley by the Inclosure Commissioners, 1828; p.62, reserved rents, Sussex sites 1–57; p. 63, land tax redeemed; pp. 66–79, dignities, prebends and Sussex livings in the bishop's gift; p. 81, Sussex livings in Crown gift; pp. 148–147, list of contents; pp. 146–110, London rental, with details of leases, sites 1–36, 1744–1837.

VI/2/13   130 ff.

ff.i–x, abstracts of Sussex and London leases, notes of fines, and memoranda, July 1825–June 1853; ff.xi–xv, index of Sussex lessees and estates; f.xvi, Sussex rental; ff.xviiiv.–36, details of Sussex leases subsisting *c.*1838; ff.39v.–57, details of London leases subsisting *c.*1838; ff.58–72, copy letters relating to London leases, 1842–1854; ff.87v.–93, accounts; f.104, list of contents; ff.104v.–109, index of lessees and premises, London and Sussex.

VI/2/14   268 pp.; this volume gives valuable information about 19th century lessees, rents, fines and *cestui qui vies*, and the eventual disposition of each site at the end of the century.

pp.iii–iv, memoranda; pp.vi–viii, index; pp.3–138, sites 1–61, from 1800; pp.141–179, site 5 as divided in 1842.

VI/2/15   Not allocated.

VI/2/16   16 ff.

ff.1–4, tenths due Christmas 1844; f.5, tenths due Christmas 1845; ff.5–6, spiritual rents, redeemed land tax on farms and benefices, corn rents and rents on leases due Lady Day 1845; ff.7–14, rents on leases, redeemed land tax on benefices and farms, corn rents and quit rents on copyholds due Mich. 1845.

VI/2/17   15 ff.

ff.1–4, tenths due Christmas 1845; ff.5–6, spiritual rents, redeemed land tax on farms and benefices and corn rents due Lady Day 1846; ff.6v.–7, redeemed land tax on farms and benefices due Mich. 1846; f.8, rents on leases due Lady Day 1846; ff.8v.–14, rents on leases, corn rents and quit rents on copyholds due Mich. 1846.

VI/2/18   14 ff.

ff.1–3, tenths due Christmas 1847; ff.4–5, spiritual rents, redeemed land tax on farms and benefices and corn rents due Lady Day 1848; ff.5v.–6, redeemed land tax on farms and benefices due Mich. 1848; f.7, rents on leases due Lady Day 1848; ff.7v.–12, rents on leases, spiritual rents, corn rents and quit rents on copyholds due Mich. 1848.

VI/2/19   56 ff.

ff.1–8, tenths, 1853–1858; ff.9–21, synodals and procurations due at episcopal visitations, 1856 and 1859; ff.21v.–22, pensions, 1854–1865; ff.23v.–25, redeemed land tax on benefices, 1854–1863; ff.25v.–26, redeemed land tax on farms, 1854–1863; ff.27–35, corn rents, 1854–1864; ff.36v.–37, redeemed land tax on farms, 1854–1859; ff.37v.–39, reserved rents, 1854–1865; ff.39v.–52, leasehold rents, 1854–1859; ff.52v.–54, quit rents on copyholds, 1854–1863.

VI/2/20   92 ff.; many papers loosely inserted.

ff.1–5, tenths, 1864–1866; ff.7–19, synodals and procurations due at episcopal visitation 1865; ff.20–21, pensions, 1864–1866; ff.21v.–30, redeemed land tax on benefices, 1864–1866; ff.30v.–33, redeemed land tax on farms, 1864–1866; ff.33v.–39, corn rents, 1864–1867; ff.39v.–45, reserved rents, 1864–1866; ff.45v.–55, leasehold rents, 1864–1866; ff.55v.–56, quit rents on copyholds, 1864–1866.

VI/2/21   192 pp.; draft book, with most entries crossed out, but giving details of all proceedings leading to enfranchisement of each property, from 1852.

pp.i–xii, index of persons; pp.1–85, enfranchisement of copyholds, mostly episcopal; pp.180–86, enfranchisement of episcopal and capitular copyholds.

VI/2/22   192 pp.; draft book (as VI/2/21), 1871–1894.

pp.i–xii, index of persons; pp.1–179, enfranchisement of copyholds on Ecclesiastical Commissioners' estates (formerly episcopal and capitular).

Ep.VI/3   LAND TAX REDEMPTION, 1798–1843

VI/3/1   (70); receipts, letters, certificates of redemption and other papers, 1798–1815. Some relate to episcopal offices as well as to estates.

VI/3/2   60 ff.; accounts for land tax on benefices, with names of incumbents, 1834–1843 (ff.1–20 only).

Ep.VI/4 ACCOUNT BOOKS, 1521–1871

These accounts supplement the Court account books (Ep.I/43).

VI/4/1 100 ff. bound in leather-covered boards, the interiors covered with part of a medieval MS.; a number of folios has been cut out. f.2, "Ric[ard]us Boughton, primo die Julij 1646"; ff.5–42, accounts, 1521–1527; ff.43–44, procurations, episcopal visitation, 1576; ff.45–50, accounts, 1528–1529; ff.51–56, survey of Streatham manor, Jan. 1552/3; ff.70–74, 1534–1535; ff.75–86, accounts, 1572–1575; ff.87–91, episcopal rental, 1555; f.94, two episcopal mandates for clerical subsidy, 1577; ff.98v.–99, two fee lists (early and late 16th cent.) and copy of Exchequer proceedings, 1351.

VI/4/2 7 ff.; receipts, 1635–1636.

VI/4/2a 8 ff.; receipts, 1635–1637.

VI/4/3 28 ff.; ff.1–14, receiver's accounts, 1636–1638; ff.28–21, household accounts, 1636–1638.

VI/4/4 7 ff.; receipts, 1638.

VI/4/5–17 John Dear's accounts, Nov. 1733, Aug. 1734, Dec. 1734, Aug. 1735, Nov. 1735, Aug. 1736, Sep. 1737, Apr. 1738, Sep. 1738, Jan. 1738/9, Sep. 1739, Jan. 1739/40, Dec. 1740.

VI/4/18 40 ff.; apparitors' and visitation accounts, July 1833–Mar. 1837, including the peculiars.

VI/4/19 60 ff.; copyhold fines, Sep. 1833–Sep. 1838 (ff.1–6 only).

VI/4/20 152 ff.; ff.1–8, notes on probate fees and other revenue; f.9, memoranda; ff.10–151, receiver's accounts, Sep. 1836–Sep. 1858; f.152, J. B. Freeland's account as acting registrar in the archdeaconry, Mar. 1837–Sep. 1839.

VI/4/21 83 ff.; receiver's accounts, Sep. 1840–Mar. 1846 (ff.1–34 only).

VI/4/22 170 ff.; receiver's accounts, Dec. 1858–Dec. 1871 (ff.1–83 only). Accounts for 1869 and 1871 are loose in this volume.

Ep.VI/5 ORIGINAL ACCOUNTS, 1724–1891

(500); these are mainly the loose papers from which the relevant volumes in Ep.VI/4 were compiled (1724–1860), many have suffered badly from damp. They also include procurations and tenths (1731–1797), chancellors' accounts (1754–1806), annual accounts for work done on the bishop's palace (1765–1796), archdeacons' accounts (1804–1840), lists of clergy cited to attend visitations (1813–1818) and Bishopstone tithe accounts (1854–1891).

Ep.VI/6 ROUGH ACCOUNT BOOKS, 1838–1900

These include payments and receipts for the Diocesan Registry and Chapter Clerk's Office.

VI/6/1 186 pp.; 1838–1856.

VI/6/2 124 ff.; 1862–1867.

VI/6/3 140 ff.; 1886–1889.

VI/6/4 184 ff.; 1892–1895.

VI/6/5 184 ff.; 1895–1898.

VI/6/6 184 ff.; 1898–1900.

Ep.VI/7 DAYBOOKS, 1833–1861

These include payments and receipts for the Diocesan Registry and Chapter Clerk's Office.

VI/7/1 262 pp.; Aug. 1833–Mar. 1838.

VI/7/2 258 pp.; Apr. 1838–Aug. 1840.

VI/7/3 358 pp.; Aug. 1840–Dec. 1843.

VI/7/4 432 pp.; Oct. 1843–Apr. 1846.

VI/7/5 452 pp.; Apr. 1846–Dec. 1849.

VI/7/6 458 pp.; Jan. 1850–1853 (pp.1–295 only).

VI/7/7 524 pp.; Jan. 1840–Dec. 1845 (not a duplicate).

VI/7/8 548 pp.; Dec. 1845–Jan. 1851 (not a duplicate).

VI/7/9 550 pp.; Probate Registry Day Book, Jan. 1858–Mar. **1861** (pp. 1–283 only).

Ep.VI/8 LEDGERS, 1832–1853

These include the business in the Diocesan Registry and Chapter Clerk's Office.

VI/8/1 514 pp.; Jan. 1832–Oct. 1842 (indexed).

VI/8/2 632 pp.; Sep. 1842–Mar. 1851 (indexed).

VI/8/3 622 pp.; Oct. 1849–Mar. 1853 (pp. 1–142 only; indexed).

Ep.VI/9 CASH BOOKS, 1836–1854

These include financial transactions in the Diocesan Registry and Chapter Clerk's Office.

VI/9/1 264 pp.; June 1836–Mar. 1841.

VI/9/2 260 pp.; Mar. 1841–Feb. 1847.

VI/9/3 358 pp.; Feb. 1847–Oct. 1852.

VI/9/4 226 ff.; Aug. 1852–Sep. 1854.

Ep.VI/10 MISCELLANEOUS ACCOUNT BOOKS, 1833–1864

These volumes are the residue from the previous groups of accounts; they often include chapter business.

VI/10/1 14 ff.; "L.D." [? Lady Day] accounts, 1833.

VI/10/2 36 ff.; tenths and procurations, July 1837–July 1840.

VI/10/3 180 ff.; cash book, June 1836–Jan. 1844.

VI/10/4 85 ff.; bank book, 1852–1858.

VI/10/5 87 ff.; bank book, 1856–1864.

Ep.VI/11 PIE POWDER COURT BOOK AND PAPERS, 1582–1801

The right to hold a fair between 5 and 13 October annually on Sloe Fair Field in Chichester was first granted to the bishop by Henry I, *c.*1107–8.[1] During that period the jurisdiction of the mayor and corporation of Chichester was completely in abeyance and during the 18th century this led to frequent disputes between the bishop and corporation. In 1807 the bishop surrendered his rights to the corporation.

VI/11/1 30 ff.; "Curia Pavilionis Cicestr[ensis] Ep[iscop]i." The order is very confused.
ff.1–2, copy of court rolls, 1582 and 1686; ff.3–5, court rolls, 1677 and 1683; ff.6–7, action for assault at the fair, 1702; ff.8–9, courts, 1752–1759; ff.10–19, courts, 1767–1801; ff.22–23, courts, 1760–1766; ff.24–30 (*recto*), courts, 1729–1736; ff.30–24 (*verso*), courts, 1737–1748; f.31 (inside back cover), courts, 1749–1751.

VI/11/2 (12); loose papers found inside VI/11/1, 1688–1800. They include accounts of the court, appointment and presentment of bailiffs and delivery of the keys. One account has been printed in *Sussex Archaeological Collections*, vol. 56, p. 97.

---

[1] Victoria County History, *Sussex*, vol. III (1935), p. 97.

Ep.VI/12 MANOR COURT BOOKS, 1502–1692

The records of later courts appear under the individual manors below. About 1561 Elizabeth I exchanged certain impropriate rectories for some of the episcopal manors (*Calendar of Patent Rolls, 1560–1563*, p. 33).

VI/12/1 62 ff., being two gatherings sewn together at a later date. ff.1–8, 51–60, Manhood Hundred, Sep. 1502–July 1505; ff.9–50, 61–62, manors of Chichester Palace, Amberley, Aldingbourne, Cakeham, Selsey, Sidlesham, Streatham, Drungewyke, Ferring, Preston, Bishopston, Bexhill and Ticehurst, and Tipnoke Hundred, Aug.–Oct. 1504.

VI/12/2 134 ff.; late 17th cent. copy with some mistakes in transcription. ff.1–92, manors of Westergate, Cakeham, Aldingbourne, Ferring, Bexhill and Amberley, and Tipnoke Hundred, Apr. 1527–May 1530; ff.93–127, Manhood Hundred, Oct. 1527–Sep. 1530.

VI/12/3 22 ff.; manors of Sidlesham, Selsey, Cakeham, Aldingbourne, Amberley, Ferring, Preston, Bishopston, Litlington and Streatham, and Hundreds of Bexhill and Tipnoke, Sep. and Oct. 1537.

VI/12/4 355 ff.; manors of Aldingbourne, Amberley, Bexhill, Bishopston, Cakeham, Ferring, Litlington, Preston, Selsey, Sidlesham and Streatham, and Hundreds of Manhood and Tipnoke.
f.4, memoranda; ff.5–25, Easter 1546; f.33v., memoranda; ff.34–55, Easter 1547; ff.60–80, Mich. 1547; ff.84–107, Easter 1548; ff.112–211, Mich. 1548; ff.212–227, Easter 1549; ff.232–250, Mich. 1549; ff.254–268, Easter 1550; ff.274–297, Mich. 1550; ff.304–322, Easter 1551; ff.326–348, Mich. 1551; ff.354–355, Sidlesham prebend, June 1552.

VI/12/5 46 ff.; manors and hundreds as in VI/12/4. See VI/12/5a for transcript. The gap between VI/12/4 and 5 is filled by a court book in the Gloucestershire Record Office (Sherborne MSS.). ff.2–23, Mich. 1553; ff.25–46, Easter 1554.

VI/12/5a 16 ff.; transcript by Mr. W. D. Peckham of VI/12/5, ff.1–19.

VI/12/6 323 pp.; manors of Aldingbourne, Amberley, Cakeham, Ferring and Streatham, and Hundreds of Manhood and Tipnoke. pp.1–315, Easter 1560–Easter 1565; pp.317–322, lists of tenants owing suits, n.d.

VI/12/7 95 ff. bound in part of a deed (1632) relating to Barngates and Lidsey tithes. Manors and hundreds as in VI/12/6. [Easter] 1582–Mich. 1585.

VI/12/8 23 ff. bound in a grant of the office of bailiff of Manhood (1593). Manors and hundreds as in VI/12/6. ff.1–16, receipts at courts, 1595–1596; f.17, recipe for ink.

VI/12/9 388 ff. in remains of blind stamped leather cover. Manors and hundreds as in VI/12/6. Easter 1605–Easter 1619.

VI/12/9a 12 ff.; contemporary index to VI/12/9.

VI/12/10 264 ff.; manors and hundreds as in VI/12/6. Mich. 1628–Easter 1643.

VI/12/11 23 ff. filed at head and wrapped in part of a contemporary mortgage from James Butler to Cicely Osbaston. Manors and hundreds as in VI/12/6. Easter 1688–Easter 1692.

ALDINGBOURNE COURT ROLLS

Ep.VI/13/1–25 1648, 1661, 1663–1665, 1667, 1670–1681, 1683–1687, 1692–1698, 1701 (48 rolls).

Ep.VI/14 ALDINGBOURNE COURT BOOKS, 1670–1948

VI/14/1 616 pp., Apr. 1670–Apr. 1751.

VI/14/2 460 pp., Oct. 1751–May 1797.

VI/14/3 420 pp., May 1798–Oct. 1831.

VI/14/4 450 pp., Jan. 1832–Oct. 1851.

VI/14/5 557 pp., Apr. 1852–Apr. 1873.

VI/14/6 554 pp., Apr. 1873–June 1896.

VI/14/7 562 pp., June 1896–Dec. 1948.

Ep.VI/15 ALDINGBOURNE DRAFT COURT BOOKS, 1737–1791

VI/15/1–6 Oct. 1737–Apr. 1791.

Ep.VI/16 ALDINGBOURNE COURT ABSTRACTS, 1606–1768

These, and the other abstracts, are the work of Francis Dear, who tried to trace the descent of each piece of land in the manor. They are abstracts of the court rolls and court books arranged by sites, each being numbered.

VI/16/1 51 ff.; ff. 1–19, 1606–1660; ff.51–23, 1670–1768.

VI/16/2 14 ff.; copy of part of VI/16/1.

VI/16/3 32 ff.; ff.1–8, rental, 1764; ff.9–15, abstract, 1670.

Ep.VI/17 ALDINGBOURNE RENTALS, 1725–1742

VI/17/0 2 ff.; Mar. 1725.

VI/17/1 2 ff.; Mar. 1728.

VI/17/2 2 ff.; Mar. 1737.

VI/17/3 6 ff.; 1742, and notes on the parliamentary survey (VI/18).

Ep.VI/18 ALDINGBOURNE SURVEY, 1647

The parliamentary survey of episcopal lands in Sussex has not survived as a whole, but there are copies of parts of it amongst these records.

VI/18/1 11 ff. filed at the head and rolled in part of an 18th century deed. A copy of the inquisition made for the compiling of the parliamentary survey, 11 Mar. 1646/7.

Ep.VI/19 ALDINGBOURNE COURT PAPERS

About 2500 documents, 1692–1925.

Ep.VI/19A and 20 AMBERLEY COURT ROLLS, 1295–1508, 1641–1687

VI/19A/1 18 membranes, now guarded and filed: 1295–1296, 1306–1307, 1348–1349, 1368–1373, 1418–1419, 1438, 1494–1508.

VI/20/1–46 1641–1665, 1667–1687 (94 rolls).

Ep.VI/21 AMBERLEY COURT BOOKS, 1670–1936

VI/21/1 642 pp., Apr. 1670–Oct. 1727.

VI/21/2 626 pp., May 1728–Oct. 1760.

VI/21/3 426 pp., May 1761–Oct. 1787.

VI/21/4 526 pp., Oct. 1787–Oct. 1814.

VI/21/5 504 pp., Nov. 1814–Mar. 1836.

VI/21/6 494 pp., Apr. 1836–Apr. 1845.

VI/21/7 550 pp., Oct. 1845–Oct. 1853.

VI/21/8 556 pp., May 1854–Apr. 1859.

VI/21/9 560 pp., Oct. 1859–Oct. 1869.

VI/21/10   572 pp., May 1870–May 1882.

VI/21/11   566 pp., Oct. 1882–July 1898.

VI/21/12   568 pp., Aug. 1898–Feb. 1915.

VI/21/13   586 pp., May 1915–Nov. 1936.

Ep.VI/22   AMBERLEY DRAFT COURT BOOKS, 1737–1844

VI/22/1–11   Oct. 1737–Oct. 1789.   **VI/22/12**   38 ff.; Oct. 1844.

Ep.VI/23   AMBERLEY COURT ABSTRACTS, 1606–1763

VI/23/1   10 ff.; abstract, 1606–1671.

VI/23/2   20 ff.; abstract, 1671–1763.

VI/23/3   8 ff.; copy of part of VI/23/2.

VI/23/4   9 ff.; copy of VI/23/3.

VI/23/5   52 ff.; ff.1–45, abstract *c*.1760; ff.49–52, index of properties.

Ep.VI/24   AMBERLEY SURVEYS, [1644]–1866

VI/24/1   193 ff., originally two separate volumes, compiled in the 18th cent.   ff.9–14, notes from court books, 1650–1722; ff.15–39, index, and memoranda from earlier court books; ff.44–136, copy of VI/20, June 1644–Oct. 1668; ff.140–193, copy of VI/20, May 1653–Apr. 1668.

VI/24/2   126 ff.   ff.1–55, copy of parliamentary survey [1647], with additional notes, 1702 and 1742; ff.57–125, abstract of court books; ff.109–103, copy of inquisition made for the compiling of the parliamentary survey, June 1647.

VI/24/3   37 ff. (incomplete at end); copy of VI/24/2, ff.1–55.

VI/24/4   16 pp.; 19th cent. copy of the customaries of the manor (see VI/24/6).

VI/24/5   22 ff.; customaries and boundaries of the manor.

VI/24/6   10 ff.; original of VI/24/4.

VI/24/7   64 ff.; ff.1*v*.–53, copy of VI/24/2, ff.1–55; ff.55*v*.–58, index of persons; ff.59*v*.–64, rentals, 1686–1719.

VI/24/8 (50); 3 files made up by the Ecclesiastical Commissioners, containing surveys, valuations, terriers and letters relating to land in Cold Waltham and Amberley parishes and the Amberley estate, 1836–66.

Ep.VI/25 AMBERLEY COURT PAPERS, 1647–1921

About 5,000 documents; the main series runs from 1690 to 1921, but there are 12 papers for 1647–1689.

Ep.VI/26, 27 AMBERLEY INCLOSURE AWARD, 1828

For details of the Amberley Inclosure Award and Map, see *Catalogue of Sussex Maps*, vol. 2,[1] The documents described below were retained by the bishop's steward.

VI/26/1 250 pp.; pp.i–xxi, Act 50 Geo. III c.35; pp.xxv–xxxii, Act 53 Geo. III c.43; pp.xxxv–xxxvii, list of contents; pp.1–204, inclosure award, with maps of Amberley, Rackham and Cold Waltham, Mar. 1828.

VI/26/2 254 pp.; pp.v–vi, index of persons; pp.1–174, admissions under the award at a special court baron, Oct. 1828; pp.213–233, Act 50 Geo. III c.35; pp.237–246, Act 53 Geo. III c.43.

VI/26/3 48 ff.; f.1, memoranda; ff.2–23, reference to the award maps; ff.46–39*v*., pencilled calculations; ff.47–48 (loose), letter and notes of surveyor.

VI/26/4 28 ff.; parish assessment in 1812 (ff.1*v*.–12 only).

VI/26/5 (1); later tracing from award for Wisborough Green and Fittleworth.

Ep.VI/27 Inclosure commissioners' minutes; bills; draft copy of award; other papers.[2]

Ep.VI/28 AMBERLEY LEASES

This was the number originally given to the group of leases relating to episcopal sites in Amberley. When the main collection of leases was catalogued these were transferred to complete the series and are now Ep.VI/56/3, 4, 25, 38, 42, 44, 45, 55 and 58.

[1] Not yet printed, 1965.
[2] Not available, 1964.

Ep.VI/29/1–49 CAKEHAM COURT ROLLS

1641–1659, 1661–1687, 1695–1697 (94 rolls).

Ep.VI/30 CAKEHAM AND MANHOOD COURT BOOKS, 1670–1937

VI/30/1 577 pp., Apr. 1670–Apr. 1762.

VI/30/2 373 pp., Oct. 1762–Nov. 1805.

VI/30/3 564 pp., Nov. 1805–Apr. 1849.

VI/30/4 552 pp., Apr. 1849–Oct. 1883.

VI/30/5 554 pp., Feb. 1884–Aug. 1937.

Ep.VI/31 CAKEHAM AND MANHOOD DRAFT COURT BOOKS, 1737–1791

VI/31/1–4 Apr. 1737–Apr. 1791.

Ep.VI/32 CAKEHAM COURT ABSTRACTS

VI/32/1 10 ff.; abstract, 1761.

Ep.VI/33 CAKEHAM SURVEYS, 1647–1853

VI/33/1 14 ff. filed at the head and rolled in part of an 18th century deed. A copy of the inquisition, 1647, made for compiling the survey. 1701.

VI/33/2 (9); surveys, valuations and terriers relating to land in West Wittering, 1841–1853.

Ep.VI/34 CAKEHAM COURT PAPERS, 1700–1920

About 1,000 documents.

Ep.VI/35/1–45 FERRING AND FURE COURT ROLLS, 1642–1687

1642–1687, and 1 undated (86 rolls).

Ep.VI/36 FERRING AND FURE COURT BOOKS, 1670–1935

VI/36/1 646 pp., Apr. 1670–Apr. 1804.

VI/36/2 555 pp., Oct. 1804–May 1862.

VI/36/3 550 pp., Dec. 1860–Nov. 1935.

Ep.VI/37 FERRING AND FURE DRAFT COURT BOOKS, 1736–
1791

VI/37/1–4 Oct. 1736–Apr. 1791.

Ep.VI/37A FERRING AND FURE COURT ABSTRACTS, 1761

VI/37A/1 18 ff.; abstracts of court rolls made Sep. 1761.

Ep.VI/37B FERRING AND FURE SURVEYS, 1647–1851

VI/37B/1 40 ff; copy [*c.*1700] of the inquisition made for compiling the parliamentary survey, June 1647.

VI/37B/2 (20); surveys, valuations, terriers and other documents in a file compiled by the Ecclesiastical Commissioners, 1840–1851.

Ep.VI/38 FERRING AND FURE COURT PAPERS, 1700–1909
About 1,050 documents.

Ep.VI/38A and 39 MANHOOD HUNDRED COURT ROLLS, 1420–
1483

VI/38A/1 12 membranes, now guarded and filed; 1420, 1437, 1454–1455, 1468–1469, 1482–1483.

VI/39/1–5 1671, 1672, 1681, 1695, 1697 (6 rolls).[1]

Ep.VI/40 MANHOOD HUNDRED COURT PAPERS, 1700–1863
About 330 documents.

---

[1] From 1670 the hundred courts were entered in the Cakeham court books (VI/30 and 31).

Ep.VI/41/1–28 STREATHAM COURT ROLLS, 1660–1688

1660–1665, 1667–1688 (71 rolls).

Ep.VI/42 STREATHAM AND TIPNOKE COURT BOOKS, 1670–1935

VI/42/1 650 pp., Apr. 1670–Apr. 1731.

VI/42/2 555 pp., Apr. 1731–Oct. 1767.

VI/42/3 458 pp., Oct. 1767–Oct. 1814.

VI/42/4 517 pp., Apr. 1815–Oct. 1846.

VI/42/5 549 pp., May 1847–Oct. 1870.

VI/42/6 559 pp., Apr. 1871–Nov. 1900.

VI/42/7 565 pp., Sep. 1901–Dec. 1935.

Ep.VI/43 STREATHAM AND TIPNOKE DRAFT COURT BOOKS, 1737–1791

VI/43/1–8 Oct. 1737–Apr. 1791.

Ep.VI/44 STREATHAM PARLIAMENTARY SURVEY, 1647

VI/44/1 63 ff. filed at head and rolled in part of an 18th cent. deed. Copy of the inquisition, 1647, made for compiling the parliamentary survey, 1679.

Ep.VI/45 MISCELLANEOUS RECORDS RELATING TO STREATHAM AND OTHER MANORS, 1619–1868

VI/45/1 Parchment roll; copy decree in Chancery establishing the customs of Streatham manor, Feb. 1618/9. An exemplification of this decree is Ep.VI/56/11/1.

VI/45/2 256 ff., consisting of several volumes of different sizes bound together, mainly 18th cent.

ff.41–57, Cakeham court rolls, Oct. 1641–Oct. 1647; ff.59–65, notes from various court books, 1641–1722; ff.66–77, an account of the bishop's liberties; ff.78–84, notes of episcopal revenues from "Mr. Greystocks book"; ff.88–101, notes and index from Ferring court books; ff.102–105, notes on Tipnoke, Manhood and Aldingbourne courts; ff.108–122, notes and index from Aldingbourne court books; ff.123–124, notes on Ferring court books; ff.125–140, notes and index from Cakeham court books; ff.141–160, notes and index from Streatham court books; ff.161–204, Streatham court rolls , Apr. 1660–Apr. 1669; ff.209–217, customs of Streatham; ff.221–246, rentals of Streatham, 1639–1724; ff.247–253, survey of Streatham, Jan. 1552/3, copied from VI/4/1, ff.51–56.

VI/45/3 (10); surveys, valuations, terriers and letters relating to land in Henfield, 1842–1868. This file was made up by the Ecclesiastical Commissioners.

Ep.VI/46 STREATHAM COURT PAPERS, 1699–1919

About 1,500 documents.

Ep.VI/47/1–13 TIPNOKE HUNDRED COURT ROLLS

1670–1672, 1677–1683, 1685–1687 (20 rolls).

Ep.VI/48 TIPNOKE HUNDRED COURT PAPERS, 1700–1848

About 200 docs.

Ep.VI/49 BIRDHAM COMMON INCLOSURE AWARD, 1793

The bishop owned the common as lord of Manhood Hundred. It was inclosed in 1793 under the Act 31 Geo. III c. 32. The official copy of the award and map are deposited in the W.S.R.O. (QDD/6/W5); for details see *Catalogue of Sussex Maps*, vol. 2 (in preparation).

VI/49/1 and 5 24 pp. (printed); Act, 31 Geo. III c. 32.

VI/49/2–4 Copies of the award, Aug. 1793.

Ep.VI/50 WEST WITTERING COMMON INCLOSURE AWARD, 1793

The bishop owned the common as lord of Manhood Hundred. It was inclosed in 1793 under the Act 31 Geo. III c. 33. The official copy of the award and map are deposited in the W.S.R.O. (QDD/6/W4); for details see *Catalogue of Sussex Maps*, vol. 2 (in preparation).

VI/50/1, 2 Copies of the award, Aug. 1793.

Ep.VI/51 LONDON ESTATE REGISTERS OF LEASES, 1700–1854

Other leases are registered in Ep.VI/55/1.

VI/51/1 186 ff. f.i, index of lessees; ff.1–182, Feb. 1699/1700–June 1789, with notes of later leases (not chronological).

VI/51/2 446 pp. pp.1–425, June 1768–Oct. 1833; pp.428–434, index of lessees.

VI/51/3 436 pp. pp.1–326, Nov. 1834–Feb. 1854, with plans of sites; pp.410–416, index of lessees.

Ep.VI/52 LONDON ESTATE RENTALS, 1722–1846

For other London rentals see Ep.VI/2/10–13.

VI/52/1 (1); gives details of leases from Feb. 1694/5–June 1722, with additions to Sep. 1737.

VI/52/1a (1); copy of VI/52/1, with additions to June 1737 and index of names.

VI/52/2 (1); gives details of leases from Feb. 1699/1700–June 1737, with additions to Feb. 1753.

VI/52/3 86 pp.; pp.3–4, list of properties; pp.5–75, rental, 1824, giving details of leases and fines; p.77, note on Symonds Inn estate; p.79, land tax redemption; p.81, reserved rents; pp.83–85, number of houses in each property.

VI/52/4 144 pp.; pp.1–43, rough copy of VI/52/3; p.54, list of Sussex livings in the Crown gift; pp.75–56, value of Cathedral dignities and Sussex livings in the bishop's gift, with list of sequestrations, 1825; p.78, land tax redemption; p.79, reserved rents; pp.140–84, rental of episcopal estates in Sussex, 1824, with later additions; pp.144–141, list of Sussex properties and index to pp.140–54.

VI/52/5 200 ff.; f.i, index of properties; f.iii, "Plan of the Estate of The Lord Bishop of Chichester situate in and about Chancery Lane"; pp. 1–13, rental, 1842–1846, with extensive notes and plans of sites.

Ep.VI/53 LONDON ESTATE LEASES

These are the surviving leases (and allied papers) relating to episcopal property in and around Chancery Lane, London. Details of other leases can sometimes be obtained from the registers (Ep.VI/51 and VI/55/1)and the rentals (particularly Ep. VI/2/11 and 13), which often give names and ages of the *cestui qui vies*. The registers are not comprehensive. The original site numbers of these properties are indicated here by the figure after VI/53/ and were as follows:—

VI/53/1   *Red Peruke*, Chancery Lane, late *The Crown*, 1751–1843 (5 docs.).

VI/53/2   Messuages in Chancery Lane, 1749–1842 (7 docs.).[1]

VI/53/3   Messuage in Chancery Lane, 1751–1853 (6 docs.).

VI/53/4   Messuages in Tenter Yard, 1768–1775 (2 docs.).[2]

VI/53/5   Breams Buildings, 1807–1849 (10 docs.).

VI/53/6   Messuage in White's Alley, 1814–1849 (13 docs.).

VI/53/7   Messuage in Chancery Lane, 1806–1853 (10 docs.).

VI/53/8   Messuage in Tenter Yard, 1800–1845 (7 docs.).

VI/53/9   Eight messuages in Chancery Lane, 1719–1854 (28 docs.).

VI/53/10   Messuage in Chancery Lane, 1786–1849 (13 docs.).

VI/53/11   Several messuages added to Bond Stables, 1742–1747 (2 docs.).

VI/53/12   A smith's shop and a little house (no docs.).

VI/53/13   Messuages in Bishop's Court and Chancery Lane, 1803–1821 (2 docs.).

VI/53/14   Messuages in White's Alley, 1806–1846 (7 docs.).

VI/53/15   *St. John's Head* Tavern, Chancery Lane, 1789–1850 (17 docs.).

VI/53/16   Messuages in Tenter Yard, 1760–1842 (9 docs.).

VI/53/17   Messuage in White's Alley 1764 (1 doc.).

VI/53/18   Messuages in White's Alley, 1756–1854 (21 docs.).

VI/53/19   *Three Crowns*, Chancery Lane, 1804–1853 (11 docs.).

VI/53/20   Symond's Inn, 1793–1877 (89 docs.).

VI/53/21   Messuage in Chancery Lane (no docs.).

VI/53/22   White's Alley House and one shilling rent, 1766–1868 (8 docs.).[3]

VI/53/23   Chancery Lane House, 1787–1813 (3 docs.).

VI/53/24   Part of Chichester Rents, 1745–1849 (10 docs.).

VI/53/25   Part of Chichester Rents, 1750–1851 (8 docs.).

---

[1] See also VI/53/4 and 22.   [2] See also VI/53/2 and 22.   [3] See also VI/53/2 and 4.

VI/53/26 Hole Out of the Wall, now Breams Buildings, 1794–1847 (10 docs.).

VI/53/27 Late Stokes's, White's Alley, 1807–1853 (11 docs.).

VI/53/28	Unnamed	Tenement in Breams Buildings, 1773–1847 (14 docs.).
VI/53/29	in the	Tenements in Breams Buildings, 1806–1845 (9 docs.).
VI/53/30	rentals	Tenement in Breams Buildings, 1790–1845 (12 docs.).

In c.1820, the properties were identified more precisely and divided into smaller units which were then re-numbered as follows:—

1. *Red Peruke*, Chancery Lane (1)
2. 21 houses in White's Alley (2 and 4)
3. Messuage in Chancery Lane (3)
4. Messuage in Chancery Lane and Rooms in Breams Buildings (5)
5. 2 messuages etc. in Breams Buildings (6)
6. 2 messuages in Chancery Lane (7)
7. Messuage corner of Breams Buildings (8)
8. 3 messuages, now 2, in Chancery Lane (9)
9. 2 messuages in Chancery Lane (9)
10. Messuage in Chancery Lane (10)
11. 12 houses in Bishop's Court, Chancery Lane (13)
12. Baptist Head Chambers (15)
13. Several messuages in Tenter Yard (16)
14. 3 messuages in White's Alley (18)
15. 6 messuages in White's Alley (18)
16. Messuage in Chancery Lane (21)
17. *City of Durham*, White's Alley (22)
18. House and yard in Chancery Lane (23)
19. 5 messuages in Chichester Rents (24)
20. 8 messuages in Chichester Rents (25)
21. 2 messuages in Breams Buildings (26)
22. Messuage in Chancery Lane (27)
23. Messuage in Breams Buildings (28)
24. 2 messuages in Breams Buildings (29)
25. Messuage in Breams Buildings (30)
26. 6 houses in White's Alley (14)
27. *Three Crowns*, Chancery Lane, and 5 messuages (19)
28. Bonds Stables (11 and 12)
29. *White Swan*, White's Alley (2 and 4)

30–36.   Symond's Inn (20)
    30.   Chambers, etc.
    31.   Cellars, etc.
    32.   Rooms, etc.
    33.   Rooms, etc.
    34.   Chambers, etc.
    35.   Shop and rooms, etc.
    36.   Coffee House, etc.

Although the original number is in brackets, it will be seen that the geographical location of the divided properties does not always appear to correspond with the site of the original property, but the deeds, whether of a whole or undivided property, are physically stored under the original number.

There are also the following bundles of later deeds, without site numbers, but identified by modern house and street names:—

VI/53/31 1–10, Lees Buildings; 1–4, Bowling Pin Alley; 10, White's Alley; 13, Little White's Alley; 1 and 2 Swan Court; and houses in Birch's Lane or Place, 1824–1880 (60 docs.).

VI/53/32 2 Breams Buildings, 1875 (1 doc.).

VI/53/33 1–3 Chancery Lane, and 191 and 192 Fleet Street, 1853 (1 doc.).

VI/53/34 22 Chancery Lane, 1874 (1 doc.).

VI/53/35 23, 24 Chancery Lane, 1865–1868 (8 docs.).

VI/53/36 77 Chancery Lane, 1883 (2 docs.).

VI/53/37 85 Chancery Lane, 1845–1859 (3 docs.).

VI/53/38 86 Chancery Lane, 1821–1863 (9 docs.).

VI/53/39 *King's Arms* Public House, Rolls Buildings, 1878 (2 docs.).

VI/53/40 The Law Courts Chambers, 1874 (1 doc.).

VI/53/41 Lonsdale Chambers, 1877–1879 (4 docs.).

VI/53/42 10, 11 Rolls Buildings, 1879 (2 docs.).

VI/53/43 8, 9, 12, 17 White's Alley, 1868–1878 (3 docs.).

VI/53/44 Agreement for widening Chancery Lane, 1875, and contract for making a road from Breams Buildings to Fetter Lane, 1881.

Many of the leases in VI/53/31–43 are endorsed with details of transactions to 1925.

EP.VI/54 LONDON ESTATE MISCELLANEA, 1548–1647

VI/54/1 46 ff. ff.1–16, copies of documents relating to lands in Chancery Lane leased to the "Guild or Fraternity of our Blessed Lady and Dunstan founded in ye parish church of St. Dunstan in ye west", 1548–1557; f.45, copy letter to Anthony Irby, Nov. 1647.

Ep.VI/55 SUSSEX ESTATE REGISTERS OF LEASES, 1661–1869

The first volume includes London estates, but the main series of London registers is in VI/51.

VI/55/1 678 pp. p.i, decorated title page; pp.1–637, June 1661–Nov. 1733; pp. 651–662, index of properties; pp. 663–675, index of lessees.

VI/55/2 346 pp.; *no leases were registered between Sep. 1755 and Feb. 1825* (see note on p. 185 in the volume). p.i, decorated title page; pp.1–323, July 1734–May 1831; pp. 324–338, index of lessees and properties; pp. 339–343 (continuation of p. 323), May 1831 and Apr. 1827.

VI/55/3 512 pp. pp.1–452, Aug. 1832–Jan. 1845; p. 453, memorandum; pp.484–500, index of lessees.

VI/55/4 552 pp. pp.1–475, June 1845–Mar. 1857; pp.509–530, index of lessees.

VI/55/5 558 pp. pp.ii–xxi, index of lessees; pp.1–498, July 1857–Nov. 1869.

Ep.VI/56 SUSSEX ESTATE LEASES

These are the surviving leases (and allied papers) relating to episcopal property in Sussex. Details of other leases can sometimes be obtained from the registers (Ep.VI/55) and the rentals (particularly Ep.VI/2/11 and 14), which often give names and ages of the *cestui qui vies*. The registers are not comprehensive, and *no episcopal leases of Sussex property were registered between Sep. 1755 and Feb. 1825.*

The site numbers of these estates (indicated here by the figure after VI/56/) remained the same, although the parts of Broyle Farm (site 5), which had been divided in 1811, were re-divided and re-numbered in 1842.[1]

VI/56/1 Aldingbourne Park or Place, 1730–1876 (40 docs.).

VI/56/2 Aldingbourne Farm, 1746–1865 (40 docs.).

VI/56/3 and 4 Amberley Rectory and Farms and Amberley Castle (held together), 1759–1868 (48 docs.).

---

[1] An incomplete calendar of these documents is available in the Diocesan Record Office (Ep.I/88/5).

VI/56/5 Broyle Farm [Chichester St. Peter the Great and St. Pancras], 1735–1869 (147 docs.).

VI/56/6 Cakeham Farm, 1780–1866 (11 docs.).

VI/56/7 Ferring Farm, 1732–1852 (23 docs.).

VI/56/8 and **9** Henfield Park and Parsonage (held together), 1722–1829 (27 docs.).

VI/56/10 Sheephouse Lands [Aldingbourne], 1721–1842 (32 docs.).

VI/56/11 Streatham Farm [Henfield], 1619–1863 (16 docs.).

VI/56/12 Brighton Rectory, 1727–1799 (14 docs.).

VI/56/13 Bishopston Prebend, 1705–1869 (45 docs.).

VI/56/14 Coldwaltham Parsonage, 1726–1853 (21 docs.).

VI/56/15 Houghton Parsonage, 1746–1800 (7 docs.).

VI/56/16 Littlehampton Rectory, 1739–1882 (12 docs.).

VI/56/17 Rudgwick Rectory, 1720, 1764 (2 docs.).

VI/56/18 Walberton Rectory, 1752–1840 (11 docs.).

VI/56/19 Butchers Row [West Street, Chichester], 1701–1816 (60 docs.).

VI/56/20 Tinkers in Amberley Manor [Wisborough Green], 1707–1854 (7 docs.).

VI/56/21 Tenement in Aldingbourne, 1752–1862 (20 docs.).

VI/56/22 Messuage and ½ acre in Aldingbourne, 1732–1839 (7 docs.).

VI/56/23 Hundred Steddle House [Birdham] (no docs.).

VI/56/24 House at Hundred Steddle [Birdham], 1738–1868 (27 docs.).

VI/56/25 Millballs in Amberley, 1754–1866 (8 docs.).

VI/56/26 Mockbeggars, Wisborough Green, 1765–1854 (11 docs.).

VI/56/27 Land at Wisborough Green, 1739–1853 (9 docs.).

VI/56/28 Cottage in Fittleworth, 1739–1852 (13 docs.).

VI/56/29 Tenement in Wisborough Green, 1726–1863 (25 docs.).

VI/56/30 Copperas Stones [Cakeham Manor in West Wittering], 1752–1860 (8 docs.).

VI/56/31 Chalk Pits in Houghton, 1754–1788 (3 docs.).

VI/56/32 Fittleworth Mills (no docs.).

VI/56/33 Birdham Mill, 1746–1859 (20 docs.).

VI/56/34 Aldingbourne Mill[s], 1708–1865 (14 docs.).

VI/56/35 Cottage and Land in Rush Lane, Aldingbourne, 1702–1862 (17 docs.).

VI/56/36 Caters and Bushey Closes, Aldingbourne, 1743–1863 (14 docs.).

VI/56/37 Messuage in Henfield, 1745–1868 (16 docs.).

VI/56/38 Cottage and Land in Amberley, 1765–1848 (13 docs.).

VI/56/39 This is the same site as VI/56/22.

VI/56/40 Cottage in Ashfold [Wisborough Green], 1735–1858 (15 docs.).

VI/56/41 Cottage in Aldingbourne, 1728–1826 (10 docs.).

VI/56/42 Land in Amberley, 1764 (1 doc.).

VI/56/43 Cottage and Land in Watersfield [Coldwaltham], 1754–1866 (14 docs.).

VI/56/44 Tavern Acre in Amberley, *temp.* Eliz. I (1 doc.).

VI/56/45 North Mead in Amberley (no docs.).

VI/56/46 Messuage and Lands in West Wittering, 1714–1869 (20 docs.).

VI/56/47 Messuage and Land in West Wittering, 1684–1869 (18 docs.).

VI/56/48 Tenement and Garden in Henfield, 1738–1868 (14 docs.).

VI/56/49 Bishops Wood in Slaugham Chace, 1732–1864 (10 docs.).

VI/56/50 Cottage in Aldingbourne, 1733–1861 (26 docs.).

VI/56/51 Part of Westergate Common, 1777–1856 (12 docs.).

VI/56/52 Part of Birdham Common, 1793–1863 (6 docs.).

VI/56/53 Part of Birdham Common, 1793–1857 (6 docs.).

VI/56/54 Part of West Wittering Common, 1793–1859 (3 docs.).

VI/56/55 Chalk Pit in Amberley, 1805 (2 docs.).

VI/56/56 Part of West Itchenor Common, 1807–1858 (11 docs.).

VI/56/57 Part of Bishop's Acre in Amberley, 1821 (1 doc.).

VI/56/58 Allotment in Amberley, 1821 (6 docs.).

VI/56/59 Allotment on Coldwaltham Common, 1828–1855 (3 docs.).

VI/56/60 Allotment on Rackham Common, 1828–1868 (2 docs.).

VI/56/61 Allotment on Coldwaltham Common (no docs.).

Ep.VI/57 MISCELLANEOUS SURVEYS, 1750–1869

These bundles consist of loose papers arranged and filed by the Ecclesiastical Commissioners in the late 19th cent.

VI/57/1 (3); valuations, land in Birdham, 1848–1860.

VI/57/2 (15); terrier, valuations and plan, the Broyle, Chichester [1750]–1859.

VI/57/3 (3); valuations and plan, land in Fittleworth, 1852–1869.

VI/57/4 (1); valuation, land in Itchenor, 1849.

VI/57/5 (10); valuations and plan, land in Slaugham, 1839–1861.

VI/57/6 (2); valuations, Walberton rectory, 1839 and 1845.

VI/57/7 (8); valuations and plan, land in Wisborough Green, 1841–1863.

VI/57/8 (20); valuations and papers, land in Aldingbourne, 1838–1861.

Ep.VI/58 CORRESPONDENCE (EPISCOPAL ESTATES), 1743–1863

(70); papers, mostly letters, relating to episcopal estates, particularly new leases, valuations, depreciation of the property and income tax returns.

Ep.VI/59 CORRESPONDENCE (RAILWAYS), 1836–1853

J. B. Freeland kept all his correspondence relating to railway schemes in one group. Consequently, besides episcopal and capitular lands acquired by the various companies, this group refers also to his own land and that of private persons for whom he was acting.

VI/59/1 (100); letters, bills, circulars, schedules, plans and other documents relating to the construction of parts of the London, Brighton and South Coast Railway, especially the Chichester–Shoreham, Chichester–Bognor and Chichester–Portsmouth extensions, and a copy of the *Case of the Municipal Corporation of Chichester*, referring to possible loss of tolls within Chichester Harbour, 1836–1853.

VI/59/2 (23); papers relating to the Direct London and Portsmouth Railway, 1844–1846.

VI/59/3 (11); papers relating to the Dorking, Brighton and Arundel railway, 1845.

VI/59/4 (4); papers relating to the Cheltenham, Oxford and London and Birmingham railway, 1836, and the London and Birmingham Railway (City of London extension), 1845.

VI/59/5 (2); papers relating to the Tunbridge to Hastings, St. Leonards and Rye railway, 1844, and the Tottenham to Farrington [*sic*] Street railway, 1845.

VI/59/6 (26); J. B. Freeland's draft accounts, 1845–1851.

THE ARCHDEACONRY OF HASTINGS

Ep.VII/1   INDUCTION MANDATES, 1912–1924

(75); episcopal mandates for induction (bishops of Chichester and Lewes).

1912	4	1916	9	1920	13	1924	1
1913	7	1917	5	1921	4		
1914	10	1918	3	1922	6		
1915	7	1919	5	1923	1		

Ep.VII/2   VISITATION PAPERS, 1913–1962

All except no. 9 relate to archidiaconal visitations.

VII/2/1   8 ff.; Liber Cleri (churchwardens only), deaneries of Hastings, Rye and Dallington (1913), Hastings, Etchingham and Rye (1914).

VII/2/2   130 ff.; book of receipts for visitation fees, deaneries of Hastings and Eastbourne (1915).

VII/2/3   124 ff.; the same (1916).

VII/2/4   5 ff.; Liber Cleri and a circular, Hastings deanery (1917).

VII/2/5   4 ff.; Liber Cleri, Eastbourne deanery (1918).

VII/2/6   119 ff.; book of receipts for visitation fees (1918).

VII/2/7   119 ff.; the same (1920).

VII/2/8   (10); letters and citations relating to the 1916, 1917, 1920 and 1921 visitations.

VII/2/9   (7); schedule of enquiries, report on his inspection of the deanery (1961) and covering letter to the archdeacon (1962), from the Rev. A. N. H. Roscamp (rural dean of Etchingham, 1957–1963).

Ep.VII/3 CHURCHWARDENS' ARTICLES OF ENQUIRY, 1913–1961

All relate to archidiaconal visitations.

VII/3/1 (100); 1915, and one unused form for 1913.

VII/3/2 (99); 1916–17.

VII/3/3 (110); 1956–57.

VII/3/4 (108); 1960–61 (financial questions only, with opportunity to raise other matters). Some with covering letters and more detailed statements of accounts.

Ep.VII/4 CHURCHWARDENS' DECLARATIONS, 1915–1922

VII/4/1 (48); 1915–16.

VII/4/2 (1); 1916–17.

VII/4/3 (80); 1917–18.

VII/4/4 (80); 1921–22.

Ep.VII/5 ASSESSORS' ELECTION PAPERS, 1912–1922

(16); citations and returns (1912, 1919, 1922) and letters from Archdeacon Cook (1922).

Ep.VII/6 SEAL MATRICES, 1912–1938

VII/6/1 Theodore Townson Churton, Archdeacon, 1912–1915.

VII/6/2 Ernest Gordon Reid, Archdeacon, 1938–1956.

Ep. VII/7 MARRIAGE LICENCE AFFIDAVITS, 1912–1936

(3,086); those for 1912–1914 are filed in one binder with those for Lewes (Ep.II/3).

1912	12	1919	369	1925	51	1931	30
1913	38	1920	111	1926	55	1932	33
1914	54	1921	72	1927	50	1933	42
1915	263	1922	74	1928	39	1934	30
1916	290	1923	62	1929	56	1935	46
1917	522	1924	76	1930	46	1936	48
1918	617						

Ep.VII/8 ORDERS IN COUNCIL, 1912–1963

VII/8/1 Copy of Order, 24 June 1912, constituting the new archdeaconry of Hastings.

VII/8/2 (2); copy of Order, 26 Mar. 1963 (with map), constituting the new district (and later parish) of Christ Church, Horam, out of parts of the existing parishes of Heathfield, Hellingly and Waldron.

THE DEAN OF BATTLE'S PECULIAR[1]

Ep.VIII/1 PROBATE AND ADMINISTRATION PAPERS, 1610–1852

For wills and administrations, 1530–1617, see *British Record Society*, vol. 24.

VIII/1/1 (16); Letters of administration, bonds and affidavits, depositions, renunciations, citations, appointments of administrators and guardians, and an original testament, relating to:

Bennett, Richard	(1718)	Leader, Mary	(1718)
Bishop, Phoebe	(1851)	Leonard, Mary	(1718)
Boys, John	(1610)	Metcalf, George	(1852)
Darby, John	(1724)	Potter, William	(1718)
Gear, Thomas	(1840)	Ridgeway, John	(1718)
Gilbert, Thomas	(1727)	Slater, Anne	(1718)
Gilmore, John	(1718)	Snepp, Thomas	(1710)
Gorham, Elizabeth	(1827)	Spiller, Robert	(1718)
Hyland, Mrs.	(n.d.)	Stevens, Richard	(1709)
Ingram, John	(1728)	Vavis, Anne	(1726)
Jarvis, Mary	(1840)	Watts, Emily Maria	(1840)

VIII/1/2 (2); memoranda, 1720–1722.

Ep.VIII/2 MISCELLANEOUS COURT PAPERS, 1689–1754

(80); churchwardens' presentments, citations to appear, acts and minutes of court, oaths, forms of penance and excommunication, lists of fees, receipts and other papers, including an "Account of the p[re]tended way between Battell & Seddlescombe" (1695).

Ep.VIII/3 VISITATION PAPERS, 1731–1844

(107); minutes of the visitation courts, 1731–1844, and churchwardens' declarations (separate documents for each person, folded with the minutes), 1836–1844.

---

[1] All the records in this section were received from Messrs. Raper & Fovargue, solicitors, Battle, in 1959. The parish register transcripts for Battle have been merged with Ep.II/16/10.

Ep.VIII/4 PRESENTATIONS, 1731–1920

VIII/4/1–3 Presentations made by the Webster family to the bishop of Chichester, 1731 and 1920, and the bishop's notice to churchwardens, 1920. (Other presentations to the deanery are in Ep.I/6).

Ep.VIII/5 MARRIAGE LICENCES AND AFFIDAVITS, 1814–1921

(63); one special licence, licences granted by the bishop of Chichester, affidavits and four documents relating to the issue of licences.

1814	1	1840	2	1853	5	1862	4
1816	1	1841	1	1854	4	1863	2
1834	1	1842	6	1855	1	1865	1
1835	1	1843	2	1856	2	1866	1
1836	2	1844	3	1857	2	1877	1
1837	2	1849	1	1858	1	1888	1
1838	1	1851	3	1859	2	1910	1
1839	2	1852	3	1861	2	1921	1

Ep.VIII/6 BUILDING PAPERS, 1863–1924

These all relate to repairs and redecorations of the Deanery and other buildings and some include inventories of fixtures and fittings in the Deanery taken at the institution of a new dean.

VIII/6/1 50 ff. and 15 documents; state of account for repairs (on 2 ff. only), and inventory, estimates, receipts and correspondence, 1863–1865 (Deanery).

VIII/6/2 (30); specifications, estimates and correspondence, 1882 (Deanery and glebe).

VIII/6/3 (10); specifications, estimates and correspondence, 1924 (Deanery, the White House and glebe).

Ep.VIII/7 LICENCES TO STIPENDIARY CURACIES, 1837–1902

(15); churchwardens' copies of Licences to stipendiary curacies at Battle and Netherfield.

1837	1	1876	1	1888	1	1896	1
1849	1	1880	1	1892	1	1900	1
1855	2	1886	1	1895	1	1902	2
1860	1						

Ep.VIII/8 SEAL

VIII/8/1 Cast of the dean's seal; see J. Lewis André, 'Battle Church', p. 23 (Ep.VIII/9/1).

Ep.VIII/9 HISTORICAL NOTES, 1899

VIII/9/1   24 pp.; J. Lewis André, 'Battle Church', reprinted from *Sussex Archaeological Collections*, vol. 42, pp. 214–236, and a letter from André to Dean Currie, 1899.

Ep.VIII/10 FACULTY PAPERS, 1919

VIII/10/1–5   Faculties to erect memorial tablets and crosses in Battle church and churchyard, all 1919.

Ep.VIII/11 TITHE BOOKS AND PAPERS, 1733–1897

From the time of Dean Birch (1801–1836) there were numerous tithe disputes between the deans and parishioners, and many of these papers relate to cases which were brought into open courts (e.g. Birch *v.* Harrison, Littler *v.* Eldridge). The later documents relate also to leases and conveyances of part of the glebe. As far as possible the papers have been kept in the original bundles in which they were received.

VIII/11/1–6   Tithe accounts and assessments (some with loose papers inserted), probably used as evidence in the 19th cent. disputes, 1733–1778.

VIII/11/7   (about 1,000); letters, accounts, receipts, assessments, precedents, case papers, and many other papers (see Ep.I/54) relating to tithe matters in Battle, *c.*1800–1897.

APPENDIX I

BISHOPS' TRANSCRIPTS

ALBOURNE

Ep.II/16/1A, 1606–10, 1612–18, 1621–30, 1632–36, 1638, 1640 [to be found in East Blatchington bundle, II/16/20], 1664, 1671–98, 1700–1812; **/1B**, 1813–88, 1890–93 (369 docs.).

ALCISTON

Ep.II/16/2A, 1608, 1609, 1611–18, 1620–38, 1664, 1665, 1668–80, 1682–85, 1687, 1692–1812; **/2B**, 1813–92 (364 docs.).

ALDINGBOURNE

Ep.I/24/1A, 1594, 1595, 1613, 1615, 1618, 1625, 1630, 1634, 1637–41, 1662, 1664, 1665, 1669–78, 1680, 1685–89, 1692–99, 1701–05, 1707–47, 1749–63, 1765–1812; **/1B**, 1813, 1814, 1816–94, 1896–1901, 1903, 1904, 1907–12 (460 docs.)

ALDRINGTON

Ep.II/16/3, 1864, 1881–91 (27 docs.).

ALFRISTON

Ep.II/16/4A, 1606, 1607, 1610–14, 1616–18, 1620–40, 1667, 1668, 1671–76, 1678, 1680, 1682–1812; **/4B**, 1813–87, 1889–93, 1908 (368 docs.).

AMBERLEY

Ep.I/24/2A, 1571, 1572, 1591–96, 1601, 1604, 1605, 1610, 1613, 1614, 1618, 1629, 1684–90, 1692–96, 1698–1763 [1758 illegible], 1765–1812; **/2B**, 1813–50, 1857, 1858 (267 docs.).

ANGMERING

Ep.I/24/3A, 1591, 1593–96, 1601, 1604, 1605, 1607, 1610, 1611, 1613, 1614, 1618, 1629, 1630, 1632–35, 1637–40, 1663–77, 1679–93, 1695–1701, 1703–63, 1765–72, 1774–1812; **/3B**, 1813–68 (392 docs.).

APPLEDRAM

Ep.I/24/4, 1594, 1604, 1605, 1610, 1613, 1614, 1618, 1634, 1681–83, 1685, 1689, 1692–1734, 1736–46, 1748, 1749, 1751–1817, 1819, 1821–30, 1832–67, 1869–71, 1873–75, 1879–83, 1887, 1889, 1892–94 (375 docs.). There are also 12 transcripts [for 1625, 1630, 1633, 1637–41, 1664, 1666, 1675–77] which are unfit for handling and cannot be produced.

ARDINGLY

Ep.II/16/5A, 1606–17, 1620–39, 1641, 1664–66, 1670, 1671, 1673–1812; **/5B**, 1813–93 (543 docs.).

ARLINGTON

Ep.II/16/6A, 1606, 1607, 1610–18, 1620, 1628, 1630–37, 1641, 1662, 1663, 1665, 1667, 1670–73, 1677–1812; **/6B**, 1813–87, 1908 (378 docs.).

ARUNDEL

Ep.I/24/5A, 1572, 1605, 1607, 1610, 1611, 1613–15, 1618, 1629, 1630, 1632–35, 1637–40, 1662, 1663, 1666, 1668, 1669, 1671–74, 1676–78, 1682–85, 1687, 1690–1735, 1737–63, 1765–80, 1782–90, 1792–1812; **/5B,** 1813–34; **/5C,** 1835–67 (706 docs.).

ASHBURNHAM

Ep.II/16/7A, 1606–18, 1620–27, 1629–40, 1664, 1671–77, 1679–94, 1696–1781, 1783–1812; **/7B,** 1813–90, 1892, 1893 (437 docs.).

ASHINGTON

Ep.I/24/6, 1571, 1572, 1591, 1594, 1596, 1607, 1610, 1611, 1613, 1614, 1618, 1623, 1630, 1633, 1634, 1637–40, 1662–64, 1667, 1677, 1679, 1681, 1682, 1685, 1687–90, 1692–99, 1701–05, 1707–1829, 1831–78 (314 docs.).

ASHURST

Ep.I/24/7, 1571, 1572, 1574, 1596, 1597, 1601, 1607, 1610, 1611, 1613, 1614, 1618, 1623, 1630, 1632–35, 1637–41, 1662–64, 1667–79, 1682, 1685, 1686, 1690, 1692–96, 1698–1763, 1765–1868, 1870, 1892–98, 1911 (292 docs.).

BALCOMBE

Ep.II/16/8A, 1606–18, 1620–40, 1675–1812; **/8B,** 1813–93 [in bad condition], (377 docs.).

BARCOMBE

Ep.II/16/9A, 1606–18, 1620–29, 1631–35, 1637, 1638, 1664–67, 1669–99, 1701–1812; **/9B,** 1813–88 (536 docs.).

BARLAVINGTON

Ep.I/24/8, 1572, 1592, 1594, 1607, 1610, 1611, 1613, 1614, 1616, 1618, 1622, 1633, 1634, 1637, 1639–41, 1662, 1664, 1665, 1667–70, 1675, 1676, 1678–87, 1698, 1701, 1703–06, 1708–30, 1732, 1735–1869 (238 docs.).

BARNHAM

Ep.I/24/9, 1590, 1592, 1594, 1604, 1605, 1610, 1611, 1613, 1614, 1618, 1629, 1630, 1633–35, 1637–40, 1663, 1666, 1667, 1670, 1674–77, 1679–91, 1693–1735, 1737–63, 1765–1817, 1819–36, 1838–49, 1857–96 (360 docs.).

BATTLE

Ep.II/16/10A, 1730–39, 1741–67, 1769–83, 1785–1809, 1811; **/10B,** 1813, 1814, 1816–28; **/10C,** 1829–35; **/10D,** 1845–60; **/10E,** 1861–81, 1883–90 (1037 docs.).

BECKLEY

Ep.II/16/11A, 1606–08, 1610–18, 1620–40, 1664, 1668, 1670–81, 1683–94, 1696–1812; **/11B,** 1813–94, 1908 (698 docs.).

BEDDINGHAM

Ep.II/16/12A, 1593–95, 1606–18, 1620–40, 1666, 1673, 1674, 1676, 1677, 1682–1699, 1701–1812; **/12B,** 1813–94 [in bad condition] (388 docs.).

Beeding, Lower

Ep.II/16/13, 1839–83, 1886–89, 1892 (223 docs.).

Beeding, Upper [*alias* Sele]

Ep.II/16/14A, 1606, 1607, 1609–18, 1620–23, 1625–29, 1631–39, 1664–67, 1672–74, 1676–77, 1679–85, 1687–1812; /**14B,** 1813–94 (501 docs.).

Bepton

Ep.I/24/10, 1592, 1594, 1610, 1611, 1613, 1614, 1618, 1622, 1631, 1633–35 [1635 in poor condition], 1637, 1639, 1640, 1662–70, 1675, 1678, 1679, 1681–84, 1689, 1690, 1692–1700, 1702–43, 1745–1854, 1857–70, 1875–79, 1882, 1883, 1885, 1887, 1889 (318 docs.).

Bersted, South

Ep.IV/7/1A, 1610, 1618, 1678, 1680–83, 1686–1702, 1704–30, 1732, 1734–54, 1756–58, 1760–64, 1766–1812; /**1B,** 1813–59; /**1C,** 1860–82; /**1D,** 1883–1912 (1102 docs.).

Berwick

Ep.II/16/15A, 1606–18, 1620–40, 1664, 1665, 1667–70, 1672, 1673, 1675–1740, 1742–1805, 1807, 1808, 1810; /**15B,**[1] 1800, 1806, 1809, 1811–97 (394 docs.).

Bexhill

Ep.II/16/16A, 1606–11, 1613, 1620–40, 1664, 1667, 1669–1812;/**16B,** 1813–60; /**16C,** 1861–94 (918 docs.).

Bexhill St. Barnabas

Ep.II/16/17, 1891–94 (21 docs.).

Bexhill St. Mark

Ep.II/16/18, 1857–85, 1887–94 (116 docs.).

Bignor

Ep.I/24/11, 1591, 1592, 1594, 1604, 1607, 1610–14, 1618, 1622, 1630, 1633, 1634, 1637, 1639–41, 1662, 1663, 1667–70, 1672, 1674–76, 1678, 1681–83, 1685–90, 1696–98, 1700–03, 1706–47, 1749–1823, 1825–53, 1855–69 (265 docs.).

Billingshurst

Ep.I/24/12A, 1591, 1592, 1594, 1596, 1601, 1607, 1610, 1611, 1613, 1614, 1618, 1623, 1630, 1632–34, 1637–39, 1663, 1664, 1667–77, 1681–83, 1685–89, 1692–94, 1696–1705, 1707, 1709–63, 1765–1812; /**12B,** 1813–62, 1901–12 (543 docs.).

Binderton *see* West Dean

---

[1] Entries for the years 1800 (duplicate of those in the previous bundle), 1806, 1809, 1811, 1812 and 1817 were copied together on 4 ff. and returned in 1828.

BINSTED

Ep.I/24/13, 1572, 1591, 1593, 1594, 1596, 1604, 1605, 1610, 1611, 1613, 1614, 1618, 1629, 1630, 1632–34, 1636–40, 1662, 1664–66, 1669, 1672–76, 1681, 1682, 1685, 1689, 1691–1701, 1703–1763, 1765–69, 1771–1820, 1822–1901 (264 docs.).

BIRDHAM

Ep.I/24/14, 1591, 1592, 1594–96, 1601, 1603, 1604, 1607, 1610, 1613, 1614, 1618, 1625, 1630, 1633, 1634, 1637, 1639–41, 1662–67, 1669, 1671, 1675–78, 1681, 1682, 1684, 1685, 1687–1811, 1813–75, 1877–80, 1882–1900 (462 docs.).

BISHOPSTONE

Ep.II/16/19A, 1592–94, 1605–18, 1620–40, 1664, 1665, 1669–89, 1693–1700, 1702–1812; **/19B,** 1813–80, 1884–92 (368 docs.).

EAST BLATCHINGTON

Ep.II/16/20A, 1592–94, 1598, 1606–08, 1610–18, 1620–41, 1665, 1672, 1673, 1675–87, 1689–1812; **/20B,** 1813–94 (366 docs.).

WEST BLATCHINGTON

Ep.II/16/21, 1635, 1636, 1638–40, 1811 (6 docs.).

BODIAM

Ep.II/16/22A, 1606–18, 1620–40, 1664, 1666, 1668, 1670–1812; **/22B,** 1813–79, 1885–93 (368 docs.).

BODLE STREET

Ep.II/16/23, 1854–93 (128 docs.).

BOGNOR

Ep.I/24/15, 1873–80, 1889, 1890, 1892–94, 1907–09 (100 docs.).

BOLNEY

Ep.II/16/24A, 1606–08, 1610–18, 1620–39, 1641, 1664–68, 1670–1812; **/24B,** 1813–70, 1885–93 (433 docs.).

BOSHAM

Ep.I/24/16A, 1590, 1591, 1594, 1601, 1610, 1613, 1614, 1618, 1625, 1630, 1633, 1634, 1637–40, 1662–65, 1669, 1670, 1672, 1676–79, 1681, 1682, 1690, 1692–1790, 1792–1812; **/16B,** 1813–23, 1825–70, 1872–78, 1888, 1890, 1893, 1894, 1896 (594 docs.).

BOTOLPHS *see* Bramber

BOXGROVE

Ep.I/24/17A, 1584, 1590–92, 1594–97, 1601, 1604, 1605, 1607, 1610, 1613, 1614, 1618, 1625, 1630, 1633, 1634, 1637–40, 1663, 1664, 1666, 1671, 1675, 1676, 1678, 1680, 1682, 1683, 1685–89, 1692–1763, 1765–1812; **/17B,** 1813–90, 1911 (504 docs.).

BRAMBER and BOTOLPHS

Ep.I/24/18, 1591, 1592, 1594, 1596, 1610, 1611, 1613, 1614, 1618, 1623, 1630, 1632–35, 1637–40, 1663, 1670, 1679, 1686, 1688, 1694, 1696–1763, 1765–1868 (423 docs.).

BREDE

Ep.II/16/25A, 1607, 1608, 1610–18, 1620–40, 1667, 1670, 1672, 1673, 1675–1812; **/25B,** 1816–45; **/25C,** 1846–93 (552 docs.).

BRIGHTLING

Ep.II/16/26A, 1596, 1598, 1600, 1605, 1606, 1608, 1610–18, 1620–40, 1664, 1670–83, 1685–1812; **/26B,** 1813–94 (566 docs.).

BRIGHTON

Ep.II/16/27A, 1606–08, 1612, 1614–18, 1620–40, 1665–67, 1673, 1675, 1677, 1679–81, 1684–1754; **/27B,** 1755–76, 1778–84, 1787–89, 1791–1812; **/27C,** 1813–18; **/27D,** 1819–22; **/27E,** 1823–25; **/27F,** 1826–29; **/27G,** 1830–32; **/27H,** 1833–34; **/27J,** 1835–37; **/27K,** 1838–41; **/27L,** 1842–45; **/27M,** 1846–49 (4944 docs.).

BRIGHTON CHAPEL ROYAL

Ep.II/16/28, 1823–26, 1834–40, 1842–47, 1877–82, 1889, 1890 (119 docs.).

BRIGHTON ALL SOULS

Ep.II/16/29, 1883–88 (48 docs.).

BRIGHTON ST. JOHN

Ep.II/16/30, 1880 (10 docs.).

BRIGHTON ST. MATTHEW

Ep.II/16/31, 1884–93 (58 docs.).

BRIGHTON ST. PAUL

Ep.II/16/32, 1873 (23 docs.).

BRIGHTON, EXTRA-MURAL CEMETERY

Ep.II/16/33, 1851–63 (Burials) (458 docs.).

BROADWATER

Ep.I/24/19A, 1571, 1572, 1591, 1592, 1601, 1607, 1610, 1611, 1613, 1614, 1618, 1632–35, 1637–40, 1662–74, 1677, 1678, 1680–90, 1692–1763, 1765–1812; **/19B,** 1813–18, 1822–24; **/19C,** 1832–34, 1836–49; **/19D,** 1850–67; **/19E,** 1868–72, 1874–82; **/19F,** 1893, 1894, 1901, 1903–36 (1681 docs.).

BROADWATER DOWN

Ep.II/16/34, 1867–88, 1890–94 (102 docs.).

BURGESS HILL

Ep.II/16/35, 1863–88, 1890–94 (348 docs.).

BURPHAM

Ep.I/24/20, 1571, 1572, 1590–92, 1594, 1595, 1597, 1601, 1604, 1605, 1610, 1611, 1613, 1614, 1618, 1629, 1630, 1632–34, 1637–40, 1662–68, 1671–75, 1678, 1679, 1681–83, 1685, 1687–98, 1700, 1701, 1703–63, 1765–1822, 1824–72, 1874–78, 1880–83, 1885, 1887–94, 1897, 1899, 1901, 1903–12 (420 docs.).

BURTON and COATES

Ep.I/24/21, 1592, 1594, 1610, 1611, 1618, 1622, 1630, 1633, 1634, 1637, 1640, 1641, 1662–64, 1669–71, 1675–77, 1680, 1687, 1705–63, 1765–1859, 1863–67, 1869, 1872–76, 1878 (241 docs.).

BURWASH

Ep.II/16/36A, 1607–12, 1614–18, 1620–40, 1664, 1667, 1670, 1672–76, 1678, 1680–84, 1686–1812; **/36B,** 1813–60; **/36C,** 1861–90 (763 docs.).

BURWASH WEALD

Ep.II/16/37, 1877–93 (64 docs.).

BURY

Ep.I/24/22, 1590–92, 1594–96, 1599, 1601, 1605, 1607, 1610, 1611, 1613, 1614, 1616, 1618, 1628, 1630, 1632–35, 1637–40, 1662, 1663, 1673, 1678–80, 1684–86, 1688–94, 1697–1763, 1765–1862 (317 docs.).

BUXTED

Ep.V/10/1A, 1662–1812; **/1B,** 1813–50, 1853–60; **/1C,** 1861–76 (640 docs.).

CATSFIELD

Ep.II/16/38A, 1606–09, 1612–18, 1620–40, 1663, 1664, 1666–72, 1676, 1678–83, 1685–91, 1693–1812; **/38B,** 1813–78, 1880, 1886–93 (425 docs.).

CHAILEY

Ep.II/16/39A, 1606–10, 1612–18, 1620–40, 1642, 1664–66, 1668–70, 1672–90, 1692–1812; **/39B,** 1813–60; **/39C,** 1861–93 (697 docs.).

CHALVINGTON

Ep.II/16/40A, 1606, 1608–18, 1620–39, 1664, 1671–79, 1681–85, 1687–1812; **/40B,** 1813–93 (356 docs.).

CHICHESTER ALL SAINTS

Ep.IV/7/2, 1610, 1611, 1682–84, 1687, 1690–96, 1699–1702, 1704, 1708–12, 1714–25, 1727–54, 1756, 1757, 1760–64, 1767–1864, 1867, 1870, 1874, 1875 (260 docs.).

CHICHESTER ST. ANDREW

Ep.III/8/1, 1610, 1614, 1617, 1620, 1621, 1630, 1632–34, 1636–39, 1677, 1678, 1684–86, 1698–1701, 1703–05, 1707, 1710, 1713–20, 1722, 1724–28, 1730, 1733–42, 1744–1861, 1863, 1868, 1870, 1871 (199 docs.).

CHICHESTER ST. BARTHOLOMEW

Ep.III/8/2, 1610, 1613, 1614, 1617, 1621, 1630, 1631, 1633, 1634, 1637, 1639, 1664, 1675, 1691, 1693, 1696, 1700, 1703, 1707, 1711, 1713, 1715–29, 1731–34, 1736–61, 1763, 1765–89, 1791–1819, 1823, 1830–58, 1860–80, 1882–91 (255 docs.).

CHICHESTER ST. MARTIN

Ep.III/8/3, 1613, 1614, 1617, 1620, 1630, 1632–34, 1636–39, 1664, 1675, 1676, 1679–90, 1692–94, 1696, 1698, 1700, 1702, 1703, 1707–09, 1711–13, 1716–20, 1722–35, 1737, 1739–46, 1748–63, 1765–1843, 1845–55, 1867, 1871, 1877, 1878 (256 docs.).

CHICHESTER ST. OLAVE

Ep.III/8/4A, 1621, 1630–34, 1636, 1637, 1639, 1664, 1665, 1675–88, 1690, 1694, 1696–1705, 1707, 1709, 1711–14, 1716–37, 1739–43, 1745–63, 1766–87, 1789, 1790, 1792–95, 1797–1812; /**4B,** 1813–24, 1826–67, 1869–79, 1881, 1882, 1911 (291 docs.).

CHICHESTER ST. PANCRAS

Ep.III/8/5A, 1610, 1613, 1614, 1617, 1620, 1630–34, 1636, 1637, 1639, 1685, 1686, 1694, 1696, 1697, 1699, 1701, 1707, 1710, 1711, 1713–15, 1718–24, 1726–28, 1732–57, 1759–1812; /**5B,** 1813–41, 1843–48, 1855–58, 1864–66, 1868, 1870–72, 1874, 1876–92 (488 docs.).

CHICHESTER ST. PETER THE GREAT *alias* SUBDEANERY

Ep.III/8/6A, 1610, 1613, 1617, 1620, 1621, 1630–34, 1636, 1637, 1639, 1664, 1678–82, 1685, 1686, 1698–1700, 1707, 1711, 1713, 1715–36, 1738–1812; /**6B,** 1813–18, 1827–32; /**6C,** 1833–35, 1837–49, 1851–55; /**6D,** 1868–87, 1889–94 (884 docs.).

CHICHESTER ST. PETER THE LESS

Ep.III/8/7, 1591, 1610, 1613, 1617, 1620, 1621, 1630–34, 1636, 1637, 1639, 1663, 1676, 1677, 1681–85, 1689–91, 1693–1705, 1707–11, 1713, 1714, 1716, 1718–37, 1739–1832, 1839–41, 1843, 1897–99 (214 docs.).

CHICHESTER, THE CLOSE

Ep.III/8/8, 1813–17, 1827–32 (21 docs.).

CHICHESTER, SOCIETY OF FRIENDS

Ep.I/24/23, 1890 (Burials) (2 docs.).

CHIDDINGLY

Ep.II/16/41A, 1605–18, 1620–40, 1665, 1667, 1668, 1671–73, 1676–82, 1684–1812; /**41B,** 1813–93 (585 docs.).

CHIDHAM

Ep.I/24/24A, 1572, 1591, 1592, 1594–96, 1601, 1604, 1605, 1610, 1613, 1614, 1625, 1630, 1633, 1634, 1637–40, 1662, 1664, 1667, 1668, 1670, 1672, 1674–77, 1681–90, 1692–1708, 1710–1812; /**24B,** 1813–53, 1885 (322 docs.).

CHILTINGTON, EAST

Ep.II/16/42A, 1607, 1609, 1630–33, 1635, 1718–27 [to be found in West-meston, II/16/197], 1608, 1611–15, 1617, 1618, 1620, 1621, 1623–29, 1631, 1634, 1636–41, 1664, 1665, 1674–77, 1682–87, 1691, 1692, 1694–1717, 1728–1812; **/42B,** 1813–87, 1889–94 (290 docs.).

See also Westmeston (until 1909 East Chiltington was a chapelry of this parish and returns for both were sometimes made together).

CHILTINGTON, WEST

Ep.I/24/25A, 1571, 1572, 1591, 1594, 1595, 1601, 1610, 1611, 1613, 1614, 1618, 1623, 1630, 1632–34, 1636–40, 1662, 1663, 1665, 1668–71, 1673–78, 1680, 1682–90, 1692–1763, 1765–1812; **/25B,** 1813–16, 1818, 1819, 1821–30, 1833–36, 1838–60, 1863–71, 1897–99, 1901–03 (364 docs.).

CHITHURST

Ep.I/24/26, 1618, 1622, 1630, 1633, 1634, 1637–39, 1662–64, 1666, 1669–71, 1675–77, 1679, 1681, 1683, 1687–89, 1691, 1692, 1695, 1696, 1702–11, 1713–28, 1731, 1733–52, 1754–57, 1759–1803, 1806, 1810–17 (141 docs.).
See also Iping.

CLAPHAM

Ep.I/24/27, 1571, 1572, 1590–96, 1605, 1607, 1610, 1611, 1613, 1614, 1618, 1629, 1632–35, 1637–40, 1662–64, 1666–83, 1685, 1687, 1688, 1690–1711, 1713–26, 1728–55, 1757, 1758, 1760–63, 1765–1808, 1810–72, 1876, 1891–94, 1896–99 (351 docs.).

CLAYTON

Ep.II/16/43A, 1606–08, 1611–18, 1620–39, 1665–69, 1671–74, 1676, 1679–88, 1690–1812; **/43B,** 1813–44, 1846–89, 1891–94 (349 docs.).

CLIFFE *see* Lewes St. Thomas

CLIMPING

Ep.I/24/28, 1572, 1591, 1595, 1596, 1601, 1607, 1610, 1611, 1613, 1614, 1618, 1629, 1630, 1632–35, 1637–40, 1662–64, 1668, 1670, 1673, 1674, 1678, 1680, 1683–1739, 1741–46, 1749–63, 1765–1811, 1813–29, 1832–94 (370 docs.).

COATES *see* Burton

COCKING

Ep.I/24/29, 1590, 1592, 1594, 1601, 1604, 1610, 1611, 1613, 1614, 1618, 1622, 1630, 1633, 1634, 1637, 1639, 1640, 1662–66, 1668–72, 1675–79, 1686, 1689, 1694–97, 1699, 1700, 1702–55, 1757–1821, 1823–58, 1860–68 (311 docs.).

COLDWALTHAM

Ep.I/24/30, 1587, 1592, 1594–96, 1601, 1605, 1607, 1610, 1611, 1613–15, 1618, 1622, 1630, 1633, 1634, 1637, 1639, 1640, 1662–68, 1670, 1671, 1675, 1676, 1679, 1683–89, 1692, 1694, 1696–98, 1700, 1701, 1703–39, 1741–57, 1759–94, 1796–1832, 1834–55, 1857, 1858 (281 docs.).

COLGATE
Ep.I/24/31, 1872–90, 1892 (77 docs.).

COMPTON
Ep.I/24/32A, 1570–72, 1591, 1594, 1601, 1604, 1605, 1613, 1618, 1625, 1630, 1632–34, 1637–41, 1662–66, 1668–70, 1672, 1675–79, 1681–84, 1686–87, 1690, 1693, 1695, 1697–99, 1701–03, 1705, 1710–39, 1741–98, 1800, 1801, 1803–10; /**32B,** 1813–87, 1889–1912 (485 docs.). *See also* Up Marden.

COOMBES
Ep.I/24/33, 1591, 1592, 1594, 1596, 1601, 1610, 1611, 1613, 1614, 1618, 1623, 1632–35, 1638–40, 1669, 1689, 1691–97, 1699–1763, 1765–81, 1783–1822, 1824–51, 1855, 1870–79, 1881–90 (248 docs.).

COPTHORNE
Ep.II/16/44, 1881–93 (48 docs.).

COWFOLD
Ep.II/16/45A, 1606–10, 1612–17, 1619–22, 1624–26, 1628–40, 1667–97, 1699–1812; /**45B,** 1813–38, 1840–44, 1846–49, 1851–89, 1891 (483 docs.).

CRAWLEY
Ep.II/16/46A, 1611–13, 1615, 1617, 1618, 1621–25, 1627–40, 1659, 1664, 1666, 1667, 1671, 1673, 1680–84, 1686–88, 1690–1812; /**46B,** 1813–94 (492 docs.).

CRAWLEY DOWN
Ep.II/16/47, 1845–93, 1908 (237 docs.).

CROWBOROUGH
Ep.II/16/48, 1883–89 (47 docs.).

CROWBOROUGH ST. JOHN, *see* Withiam St. John

CROWHURST
Ep.II/16/49A, 1604–08, 1610–18, 1620–39, 1669–74, 1676–88, 1690–95, 1697–1777, 1779–1812; /**49B,** 1813–85, 1889–94 (412 docs.).

CUCKFIELD
Ep.II/16/50A, 1606–18, 1620–40, 1664, 1665, 1667–91, 1695–1752, 1754–1812; /**50B,** 1813–60; /**50C,** 1861–94, 1908 (959 docs.).

DALLINGTON
Ep.II/16/51A, 1598–1600, 1602, 1606–18, 1620–27, 1630–39, 1664, 1667, 1670, 1672–1812; /**51B,** 1813–40, 1842–93 (484 docs.).

DANEHILL
Ep.II/16/52, 1851–86, 1888, 1890–94 (260 docs.).

EAST DEAN (Lewes)

Ep.II/16/53A, 1606–18, 1620–40, 1670–74, 1678, 1679, 1681–93, 1695–1812; **/53B,** 1813–59, 1861–88, 1890, 1891 (356 docs.).

EAST DEAN (Chichester)

Ep.I/24/34, 1571, 1572, 1591, 1592, 1594–97, 1601, 1604, 1605, 1610, 1613, 1618, 1625, 1630, 1633, 1637–40, 1666, 1669, 1671, 1672, 1675–79, 1681, 1683–1710, 1712–1853, 1855 (267 docs.).

WEST DEAN (Lewes)

Ep.II/16/54A, 1607, 1609, 1610, 1612–18, 1620, 1664, 1667–69, 1674, 1678–84, 1686–90, 1692, 1696–98, 1700, 1702–1812; **/54B,** 1813–94, 1897, 1899, 1902, 1905, 1907 (309 docs.).

WEST DEAN (Chichester)

Ep.I/24/35A, [including Binderton—1592, 1610, 1618, 1626, 1633, 1634, 1637–41] 1592–96, 1604, 1605, 1610, 1613, 1615, 1630, 1632–34, 1637, 1638, 1640, 1667, 1672, 1677, 1678, 1681–85, 1689, 1693, 1695–98, 1700–07, 1709–45, 1747, 1749, 1751–86, 1788–1802, 1804–1812; **/35B,** 1813–61, 1869–1911 (483 docs.).

DENTON

Ep.II/16/55A, 1593, 1594, 1604, 1606–18, 1620–40, 1664, 1665, 1667, 1668, 1670–72, 1674–82, 1684–86, 1689, 1691–1787, 1789–1812; **/55B,** 1813–94 (384 docs.).

UPPER DICKER

Ep.II/16/56, 1845–93 (240 docs.).

DIDLING *see* Treyford

DITCHLING

Ep.II/16/57A, 1606, 1607, 1609–36, 1638–40, 1669, 1671–1812; **/57B,** 1813–73; **/57C,** 1874–92 (565 docs.).

DONNINGTON

Ep.I/24/36, 1584, 1591, 1594, 1595, 1607, 1610, 1613, 1614, 1618, 1625, 1630, 1633, 1634, 1637–40, 1662, 1669, 1673–75, 1678, 1679, 1681–85, 1688–90, 1694, 1695, 1697–1702, 1704–07, 1711–58, 1760–1911 (359 docs.).

DUNCTON

Ep.I/24/37, [1571 and 1572 to be found in Petworth, I/24/89A] 1592, 1594, 1607, 1610, 1611, 1614, 1622, 1630, 1634, 1635, 1637–40, 1662–71, 1675, 1676, 1678, 1679, 1681, 1682, 1685–87, 1693, 1695, 1697, 1698, 1705–47, 1749–63, 1765–1874, 1876–85 (410 docs.).

DURRINGTON

Ep.IV/7/3, 1683–85, 1687, 1692, 1693, 1695–1700, 1702–58, 1761, 1762, 1764, 1767–1808, 1810, 1812–1820, 1822–36, 1838–55, 1857–64, 1867, 1869, 1872–77, 1889 (198 docs.). *See also* West Tarring.

Earnley

Ep.I/24/38, 1590, 1592, 1594–96, 1607, 1610, 1613, 1614, 1618, 1624, 1625, 1630, 1633, 1634, 1637–40, 1662, 1667, 1675, 1677–82, 1686, 1687, 1691, 1694, 1695, 1697, 1699–1718, 1720, 1722-28, 1730–41, 1743–45, 1747–1850, 1854–57, 1860–67, 1869–98 (265 docs.).

Eartham

Ep.I/24/39, 1591, 1592, 1594, 1595, 1597, 1601, 1604, 1607, 1610, 1613, 1614, 1618, 1626, 1632–34, 1637–40, 1662, 1665, 1666, 1675, 1680, 1695–1726, 1728–1816, 1818–62, 1864–67, 1871, 1873–80, 1882–1911(360 docs.).

Easebourne

Ep.I/24/40A, 1591, 1592, 1594, 1607, 1610, 1611, 1618, 1622, 1630, 1633–35, 1637–41, 1662–71, 1675, 1677–79, 1683–90, 1692–1707, 1709–1812; **/40B,** 1813–78 (552 docs.).

Eastbourne

Ep.II/16/58A, 1593, 1594, 1606–08, 1610–18, 1620–40, 1664, 1665, 1669–1812; **/58B,** 1813–60; **/58C,** 1861–88, 1890, 1892, 1894 (1111 docs.).

Eastbourne All Saints

Ep.II/16/59, 1879–93 (36 docs.).

Eastbourne All Souls

Ep.II/16/60, 1882–91, 1893 (Baptisms) (76 docs.).

Eastbourne Christchurch

Ep.II/16/61, 1864–93 (299 docs.).

Eastbourne Holy Trinity

Ep.II/16/62, 1848–80, 1892 (173 docs.).

Eastbourne St. John

Ep.II/16/63, 1892, 1893 (8 docs.).

Eastbourne St. John, All Saints Convalescent Home

Ep.II/16/64, 1884, 1887–93 (Baptisms) (12 docs.).

Eastbourne St. Saviour

Ep.II/16/65, 1868–80, 1882–93 (93 docs.).

Eastergate

Ep.I/24/41, 1590, 1593–95, 1601, 1604, 1605, 1610, 1611, 1613, 1614, 1618, 1630, 1633–35, 1637–40, 1662–66, 1668, 1670, 1673, 1677, 1678, 1680, 1681, 1683–1744, 1746, 1747, 1750, 1752–63, 1765–77, 1779–1817, 1819–28, 1830–35, 1837–51, 1853–61, 1879–97, 1899–1901 (186 docs.).

Ebernoe

Ep.I/24/42, 1875, 1876, 1884, 1885, 1888–92, 1896, 1897, 1899 (40 docs.).

EDBURTON

Ep.V/10/2A, 1662–68, 1670, 1671, 1673, 1675, 1676, 1678, 1681–1812; **/2B,** 1813–83, 1891–94 (344 docs.).

EGDEAN

Ep.I/24/43, 1630, 1633–35, 1637–40, 1663, 1665, 1667, 1670, 1674, 1675, 1677, 1681, 1687, 1688, 1695, 1696, 1699, 1701, 1703, 1706–1716, 1718–62, 1764–71, 1773–1857, 1859, 1872–77, 1879–1903, 1906, 1907 (274 docs.).

ELSTED

Ep.I/24/44A, 1592, 1601, 1610, 1614, 1618, 1622, 1630, 1633–35, 1637–41, 1662–65, 1668–71, 1675, 1677, 1681–83, 1685–94, 1696–1700, 1702–19, 1721, 1722, 1724-70, 1772–1812; **/44B,** 1813–49, 1851–58, 1860–66, 1868–84, 1899–1902 (356 docs.).

ERIDGE GREEN

Ep.II/16/66, 1857–81, 1891–94, 1903–09 (105 docs.).

ETCHINGHAM

Ep.II/16/67A, 1604–08, 1610–16, 1618, 1620–40, 1664, 1669–73, 1675, 1677–83, 1686, 1689–1812; **/67B,** 1813–46, 1849–84, 1886, 1887 (447 docs.).

EWHURST

Ep.II/16/68A, 1606–08, 1610–18, 1620–40, 1664, 1667–1750, 1752–1812; **/68B,** 1813–63, 1869–72, 1883, 1886 (505 docs.).

FAIRLIGHT

Ep.II/16/69A, 1606–17, 1620–39, 1664, 1669–83, 1685–88, 1692–96, 1698–1782, 1784–1812; **/69B,** 1813–54, 1856–92 (592 docs.).

FALMER

Ep.II/16/70A, 1606–18, 1620–27, 1629–40, 1664, 1670–76, 1680, 1682–98, 1700–1812; **/70B,** 1813–89 (409 docs.).

FELPHAM

Ep.I/24/45A, 1592, 1593, 1595, 1596, 1605, 1610–14, 1629, 1630, 1632–35, 1637–40, 1662, 1663, 1677, 1681–90, 1692–1747, 1749–63, 1765–1812; **/45B,** 1813–49, 1852, 1853, 1856–59, 1861, 1866, 1870–1911 (444 docs.).

FERNHURST

Ep.I/24/46A, 1590–92, 1594, 1601, 1604, 1607, 1610, 1611, 1613, 1614, 1618, 1622, 1630, 1633–35, 1637, 1639–41, 1662–69, 1671, 1672, 1675, 1678, 1681, 1683, 1685–1732, 1734–39, 1741, 1743–1812; **/46B,** 1813–16, 1818–74 (482 docs.).

FERRING

Ep.I/24/47, 1591–97, 1604, 1605, 1610, 1611, 1613, 1614, 1618, 1629, 1630, 1632–35, 1637–40, 1662, 1664, 1670–74, 1676, 1680–83, 1685, 1689–1729, 1731–63, 1765–1892 (337 docs.).

FINDON

Ep.I/24/48, 1592, 1594, 1596, 1601, 1607, 1610, 1611, 1613, 1614, 1618, 1623, 1630, 1632–35, 1637–41, 1662, 1663, 1668, 1670, 1672–79, 1682, 1683, 1685, 1688–92, 1694, 1696, 1697, 1699, 1700, 1702–35, 1737, 1739– 41, 1743–63, 1765–1831, 1833–79, 1881, 1882, 1885–91, 1894, 1896–99, 1901–10 (505 docs.).

WEST FIRLE

Ep.II/16/71A, 1606–18, 1620–38, 1664, 1671, 1672, 1682–89, 1691–1812; **/71B,** 1813–94 (466 docs.).

NEW FISHBOURNE

Ep.III/8/9, 1591, 1594, 1595, 1610, 1613, 1614, 1617, 1620, 1621, 1629–34, 1636, 1637, 1639, 1675, 1676, 1678–81, 1683–86, 1689–94, 1696–1705, 1707–63, 1765–1770, 1772–87, 1789, 1790, 1795, 1797–1872, 1875–1907, 1910, 1911 (427 docs.).

FITTLEWORTH

Ep.I/24/49, 1584, 1592, 1594, 1610, 1611, 1613, 1614, 1618, 1622, 1633, 1634, 1637, 1639–41, 1662–65, 1667–70, 1672, 1674–80, 1683, 1685–88, 1690–1755, 1757–1866, 1875–99, 1901, 1903, 1904, 1906–08 (365 docs.).

FLETCHING

Ep.II/16/72A, 1606–18, 1620–40, 1664, 1665, 1667–79, 1681–1812; **/72B,** 1813–60; **/72C,** 1861–96, 1898 (904 docs.).

FLIMWELL

Ep.II/16/73, 1844–82, 1885–93 (280 docs.).

FOLKINGTON

Ep.II/16/74A, 1606–18, 1620–40, 1671–74, 1678, 1679, 1681, 1682, 1684– 87, 1690–1812; **/74B,** 1813–78, 1881, 1882 (404 docs.).

FORD

Ep.I/24/50, 1572, 1590–95, 1610, 1611, 1613, 1614, 1618, 1629, 1630, 1633–35, 1637–40, 1662–66, 1679–89, 1692, 1694–1700, 1702–15, 1717, 1719–45, 1747–53, 1755–63, 1765–1821, 1823–29, 1832–98 (414 docs.).

FOREST ROW

Ep.II/16/75, 1850–93 (273 docs.).

FRAMFIELD

Ep.V/10/3A, 1662, 1665–1812; **/3B,** 1813–38, 1841, 1845–82, 1886–93 (532 docs.).

FRANT

Ep.II/16/76A, 1598–1600, 1604–18, 1620–40, 1662–65, 1667, 1668, 1672– 1812; **/76B,** 1813–60; **/76C,** 1861–87 (870 docs.).

FRISTON

Ep.II/16/77A, 1603–06, 1608–12, 1614, 1615, 1617, 1618, 1620–40, 1667, 1669–73, 1675–88, 1690, 1692, 1695–97, 1700–68, 1770–1812; /**77B,** 1813–27, 1829–82, 1884, 1885, 1888, 1890, 1891 (255 docs.).

FUNTINGTON

Ep.I/24/51A, 1590, 1592, 1594–96, 1601, 1610, 1613, 1614, 1618, 1625, 1630, 1632, 1634, 1637–41, 1667, 1670, 1672, 1674–79, 1681–1705, 1707–52, 1754–1812; /**51B,** 1813–52, 1854–68, 1870, 1872–1908 (514 docs.).

GLYNDE

Ep.V/10/4A, 1662–64, 1669–71, 1673, 1678–85, 1688–1811; /**4B,** 1813–93 (325 docs.).

GORING

Ep.I/24/52, 1571, 1572, 1596, 1597, 1610, 1611, 1613, 1614, 1618, 1623, 1632–35, 1637–41, 1662–64, 1670–72, 1674–78, 1680–1763, 1765–1861, 1863–67, 1870, 1872–76, 1878, 1879, 1881, 1882, 1884–88, 1890, 1891, 1893, 1894, 1898, 1899, 1901, 1902 (413 docs.).

GRAFFHAM

Ep.I/24/53, 1590–92, 1594, 1604, 1610, 1611, 1613, 1614, 1618, 1622, 1631, 1633, 1634, 1637–41, 1662–65, 1667, 1668, 1670–72, 1674–78, 1681–83, 1685–90, 1695, 1698–1709, 1711–1871 (423 docs.).

EAST GRINSTEAD

Ep.II/16/78A, 1606, 1609, 1610, 1616–18, 1621, 1622, 1624–26, 1628–40, 1667–77, 1679–1812; /**78B,** 1813–36; /**78C,** 1837–60; /**78D,** 1861–90, 1892–94, 1896, 1897, 1899 (1348 docs.).

WEST GRINSTEAD

Ep.I/24/54A, 1591, 1592, 1594, 1596, 1601, 1610, 1611, 1613, 1614, 1618, 1623, 1630, 1632–35, 1637–40, 1662–69, 1671, 1675, 1676, 1679, 1682–86, 1689–1763, 1765–1812; /**54B,** 1813–15, 1831–72, 1888–94, 1896–99, 1901–04, 1906, 1908–12 (506 docs.).

NEW GROOMBRIDGE

Ep.II/16/79, 1886, 1887, 1889 (10 docs.).

GUESTLING

Ep.II/16/80A, 1606–18, 1620–27, 1629–40, 1667–69, 1671–1812; /**80B,** 1813–89 (409 docs.).

EAST GULDEFORD

Ep.II/16/81A, 1605–08, 1611, 1612, 1614–18, 1620–40, 1664, 1666, 1670, 1671, 1673–83, 1688–1812; /**81B,** 1813–93 (409 docs.).

HADLOW DOWN

Ep.II/16/82, 1836–41, 1846–94, 1908 (228 docs.).

HAILSHAM

Ep.II/16/83A, 1593–97, 1604, 1607–18, 1620–40, 1671–74, 1676–78, 1680–87, 1689–1812; **/83B,** 1813–86 (602 docs.).

HAMMERWOOD

Ep.II/16/84, 1879–86 (22 docs.).

HAMSEY

Ep.II/16/85A, 1607–18, 1620–37, 1639, 1664, 1665, 1669–75, 1678, 1679, 1681–1812; **/85B,** 1813–94 (390 docs.).

HANGLETON

Ep.II/16/86A, 1635, 1678, 1697–1765, 1767–94, 1796–1812; **/86B,** 1813–37, 1839–47, 1849–53, 1855–75 (173 docs.). *See also* Portslade.

HARDHAM

Ep.I/24/55, 1591, 1592, 1594, 1604, 1607, 1614, 1618, 1622, 1630, 1633–35, 1639, 1640, 1662–64, 1668, 1670, 1675, 1676, 1681–91, 1694, 1695, 1697, 1699–1706, 1708–25, 1727–30, 1732–38, 1740–47, 1749, 1751–53, 1755, 1757–1804, 1806–58 (220 docs.).

HARTFIELD

Ep.II/16/87A, 1594, 1604, 1606, 1608–18, 1620–22, 1624, 1626–40, 1664, 1665, 1667–1812; **/87B,** 1813–60; **/87C,** 1861–88, 1890–99 (724 docs.).

HARTING

Ep.I/24/56A, 1584, 1590, 1591, 1594, 1601, 1604, 1610, 1611, 1613, 1614, 1618, 1622, 1630, 1633–35, 1637–40, 1661–65, 1667–79, 1681–84, 1693, 1695, 1696, 1698–1719, 1721–1812; **/56B,** 1813–69; **/56C,** 1870–1912 (746 docs.).

HASTINGS ALL SAINTS

Ep.II/16/88A, 1606–18, 1620–36, 1638–40, 1667, 1668, 1671–73, 1677–83, 1685–1812; **/88B,** 1813–34; **/88C,** 1835–60; **/88D,** 1861–95 (1265 docs.).

HASTINGS CHRIST CHURCH

Ep.II/16/89, 1888 (6 docs.).

HASTINGS EMMANUEL

Ep.II/16/90, 1874–79, 1887 (34 docs.).

HASTINGS HOLY TRINITY

Ep.II/16/91, 1864–87, 1890, 1892 (121 docs.).

HASTINGS ST. CLEMENT

Ep.II/16/92A, 1608, 1610–12, 1614, 1615, 1617, 1618, 1620–29, 1632–35, 1637, 1638, 1640, 1667, 1670–1740, 1742–1812; **/92B,** 1813–60; **/92C,** 1861–98, 1900 (825 docs.).

HASTINGS ST. CLEMENT, HALTON
Ep.II/16/93, 1840–92 (322 docs.).

HASTINGS ST. MARY-IN-THE-CASTLE
Ep.II/16/94, 1828–97 (472 docs.).

HAYWARDS HEATH
Ep.II/16/95, 1866–1909 (351 docs.).

HAYWARDS HEATH, SUSSEX LUNATIC ASYLUM
Ep.II/16/96, 1867–83, 1893 (Burials) (86 docs.).

HEATHFIELD
Ep.II/16/97A, 1598–1600, 1603, 1604, 1606–10, 1612–18, 1620–41, 1667–75, 1678, 1679, 1681–84, 1686–1731, 1734–1812; **/97B,** 1813–60; **/97C,** 1861–72, 1874–85, 1887 (658 docs.).

HEENE
Ep.IV/7/4, 1610, 1618, 1662–64, 1677, 1680–86, 1702, 1704–20, 1722–51, 1753, 1754, 1758, 1759, 1761, 1762, 1767, 1768, 1770–74, 1776–91, 1793–1817, 1819, 1820, 1822–35, 1838–55, 1857–64, 1867, 1869, 1873–77, 1892–1906 (262 docs.). *See also* West Tarring.

SOUTH HEIGHTON
Ep.II/16/98, 1604, 1606–18, 1620–24, 1626–28, 1630–40, 1664, 1665, 1667, 1669–76, 1678–87, 1689–97, 1699–1812 [including Tarring Neville from 1775] (164 docs.). *See also* Tarring Neville.

HELLINGLY
Ep.II/16/99A, 1607, 1608, 1610–18, 1620–40, 1670, 1671, 1673, 1675, 1677–81, 1683–85, 1687, 1689–1812; **/99B,** 1813–91 (637 docs.).

HENFIELD
Ep.II/16/100A, 1606–18, 1620–26, 1628–41, 1666–68, 1670–72, 1674, 1675, 1677–1812; **/100B,** 1813–60; **/100C,** 1861–93 (811 docs.).

HERSTMONCEUX *see* Hurstmonceux

HEYSHOTT
Ep.I/24/57, 1590–92, 1594, 1601, 1607, 1610, 1611, 1613, 1614, 1618, 1622, 1630, 1633–35, 1637–40, 1662–65, 1667–70, 1672, 1675–79, 1681, 1683, 1687, 1689–96, 1698–1755, 1757–1816, 1818, 1822–25, 1845, 1846, 1875, 1876, 1878, 1883, 1884, 1897, 1898 (203 docs.).

HIGHBROOK ALL SAINTS
Ep.II/16/101, 1885, 1886, 1888–99 (29 docs.).

HIGH HURST WOOD
Ep.II/16/102, 1872–79 (40 docs.).

HOATHLY, EAST
Ep.II/16/103A, 1607–18, 1620–40, 1664, 1665, 1667, 1671, 1673–79, 1682, 1684–1812; /**103B,** 1813–82 (455 docs.).

HOATHLY, WEST
Ep.II/16/104A, 1606, 1608, 1610–18, 1620–40, 1665–69, 1671–1812; /**104B,** 1813–96, 1908, 1909 (637 docs.).

HOLLINGTON
Ep.II/16/105A, 1606, 1607, 1609–18, 1620–40, 1664, 1667, 1670–79, 1681–1812; /**105B,** 1813–93 (644 docs.).

HOLLINGTON ST. JOHN
Ep.II/16/106, 1870–93 (68 docs.).

HOOE
Ep.II/16/107A, 1606–18, 1620–40, 1667, 1669–71, 1674–76, 1678–1812; /**107B,** 1813–93, 1902, 1908 (417 docs.).

HORSHAM
Ep.I/24/58A, 1571, 1572, 1584, 1592, 1601, 1610, 1611, 1613, 1614, 1618, 1623, 1630, 1632–35, 1637–40, 1662–71, 1673, 1674, 1676–79, 1681–86, 1689–1726, 1728–49; /**58B,** 1751–63, 1765–1810; /**58C,** 1813–23, 1825, 1826; /**58D,** 1827–39; /**58E,** 1840–59; /**58F**[1], 1860–64, 1866–77, 1879–83 (1745 docs.).

HORSHAM SOCIETY OF FRIENDS
Ep.I/24/59[2], 1866, 1876, 1880, 1881, 1887 (Burials) (5 docs.).

HORSTED KEYNES
Ep.II/16/108A, 1605–18, 1620–40, 1664–1665, 1671–1812; /**108B,** 1813–93 (516 docs.).

LITTLE HORSTED
Ep.II/16/109A, 1593, 1594, 1605–10, 1613–18, 1620–40, 1664, 1665, 1667–69, 1673–80, 1682–94, 1697–1782, 1784–1812; /**109B,** 1813–82, 1885, 1888, 1891, 1893 (482 docs.).

HOUGHTON
Ep.I/24/60, 1591–95, 1605, 1610, 1613, 1614, 1618, 1629, 1633, 1634, 1637–40, 1662–65, 1668, 1669, 1672, 1674, 1676, 1679, 1681–83, 1685, 1686, 1688, 1689, 1691–98, 1700–63, 1765–1850 (251 docs.).

HOVE
Ep.II/16/110A, 1606–08, 1610, 1613–17, 1620–40, 1672, 1674–78, 1681–85, 1688, 1692–1715, 1717–32, 1735–40, 1742–47, 1749–53, 1758, 1759, 1770–75, 1777, 1778, 1780–82, 1785–96, 1798–1812; /**110B,** 1813–27 [the

[1] This is in the same bundle as Ep.I/24/59.
[2] This is in the same bundle as Ep.I/24/58F.

transcripts in this bundle are illegible, and cannot be produced]; /**110C,** 1828–64; /**110D,** 1865–74, 1877–82 (913 docs.).

HOVE HOLY TRINITY
Ep.II/16/111, 1878, 1879, 1884, 1885 (4 docs.).

HOVE ST. ANDREW
Ep.II/16/112, 1831–57, 1862–93 (86 docs.).

HOVE ST. JOHN
Ep.II/16/113, 1869, 1871–83 (33 docs.).

HOVE ST. PATRICK
Ep.II/16/114, 1885–93 (25 docs.).

HUNSTON
Ep.I/24/61A, 1584, 1590, 1592, 1594, 1596, 1601, 1604, 1605, 1610, 1613, 1618, 1625, 1633, 1634, 1637–41, 1662, 1664, 1665, 1669, 1670, 1675–78, 1680–1737, 1740–1812; /**61B,** 1813–76, 1878–1908 (412 docs.).

HURSTMONCEUX
Ep.II/16/115A, 1606–08, 1610–18, 1620–25, 1627, 1629–40, 1665, 1666, 1671–78, 1682–87, 1692–1812; /**115B,** 1813–93 (538 docs.).

HURSTPIERPOINT
Ep.II/16/116A, 1607–13, 1615–18, 1620–41, 1664, 1665, 1672, 1673, 1675–78, 1680–82, 1684–1812; /**116B,** 1813–61; /**116C,** 1862–94 (798 docs.).

ICKLESHAM
Ep.II/16/117A, 1606–18, 1620–37, 1639–1640, 1664, 1667, 1671–73, 1675–85, 1687–89, 1691, 1693–1812; /**117B,** 1813–79, 1881, 1882, 1884–92 (470 docs.).

IDEN
Ep.II/16/118A, 1606–08, 1610–18, 1620–40, 1664, 1665, 1673–1812; /**118B,** 1813–81, 1883, 1884, 1886–94 (476 docs.).

IFIELD
Ep.II/16/119A, 1606, 1609–18, 1620–38, 1640, 1670, 1672, 1673, 1677, 1679–83, 1687–1812; /**119B,** 1813–93 (606 docs.).

IFIELD SOCIETY OF FRIENDS
Ep.II/16/120, 1865–67 (3 docs.).

IFORD
Ep.II/16/121A, 1606–18, 1620–41, 1667–1812; /**121B,** 1813–83 (354 docs.).

IPING
Ep.I/24/62A, 1592, 1594, 1611, 1613, 1614, 1618, 1622, 1630, 1633–35, 1637–40, 1662–72, 1675–78, 1681–86, 1688–91, 1693–1700, 1703–11, 1713–

1812; /**62B,** 1813–20, 1838–49, 1851–75, 1888–90 [including Chithurst from 1818] (296 docs.).

ISFIELD

Ep.V/10/5A, 1667–1812; /**5B,** 1813–93 (380 docs.).

ITCHENOR, WEST

Ep.I/24/63A, 1591, 1594, 1597, 1601, 1604, 1610, 1613, 1614, 1618, 1630, 1631, 1633, 1634, 1637–40, 1662, 1664, 1665, 1677, 1678, 1681, 1682, 1685, 1687, 1688, 1690–94, 1697, 1700–07, 1709, 1711–19, 1721–31, 1733–90, 1792–1812; /**63B,** 1813–27, 1829–80 (300 docs.).

ITCHINGFIELD

Ep.I/24/64A, 1591, 1592, 1594, 1596, 1601, 1603, 1610, 1611, 1614, 1618, 1623, 1630, 1632–35, 1637–40, 1662–70, 1672–1812; /**64B,** 1813, 1819, 1824, 1827, 1828, 1830–64, 1866–69, 1871–88 (341 docs.).

JEVINGTON

Ep.II/16/122A, 1606–18, 1620–41, 1664, 1670–1812; /**122B,** 1813–77, 1886–92 (359 docs.).

KEYMER

Ep.II/16/123A, 1626–40, 1665–67, 1669, 1671, 1672, 1674, 1676, 1677, 1679–86, 1691–1812, /**123B,** 1813–37, 1839–58, 1860–94 (411 docs.).

KINGSTON-BY-LEWES

Ep.II/16/124A, 1606, 1608, 1610–18, 1620–40, 1664–66, 1668–73, 1675–78, 1680–85, 1687–1812; /**124B,** 1813–83 (400 docs.).

KINGSTON-BY-SEA

Ep.II/16/125A, 1606–09, 1611–18, 1620–41, 1682–1812; /**125B,** 1813–41, 1843–93 (244 docs.).

KINGSTON GORSE

Ep.I/24/65, 1590–97, 1600, 1601, 1604, 1605, 1607, 1610, 1611, 1613, 1618, 1629, 1630, 1633–35, 1637–40 (30 docs.). *See also* East Preston.

KIRDFORD

Ep.I/24/66A, 1571, 1572, 1591, 1592, 1594, 1610, 1611, 1613, 1614, 1618, 1622, 1630, 1633–35, 1638–40, 1662–65, 1667–71, 1674–76, 1678, 1679, 1681, 1682, 1684–93, 1696–1733, 1735–1812; /**66B,** 1813–57, 1881, 1882, 1887–90 (528 docs.).

LANCING

Ep.I/24/67A, 1591, 1594, 1596, 1601, 1610, 1611, 1613, 1614, 1618, 1630, 1632–35, 1637–40, 1664, 1667, 1670–77, 1679, 1683, 1684, 1688–1749, 1751–63, 1765–1812; /**67B,** 1813–15, 1823–81, 1883–1916, 1918 (578 docs.).

LAUGHTON

Ep.II/16/126A, 1605–07, 1609–11, 1614–18, 1620, 1622–41, 1664, 1667, 1670–1812; /**126B,** 1813–91 (491 docs.).

East Lavant

Ep.IV/7/5, 1610, 1618, 1662, 1671, 1679–81, 1683, 1684, 1686–91, 1693–1704, 1706–38, 1740, 1741, 1743–64, 1766–1808, 1812–78 (320 docs.).

Mid Lavant

Ep.I/24/68, 1591, 1592, 1594, 1597, 1601, 1610, 1613, 1614, 1618, 1625, 1630, 1632–34, 1637–41, 1662–65, 1675, 1678, 1684, 1687–91, 1694, 1696–1700, 1702, 1703, 1705–20, 1722–34, 1736–1817, 1819, 1821–23, 1825–64, 1866–70, 1876, 1878 (307 docs.).

West Lavington

Ep.I/24/69, 1851–62, 1878–98, 1901, 1902 (55 docs.).

Lewes All Saints

Ep.II/16/127A, 1606–11, 1613, 1617, 1618, 1620, 1623, 1626–28, 1631, 1664, 1672, 1674, 1678–88, 1690–1812; **/127B,** 1813–37; **/127C,** 1838–77; **/127D,** 1878–89 (619 docs.).

Lewes St. Anne

Ep.II/16/128A, 1608, 1610, 1611, 1616, 1620, 1625, 1627–33, 1636, 1672, 1673, 1677, 1678, 1682–1812; **/128B,** 1813–65 (430 docs.).

Lewes St. John

Ep.II/16/129A, 1606–09, 1611–13, 1615–18, 1620–29, 1631–39, 1665, 1672–77, 1681, 1684–96, 1698–1812; **/129B,** 1813–60; **/129C,** 1861–89 (928 docs.).

Lewes St. John Southover

Ep.II/16/130A, 1607–18, 1620–41, 1666, 1671–77, 1679–1782, 1784–1812; **/130B,** 1813–86 (530 docs.).

Lewes St. Mark Westout *see* Lewes St. Anne

Lewes St. Michael

Ep.II/16/131A, 1606–14, 1616–18, 1620, 1622–24, 1626–38, 1640, 1642, 1666, 1672–74, 1676–80, 1682–1812; **/131B,** 1813–45; **/131C,** 1846–51, 1855–86, 1888, 1890–92, 1894, 1895 (763 docs.).

Lewes St. Thomas at Cliffe

Ep.V/10/6A, 1667, 1668, 1671–74, 1676–1812; **/6B,** 1813–60; **/6C,** 1861–87, 1892, 1893 (717 docs.).

Lewes Society of Friends

Ep.II/16/132, 1865–68, 1870, 1874–78, 1882, 1884–86, 1890–93, 1895, 1901 (Burials) (18 docs.).

Linch

Ep.I/24/70, 1704, 1706, 1708–10, 1713, 1716–19, 1721–38, 1742, 1744–57, 1759–1805, 1807–81 (227 docs.).

LINCHMERE

Ep.I/24/71, 1590–92, 1594, 1601, 1610, 1611, 1618, 1622, 1630, 1633–35, 1637–41, 1662–67, 1669, 1670, 1672, 1675–78, 1681–85, 1687, 1688, 1690–93, 1697, 1699, 1700, 1702, 1704–26, 1728–1802, 1804–13, 1816–94, 1907–10 (337 docs.).

LINDFIELD

Ep.V/10/7A, 1662, 1664–68, 1670–1812; **/7B,** 1813–43, 1845–60; **/7C,** 1861–94 (683 docs.).

LITLINGTON

Ep.II/16/133A, 1593–95, 1606–18, 1620–40, 1675, 1678, 1679, 1681–83, 1685, 1686, 1690, 1692, 1693, 1695–1800, 1802–12; **/133B,** 1813–94, 1909 (339 docs.).

LITTLEHAMPTON

Ep.I/24/72A, 1591, 1594–96, 1601, 1604, 1610, 1611, 1613, 1614, 1618, 1629, 1630, 1632–35, 1637–40, 1663–68, 1671, 1674, 1675, 1677, 1678, 1680–83, 1685–1733, 1735–63, 1765–1812; **/72B,** 1813–63, 1869–72, 1881, 1891, 1892 (499 docs.).

LODSWORTH

Ep.I/24/73A, 1572, 1592, 1594, 1601, 1604, 1607, 1610, 1611, 1613, 1614, 1618, 1622, 1630, 1633–35, 1637–40, 1662–70, 1672, 1674–76, 1679, 1681, 1682, 1684–86, 1688–99, 1701–1812; **/73B,** 1813–73, 1876–79, 1885, 1886, 1890–93 (371 docs.).

LULLINGTON

Ep.II/16/134A, 1606–09, 1611–18, 1620–40, 1698–1812; **/134B,** 1813–48, 1850, 1857, 1861–64, 1869, 1879–85, 1887–89, 1892, 1894 (186 docs.).

LURGASHALL

Ep.I/24/74A, 1591, 1592, 1594, 1604, 1610, 1613, 1614, 1618, 1622, 1630, 1633–35, 1637, 1639–41, 1662, 1664, 1665, 1667–69, 1672, 1675, 1678, 1679, 1681–1704, 1706–16, 1718–44, 1746–1812; **/74B,** 1819–49, 1855–62, 1864, 1875, 1876, 1878, 1879, 1881, 1883, 1885–94, 1896–99, 1901–11 (408 docs.).

LYMINSTER

Ep.I/24/75A, 1571, 1572, 1591, 1592, 1595–97, 1601, 1605, 1607, 1610, 1611, 1613, 1614, 1618, 1630, 1632–35, 1637–39, 1641, 1662–64, 1666–68, 1671, 1672, 1674, 1675, 1677–83, 1685–87, 1690–1701, 1703–28, 1730–63, 1765–1812; **/75B,** 1813–24, 1833–51, 1856–67, 1871, 1878–84 (391 docs.).

MADEHURST

Ep.I/24/76, 1572, 1591–95, 1605, 1607, 1610, 1611, 1613, 1614, 1618, 1629, 1630, 1633–35, 1638–40, 1662–66, 1668, 1670–74, 1680, 1681, 1683, 1685–88, 1690, 1692–1716, 1718–46, 1748–63, 1765–1804, 1806–1813, 1815–24, 1827–29, 1831–34, 1836–55, 1858, 1859, 1861–75 (229 docs.).

South Malling

Ep.V/10/8A, 1667, 1668, 1675, 1678, 1681–83, 1685, 1687–93, 1698–1812; **/8B,** 1813, 1815–94, 1908, 1909 (404 docs.).

East Marden

Ep.I/24/77, 1571, 1584, 1590–92, 1594, 1601, 1605, 1610, 1613, 1614, 1618, 1625, 1630, 1633, 1634, 1637–40, 1664–66, 1668, 1669, 1676–78, 1683, 1684, 1686–91, 1693–95, 1697–1718, 1720–36, 1738–46, 1748, 1750, 1751, 1753–96, 1798, 1799, 1801–06, 1808, 1809, 1811, 1813–65, 1867–74, 1877–83, 1885, 1886, 1888–1902, 1910, 1911 (317 docs.).

North Marden

Ep.I/24/78, 1590–92, 1601, 1605, 1607, 1610, 1613, 1618, 1625, 1630, 1633, 1634, 1637–40, 1666, 1674–76, 1678, 1681–83, 1685–90, 1693, 1694, 1696–1715, 1717–19, 1721–33, 1735–38, 1740, 1742–45, 1747–97, 1799–1811, 1813–27, 1829, 1830, 1832–55, 1857, 1859–65, 1870–76, 1884, 1887, 1889–1902 (334 docs.).

Up Marden

Ep.I/24/79, 1601, 1607, 1612, 1618, 1630, 1633, 1634, 1637–40, 1662–66, 1668–70, 1672, 1674, 1675, 1677, 1679, 1681, 1688, 1694, 1695, 1700, 1704, 1706–09, 1713–96, 1798–1801, 1803–10, 1813–82, 1884–89, 1891–1909 [including Compton 1704–09] (318 docs.).

Maresfield

Ep.II/16/135A, 1594, 1605–08, 1610–23, 1625–40, 1663, 1664, 1668–70, 1672–1812; **/135B,** 1813–90, 1892 (637 docs.).

Mark Cross

Ep.II/16/136, 1875–84, 1891 (20 docs.).

Mayfield

Ep.V/10/9A, 1666, 1669, 1673–76, 1678–87, 1689–1754; **/9B,** 1755–94; **/9C,** 1795, 1796, 1800–34; **/9D,** 1835–97 (985 docs.).

Meeching see Newhaven

Merston

Ep.I/24/80, 1594, 1601, 1610, 1613, 1614, 1618, 1625, 1630, 1633, 1634, 1637–41, 1663–66, 1675, 1677–81, 1683–88, 1690–93, 1695–1717, 1719–1818, 1827–49, 1856–61, 1864, 1870, 1873–92 (274 docs.).

Middleton

Ep.I/24/81, 1592, 1610, 1618, 1629, 1632–34, 1637, 1639, 1640, 1662–67, 1670, 1675, 1682–85, 1689, 1698–1718, 1720–57, 1759–63, 1765–99, 1801–11, 1813–20, 1822, 1823, 1825–37, 1849–64, 1866–68, 1906–09 (223 docs.).

Midhurst

Ep.I/24/82A, 1591, 1594, 1610, 1613, 1614, 1618, 1622, 1630, 1633–35, 1637–41, 1662–73, 1675–1812; **/82B,** 1813–79, 1881, 1882, 1885, 1890–1905 (645 docs.).

MILLAND *alias* TUXLITH
Ep.I/24/83, 1861–1904, 1908 (222 docs.).

MOUNTFIELD
Ep.II/16/137A, 1604–39, 1664–82, 1684–1812; /**137B,** 1813–96 (524 docs.).

NORTH MUNDHAM
Ep.I/24/84A, 1591, 1592, 1594, 1601, 1605, 1607, 1610, 1613, 1614, 1618, 1625, 1630, 1632–34, 1637–39, 1664, 1668, 1670, 1677, 1681, 1682, 1688–91, 1694, 1695, 1697–1737, 1740–1812; /**84B,** 1813–56, 1858–1903, 1905–09 (463 docs.).

NETHERFIELD
Ep.II/16/138, 1862–93 (92 docs.).

NEWHAVEN *alias* MEECHING
Ep.II/16/139A, 1606–08, 1610–13, 1615–18, 1620–37, 1639, 1640, 1664, 1667, 1668, 1672–88, 1692–1738, 1741–1812; /**139B,** 1813–94, 1897, 1898 (641 docs.).

NEWICK
Ep.II/16/140A, 1606–17, 1620–40, 1665–67, 1669, 1672–1812; /**140B,** 1813–79, 1885–93 (488 docs.).

NEWTIMBER
Ep.II/16/141A, 1606, 1609–18, 1620–27, 1629–38, 1640–42, 1664, 1672–76, 1678–85, 1688–1812; /**141B,** 1813–94 (320 docs.).

NINFIELD
Ep.II/16/142A, 1599, 1600, 1605–08, 1610, 1611, 1613, 1615–18, 1620–39, 1664, 1666, 1667, 1669–1812; /**142B,** 1813–77 (440 docs.).

NORTHCHAPEL
Ep.I/24/85A, 1592, 1593, 1611, 1614, 1618, 1622, 1630, 1633, 1634, 1637–41, 1662–72, 1675, 1676, 1678, 1683, 1684, 1687, 1690, 1692–97, 1699, 1700, 1702–04, 1706–17, 1719–1812; /**85B,** 1813, 1815–18, 1820–66, 1869, 1870, 1872, 1873, 1881–1900 (338 docs.).

NORTHIAM
Ep.II/16/143A, 1606–09, 1611–18, 1620–26, 1628–41, 1664–1812; /**143B,** 1813–52, 1855–94, 1908, 1909 (515 docs.).

NUTHURST
Ep.I/24/86A, 1571, 1572, 1591, 1592, 1594, 1596, 1601, 1610, 1613, 1614, 1618, 1623, 1630, 1632–35, 1637–40, 1664, 1669, 1671, 1672, 1674, 1675, 1684–86, 1689–1749, 1751–63, 1765–1812; /**86B,** 1813–15, 1817–21, 1823–69 (437 docs.).

NUTLEY
Ep.II/16/144, 1847–81 (134 docs.).

ORE

Ep.II/16/145A, 1606–18, 1620–37, 1664, 1670–79, 1681–89, 1691–1812; **/145B,** 1813–55; **/145C,** 1856–93 (713 docs.).

OVING

Ep.I/24/87, 1591, 1592, 1596, 1601, 1604, 1605, 1607, 1610, 1613, 1618, 1630, 1633, 1634, 1637–40, 1662–65, 1669–71, 1674, 1675, 1677–81, 1684, 1687–89, 1691–1701, 1703–11, 1713–35, 1738–1850, 1876, 1879–99 (366 docs.).

OVINGDEAN

Ep.II/16/146, 1606–13, 1615–18, 1620, 1621, 1623–36, 1638, 1639, 1685–87, 1691, 1695, 1698–1887 (262 docs.).

PAGHAM

Ep.IV/7/6A, 1610, 1618, 1662–64, 1674, 1676, 1679–81, 1683, 1685–93, 1695–1704, 1706–59, 1761–1810, 1812; **/6B,** 1813–1911 (563 docs.).

PARHAM

Ep.I/24/88, 1571, 1572, 1585, 1591, 1592, 1594, 1596, 1601, 1602, 1607, 1610, 1611, 1613, 1614, 1618, 1623, 1630, 1632–35, 1637–40, 1663, 1667–69, 1675–79, 1684, 1685, 1692–96, 1698, 1699, 1701, 1703–43, 1745–52, 1754–63, 1765–1865, 1867–70, 1873, 1876, 1890, 1893–98 (312 docs.).

PATCHAM

Ep.II/16/147A, 1606, 1607, 1609–18, 1620–40, 1672–77, 1679–91, 1694–1812; **/147B,** 1813–76, 1885–93 (309 docs.).

PATCHING

Ep.IV/7/7, 1610, 1618, 1676, 1677, 1679, 1683, 1684, 1686–89, 1693–1704, 1706–44, 1746–51, 1754–58, 1761–63, 1766–1868, 1891, 1892, 1894, 1896–99, 1906–08 (280 docs.).

PEASMARSH

Ep.II/16/148A, 1607, 1610–18, 1620–40, 1664, 1667–80, 1682, 1684–89, 1691–1812; **/148B,** 1813–83 (532 docs.).

PENHURST

Ep.II/16/149, 1599, 1600, 1606–08, 1610–18, 1620–38, 1640, 1641, 1664, 1666, 1667, 1669–82, 1685–1758, 1760–1890 (306 docs.).

PETT

Ep.II/16/150A, 1606–15, 1617, 1618, 1620–40, 1667, 1668, 1672–1812; **/150B,** 1813–81 (373 docs.).

PETWORTH

Ep.I/24/89A, 1571, 1572, 1594, 1610, 1611, 1613, 1614, 1618, 1622, 1630, 1633, 1634, 1637, 1639, 1640, 1662–72, 1675, 1676, 1678, 1679, 1681, 1682, 1684, 1685, 1690–1738, 1740–1812; **/89B,** 1813–33; **/89C,** 1834–58; **/89D,** 1859–68, 1870–94, 1897 (911 docs.).

PEVENSEY

Ep.II/16/151A, 1596, 1604–18, 1620, 1621, 1623–40, 1664, 1665, 1667, 1673–91, 1693–1812; **/151B,** 1813–86, 1888–91 (369 docs.).

PIDDINGHOE

Ep.III/16/152A, 1607, 1608, 1610–18, 1620–32, 1634–39, 1664–67, 1669, 1670, 1672–98, 1700–1812; **/152B,** 1813–18, 1820–77, 1879–84 (347 docs.).

PLAYDEN

Ep.II/16/153A, 1600, 1605–13, 1615, 1616, 1618, 1620–40, 1670–77, 1679–83, 1685–88, 1690–93, 1695–1812; **/153B,** 1813–47, 1849–51, 1853–95 (420 docs.).

PLUMPTON

Ep.II/16/154A, 1606–18, 1620–41, 1666, 1672, 1677–87, 1689–1812; **/154B,** 1813–71, 1873–93 (406 docs.).

POLEGATE

Ep.II/16/155, 1879–85 (19 docs.).

POLING

Ep.I/24/90A, 1591, 1605, 1607, 1610, 1611, 1613, 1614, 1618, 1629, 1632–35, 1637, 1639–41, 1662, 1663, 1665–67, 1669, 1670, 1673, 1675–80, 1682–94, 1696–1763, 1765–1802, 1804, 1805, 1807–12; **/90B,** 1813–66, 1869, 1875–77, 1879–1901 (453 docs.).

PORTFIELD

Ep.I/24/91, 1871–75, 1877, 1878, 1881–92 (108 docs.).

PORTSLADE

Ep.II/16/156A, 1608–18, 1620–23, 1625–40, 1664, 1669, 1671–74, 1676, 1677, 1679–86, 1688–97, 1699–1812; **/156B,** 1813–75, 1888–90 [including Hangleton 1700–05] (384 docs.).

POYNINGS

Ep.II/16/157A, 1606, 1607, 1609, 1611, 1613, 1615–18, 1620–38, 1664, 1665, 1671, 1672, 1675–86, 1688, 1689, 1691–1812; **/157B,** 1813–1889, 1892–94 (447 docs.).

PRESTON

Ep.II/16/158A, 1606–18, 1620–40, 1664, 1666, 1668, 1672–1812; **/158B,** 1813–74 (419 docs.).

PRESTON ST. LUKE

Ep.II/16/159, 1877–90 (15 docs.).

PRESTON ST. SAVIOUR

Ep.II/16/160, 1884–89, 1893 (22 docs.).

EAST PRESTON

Ep.I/24/92, 1590, 1591, 1593–95, 1604, 1605, 1607, 1610, 1611, 1614, 1618, 1629, 1630, 1633–35, 1637–41, 1662–69, 1672, 1674–86, 1688–90, 1692–1728, 1730–63, 1765–1899, 1910, 1911 (342 docs.).

PULBOROUGH

Ep.I/24/93A, 1590–92, 1594–96, 1607, 1610, 1611, 1613, 1614, 1618, 1623, 1630, 1632–35, 1637, 1639, 1640, 1662, 1663, 1666–70, 1672–75, 1677, 1680–83, 1685, 1686, 1688–90, 1692–99, 1701, 1703–63, 1765–1812; **/93B,** 1813–29, 1831–47; **/93C,** 1848–79 (841 docs.).

PYECOMBE

Ep.II/16/161A, 1606–18, 1620–37, 1639–41, 1664, 1667, 1671–73, 1675–1812; **/161B,** 1813–94 (454 docs.).

RACTON

Ep.I/24/94, 1601, 1610, 1625, 1634, 1636, 1638–40, 1677, 1678, 1681–85, 1690, 1695–1705, 1707, 1709–28, 1730–38, 1740–1810, 1812–14, 1817–21, 1823–28, 1831–36, 1838–56, 1860–67, 1869, 1870, 1872, 1875, 1876, 1878, 1879, 1881, 1907–12 (242 docs.).

RINGMER

Ep.V/10/10A, 1666–1758, 1760–1812; **/10B,** 1813–60; **/10C,** 1861–67, 1870–85, 1887–89, 1891, 1892 (600 docs.).

RIPE

Ep.II/16/162A, 1606–08, 1610–16, 1618, 1620–41, 1643, 1663, 1664, 1668, 1669, 1671, 1672, 1674–77, 1680–85, 1687–1812; **/162B,** 1813–93 (384 docs.).

RODMELL

Ep.II/16/163A, 1610, 1612–18, 1620, 1622–40, 1671–76, 1678–86, 1688–1812; **/163B,** 1813–84, 1886, 1889, 1891–93, 1908 (365 docs.).

ROFFEY

Ep.I/24/95, 1879–86 (35 docs.).

ROGATE

Ep.I/24/96A, 1594, 1597, 1607, 1610, 1611, 1613, 1614, 1618, 1622, 1633–35, 1637, 1639–41, 1662–67, 1669–72, 1676–78, 1681–83, 1685, 1687, 1690, 1691, 1693–99, 1701–31, 1733–1812; **/96B,** 1813–72, 1878–1911 (435 docs.).

ROTHERFIELD

Ep.II/16/164A, 1593, 1594, 1597, 1605–07, 1609–18, 1620–40, 1664, 1665, 1667, 1668, 1671, 1674–1708; **/164B,** 1709–1812; **/164C,** 1813–37; **/164D,** 1838–60; **/164E,** 1861–86 (1,092 docs.).

ROTTINGDEAN

Ep.II/16/165A, 1606–18, 1620–40, 1664, 1673–76, 1679, 1681–83, 1685–89, 1691–1812; **/165B,** 1813–82, 1884–93 (431 docs.).

Rottingdean Society of Friends
Ep.II/16/166, 1865–73, 1875–1901 (Burials) (66 docs.).

Rudgwick
Ep.I/24/97A, 1571, 1572, 1591, 1594, 1596, 1601, 1610, 1613, 1614, 1618, 1623, 1684–1701, 1703–30, 1732–37, 1772, 1788, 1811; **/97B,** 1813–33; **/97C,** 1834–57, 1859–64 (348 docs.).

Rumboldswyke
Ep.III/8/10A, 1610, 1613, 1617, 1629–34, 1636, 1637, 1639, 1663, 1673–75, 1677, 1678, 1680, 1683, 1684, 1686, 1688–90, 1692, 1693, 1696, 1697, 1699–1705, 1707–09, 1711, 1714–22, 1724, 1726, 1728–34, 1736–63, 1765–1812; **/10B,** 1813–1855, 1857–82, 1896–1912 (467 docs.).

Rusper
Ep.I/24/98A, 1571, 1572, 1592, 1594, 1596, 1601, 1607, 1610, 1611, 1613, 1614, 1618, 1623, 1630, 1632, 1633, 1635, 1637–40, 1662–69, 1672–74, 1676–86, 1689, 1691–98, 1700–63, 1765–1812; **/98B,** 1813–25, 18?8–71, 1873–88, 1890–1912 (482 docs.).

Rustington
Ep.I/24/99A, 1593–96, 1601, 1604, 1605, 1607, 1610, 1613, 1614, 1618, 1629, 1630, 1632–35, 1639–41, 1662–64, 1666–77, 1679–85, 1687, 1688, 1690–93, 1695–1763, 1765–1812; **/99B,** 1813–99, 1901–04, 1906 (444 docs.).

Rye
Ep.II/16/167A, 1606–09, 1611–18, 1620–39, 1664–67, 1670–1759; **/167B,** 1760–1812; **/167C,** 1813–34; **/167D,** 1835–60; **/167E,** 1861–93 (1613 docs.).

St. Leonards Christ Church
Ep.II/16/168, 1885–93 (71 docs.).

St. Leonards St. Mary Magadalene
Ep.II/16/169, 1834, 1835, 1839–42, 1844–97 (428 docs.).

St. Leonards St. Matthew, Silverhill
Ep.II/16/170, 1871–79, 1881–93 (158 docs.).

St. Leonards St. Paul
Ep.II/16/171, 1869–79 (Baptisms) (45 docs.).

Salehurst
Ep.II/16/172A, 1600, 1606–11, 1613–18, 1620–38, 1640, 1666–1812; **/172B,** 1813–60; **/172C,** 1861–94, 1908 (873 docs.).

Sayers Common
Ep.II/16/173, 1882, 1887–94 (21 docs.).

Ep.II/16/174A, 1606–18, 1620–40, 1664, 1665, 1676–83, 1685, 1686, 1688, 1690–95, 1697–1812; **/174B,** 1813–45, 1847–92 (497 docs.).

Ep.II/16/175A, 1607, 1608, 1610–18, 1620–25, 1627–38, 1640, 1669, 1671–1812; **/175B,** 1813–74 (405 docs.).

SELE *see* Upper Beeding

SELHAM

Ep.I/24/100, 1572, 1594, 1601, 1610, 1611, 1613, 1614, 1618, 1622, 1630, 1633–35, 1637, 1639, 1640, 1662, 1663, 1669, 1670, 1674–79, 1681, 1683, 1685, 1696, 1707, 1723, 1725, 1726, 1728–63, 1765–1862, 1865, 1872, 1902–10 (272 docs.).

SELMESTON

Ep.II/16/176A, 1608–18, 1620–27, 1629–39, 1664, 1672, 1673, 1675, 1677–86, 1688–1812; **/176B,** 1813–93 (364 docs.).

SELSEY

Ep.I/24/101, 1571, 1594–96, 1601, 1604, 1605, 1610, 1613, 1614, 1618, 1625, 1630, 1633, 1634, 1637–40, 1664, 1674, 1675, 1677, 1681, 1683, 1685–87, 1689, 1695–1705, 1707–1813, 1816–35, 1838–50, 1852, 1854, 1855, 1862 (358 docs.).

SHERMANBURY

Ep.II/16/177A, 1606, 1607, 1609–18, 1620–40, 1671–1812; **/177B,** 1813–81, 1883–91, 1895–1900 (361 docs.).

SHIPLEY

Ep.I/24/102A, 1591, 1592, 1594, 1596, 1601, 1607, 1610, 1611, 1613, 1614, 1618, 1623, 1630, 1632–35, 1637–40, 1662–64, 1667–71, 1676, 1678, 1679, 1683, 1690, 1692–1757, 1759–63, 1765–1812; **/102B,** 1813, 1821–66, 1871, 1872 (445 docs.).

SHOREHAM, NEW

Ep.II/16/178A, 1606–08, 1610–12, 1615–17, 1622, 1624–27, 1629–39, 1673, 1675, 1679, 1681–1812; **/178B,** 1813–54, 1857; **/178C,** 1861–77, 1879–86, 1888–93 (826 docs.).

SHOREHAM, OLD

Ep.II/16/179A, 1606, 1607, 1610, 1612–18, 1620–39, 1665, 1669–74, 1676–79, 1681–84, 1686, 1687, 1689–92, 1694–1812; **/179B,** 1813–49, 1852–95 (376 docs.).

SIDLESHAM

Ep.I/24/103A, 1591, 1592, 1594–97, 1601, 1604, 1605, 1610, 1613, 1614, 1618, 1625, 1630, 1633, 1634, 1637–40, 1662, 1663, 1667, 1669, 1671, 1672, 1676–78, 1686–93, 1695–1701, 1704–10, 1712–1812; **/103B,** 1813–24, 1826–79, 1881–86, 1890, 1897–1909 (577 docs.).

SINGLETON

Ep.I/24/104A, 1591, 1592, 1594–96, 1601, 1604, 1605, 1610, 1613, 1614, 1618, 1625, 1630, 1632–34, 1637–39, 1662–64, 1671, 1677, 1678, 1685, 1687, 1688, 1691–96, 1698–1707, 1709–1812; /**104B,** 1813–96 (452 docs.).

SLAUGHAM

Ep.II/16/180A, 1606, 1609, 1610, 1614–18, 1620–26, 1628–41, 1664–1812; /**180B,** 1813–85, 1890, 1892–94 (537 docs.).

SLINDON

Ep.IV/7/8, 1610, 1618, 1663, 1678–80, 1682–84, 1686–90, 1693–1704, 1706–38, 1740–64, 1766–1820, 1827–63, 1896–1902 (259 docs.).

SLINFOLD

Ep.I/24/105A, 1571, 1572, 1591, 1592, 1594, 1601, 1607, 1610, 1611, 1613, 1614, 1618, 1623, 1630, 1632–35, 1637–41, 1662, 1663, 1665–69, 1671–79, 1683–86, 1688–1716, 1718–1812; /**105B,** 1813–46, 1848–54, 1856–61, 1863, 1864, 1866–94, 1896–99 (452 docs.).

SOCIETY OF FRIENDS

See Chichester, Horsham, Ifield, Lewes, Rottingdean

SOMPTING

Ep.I/24/106A, 1590–92, 1594, 1596, 1601, 1610, 1611, 1613, 1614, 1618, 1623, 1630, 1632–35, 1637–41, 1663, 1665–70, 1672–78, 1682–93, 1695–1763, 1765–1812; /**106B,** 1813–21, 1824–29, 1831–56, 1858–1908 (460 docs.).

SOUTHEASE

Ep.II/16/181A, 1606–18, 1620–40, 1664–67, 1671, 1673–1812; /**181B,** 1813–89, 1891–94, 1909 (333 docs.).

SOUTHOVER *see* Lewes St. John Southover

SOUTHWATER

Ep.I/24/107, 1850–73, 1897, 1898 (84 docs.).

SOUTHWICK

Ep.II/16/182A, 1606, 1607, 1609–12, 1615, 1617, 1618, 1620–40, 1664, 1665, 1673–76, 1679, 1681–88, 1692–1723, 1725–89, 1791–1812; /**182B,** 1813–38, 1840–42, 1848–85, 1890 (512 docs.).

STANMER

Ep.V/10/11A, 1663, 1664, 1666, 1667, 1669, 1670, 1672–85, 1687, 1689, 1691–97, 1699–1711, 1713–1812; /**11B,** 1813–89 (284 docs.).

STAPLEFIELD

Ep.II/16/183, 1852–82, 1884–91, 1893 (158 docs.).

STEDHAM

Ep.I/24/108, 1570, 1572, 1591, 1592, 1594, 1610, 1611, 1618, 1622, 1630, 1633–35, 1637, 1639, 1640, 1662–64, 1666–71, 1675–79, 1684, 1685, 1693, 1695–99, 1701, 1703–30, 1732–1816, 1818, 1824, 1845, 1846, 1876, 1882, 1884, 1885, 1889–90, 1892, 1893, 1897–1904, 1906, 1907 (216 docs.).

STEYNING

Ep.I/24/109A, 1591, 1592, 1594, 1596, 1601, 1605, 1610, 1611, 1613–15, 1618, 1623, 1630, 1632–35, 1637–40, 1663, 1668, 1669, 1671, 1675, 1676, 1679, 1685–94, 1696–1801, 1803–12; /**109B,** 1813–38, 1840–50; /**109C,** 1851–64, 1866–81, 1883–86, 1904, 1908, 1909 (718 docs.).

NORTH STOKE

Ep.I/24/110, 1572, 1590–95, 1597, 1601, 1604, 1605, 1610, 1611, 1613, 1614, 1618, 1629, 1630, 1633–35, 1637–40, 1662, 1663, 1666–68, 1671–73, 1677, 1682–95, 1698–1703, 1705–42, 1744–1820, 1822–36, 1838–58, 1860–69, 1890, 1891 (258 docs.).

SOUTH STOKE

Ep.I/24/111, 1567, 1569, 1590, 1591, 1593–95, 1604, 1610, 1611, 1613, 1614, 1618, 1629, 1633, 1635, 1637–40, 1663–65, 1667–73, 1675, 1677–81, 1683, 1685–87, 1690–1728, 1730–63, 1765–1835, 1837–64, 1866, 1867 (293 docs.).

WEST STOKE

Ep.I/24/112, 1594, 1601, 1610, 1614, 1618, 1625, 1630, 1633, 1634, 1637–40, 1662, 1670, 1672, 1675, 1679–87, 1689–99, 1701–46, 1748–57, 1759–1804, 1806–56, 1858–63, 1865, 1899, 1902, 1908 (275 docs.).

STONEGATE

Ep.II/16/184, 1850–94 (117 docs.).

STOPHAM

Ep.I/24/113, 1572, 1584, 1590–92, 1594, 1601, 1604, 1610, 1613, 1614, 1618, 1622, 1630, 1633–35, 1637, 1639–41, 1662–65, 1667, 1668, 1670–72, 1675, 1676, 1678, 1685–87, 1689, 1691, 1692, 1694–96, 1698–1700, 1702–08, 1710–32, 1734–1868, 1870–76, 1879–1915 (380 docs.).

STORRINGTON

Ep.I/24/114A, 1590–94, 1598, 1601, 1604, 1610, 1611, 1613, 1614, 1618, 1623, 1630, 1632, 1633, 1635, 1637–40, 1663–65, 1668–71, 1673–77, 1687, 1688, 1690, 1692–1758, 1760–63, 1765–1812; /**114B,** 1813–46, 1848–51, 1854–63, 1865–94 (509 docs.).

STOUGHTON

Ep.I/24/115A, 1571, 1591, 1592, 1594, 1601, 1604, 1610, 1613, 1618, 1625, 1630, 1633, 1634, 1637–40, 1662–64, 1666, 1667, 1669–72, 1675–77, 1684, 1687, 1688, 1691–95, 1697–1812; /**115B,** 1813, 1814, 1816–99 (431 docs.).

Ep.II/16/185A, 1606–10, 1612–18, 1620–22, 1624, 1625, 1627–29, 1632–40, 1664, 1665, 1676, 1677, 1679, 1682–86, 1688–1812; **/185B,** 1813–47, 1849–93, 1908 (462 docs.).

SULLINGTON

Ep.I/24/116, 1590–92, 1594, 1596, 1601, 1604, 1607, 1610, 1611, 1613, 1614, 1618, 1623, 1630, 1632–35, 1637, 1638, 1640, 1660–65, 1667–70, 1672–75, 1677–79, 1681–84, 1689, 1690, 1692, 1694–96, 1698–1712, 1714–27, 1729–63, 1765–1830, 1832–85, 1887 (454 docs.).

SUSSEX LUNATIC ASYLUM *see* Haywards Heath

SUTTON

Ep.I/24/117, 1590–92, 1594, 1601, 1610, 1611, 1613, 1614, 1618, 1622, 1633–35, 1637, 1639–41, 1662–87, 1689–91, 1693–97, 1701, 1702, 1704, 1706, 1707, 1709–30, 1732–39, 1741, 1744–1823, 1825–71 (305 docs.).

TANGMERE

Ep.IV/7/9, 1610, 1618, 1662, 1664, 1679–81, 1683, 1684, 1686–89, 1691, 1693–1701, 1703, 1704, 1706–14, 1716, 1717, 1719–23, 1725, 1726, 1729, 1732–64, 1766–1810, 1812–56, 1858–67, 1869–71, 1874 (297 docs.).

TARRING NEVILLE

Ep.II/16/186A, 1606–08, 1612–18, 1620–40, 1664, 1665, 1667, 1669–86, 1688–97, 1699–1811; **/186B,** 1813–94 [including South Heighton from 1775] (451 docs.). *See also* South Heighton.

WEST TARRING

Ep.IV/7/10A, 1610, 1662–64, 1679, 1681–84, 1686–98, 1700, 1702, 1704, 1706–58, 1761–64, 1766–1806, 1808–12; **/10B,** 1813–91, 1893, 1897 [including Durrington and Heene, 1837–97] (465 docs.).

TELSCOMBE

Ep.II/16/187, 1606, 1608–18, 1620–31, 1633–40, 1667, 1672, 1673, 1677–79, 1682, 1684–87, 1691, 1697, 1700–47, 1750–63, 1784–1877, 1879–84 (290 docs.).

TERWICK

Ep.I/24/118, 1571, 1572, 1590, 1592, 1607, 1610, 1611, 1614, 1618, 1622, 1630, 1633, 1634, 1637, 1639–41, 1662, 1663, 1665, 1668–72, 1676, 1677, 1679–81, 1683, 1684, 1693, 1695, 1701, 1704–06, 1708–13, 1716–30, 1734–39, 1741–63, 1765–1801, 1804–06, 1808, 1811–63, 1865–80 (242 docs.).

THAKEHAM

Ep.I/24/119, 1590–92, 1594, 1596, 1601, 1604, 1607, 1610, 1611, 1613, 1614, 1618, 1623, 1630, 1632, 1633, 1637–40, 1662–64, 1669, 1672, 1674–79, 1681, 1683–86, 1688–90, 1692–97, 1699, 1700, 1702–63, 1765–1836, 1838–49 [including Society of Friends, Baptisms, 1888, 1889] (265 docs.).

West Thorney

Ep.I/24/120, 1592, 1594, 1618, 1626, 1633, 1634, 1637, 1639, 1640, 1662, 1663, 1665, 1666, 1668–70, 1672, 1673, 1677, 1680–89, 1691, 1693–1734, 1736–87, 1789–1885 (310 docs.).

Ticehurst

Ep.II/16/188A, 1593, 1594, 1600, 1605–18, 1620–22, 1624–39, 1664, 1666, 1669–1812; /**188B,** 1813–60; /**188C,** 1861–94 (661 docs.).

Tidebrook

Ep.II/16/189, 1856–91 (222 docs.).

Tillington

Ep.I/24/121A, 1571, 1572, 1592, 1594, 1610, 1611, 1614, 1618, 1622, 1633–35, 1637, 1639–41, 1662–70, 1672–75, 1677–79, 1681–1702, 1704–56, 1759–82, 1784–1808, 1810–12; /**121B,** 1813–18, 1821–75, 1899, 1902 (494 docs.).

Tortington

Ep.I/24/122, 1593, 1594, 1604, 1605, 1607, 1611, 1613, 1614, 1618, 1629, 1630, 1633, 1634, 1637, 1639, 1640, 1663, 1664, 1667, 1668, 1678, 1680, 1681, 1683–85, 1687, 1688, 1690–99, 1706–20, 1722–25, 1728, 1729, 1731–37, 1739, 1741–54, 1761–63, 1765–1818, 1820–78 (280 docs.).

Treyford with Didling

Ep.I/24/123, 1573, 1590, 1592, 1596, 1610, 1614, 1618, 1622, 1630, 1633–35, 1637, 1639, 1640, 1662–65, 1669–71, 1675, 1677, 1680–83, 1685–97, 1699, 1701, 1704–11, 1713–17, 1719–30, 1732–1800, 1802–83, 1902–10 (284 docs.).

Trotton

Ep.I/24/124, 1571, 1572, 1584, 1592, 1593, 1595–97, 1606, 1611, 1613–16, 1618, 1622, 1630, 1633–35, 1637, 1639–41, 1662–71, 1675–79, 1681–84, 1691–93, 1695–97, 1700–03, 1705–15, 1717–1813, 1815–20, 1822–29, 1833–70, 1872, 1873, 1885–96, 1898, 1899 [including Tuxlith to 1860] (395 docs.).

Tuxlith *see* Milland and Trotton

Twineham

Ep.II/16/190, 1606–18, 1620–41, 1664, 1666, 1667, 1674–78, 1680–1889, 1893 (346 docs.).

Uckfield

Ep.V/10/12A, 1664–69, 1671–85, 1687–1812; /**12B,** 1813–54; /**12C,** 1855–83 (594 docs.).

Udimore

Ep.II/16/191, 1600, 1607, 1608, 1610–18, 1620–29, 1631–40, 1664, 1666, 1667, 1669–1893 (454 docs.).

UPWALTHAM

Ep.I/24/125, 1592, 1601, 1607, 1610, 1613, 1618, 1626, 1630, 1633, 1634, 1637–40, 1667, 1670, 1674, 1685, 1698, 1701, 1703, 1705–33, 1735–1819, 1821–29, 1832–53, 1855 (204 docs.).

WADHURST

Ep.V/10/13A, 1666–90, 1693–1812; **/13B,** 1813–30; **/13C,** 1831–48; **/13D,** 1849–77 (766 docs.).

WALBERTON

Ep.I/24/126, 1572, 1590–94, 1604, 1605, 1607, 1610, 1611, 1613, 1618, 1629, 1630, 1632–35, 1637–39, 1662–69, 1672, 1674–77, 1679, 1681–83, 1688, 1690–94, 1696–1717, 1721–43, 1745, 1747, 1749–63, 1765–1817, 1819–58, 1860, 1861, 1875, 1876, 1880, 1889–1912 (361 docs.).

WALDRON

Ep.II/16/192A, 1605–10, 1612–18, 1620–30, 1632–41, 1663–65, 1667, 1668, 1670–83, 1685–1812; **/192B,** 1813–43, 1845–82, 1884–93 (508 docs.).

WARBLETON

Ep.II/16/193A, 1598–1600, 1606, 1608–18, 1620–39, 1666–68, 1670–89, 1691–1812; **/193B,** 1813–37, 1839–93, 1896 (444 docs.).

WARMINGHURST

Ep.I/24/127, 1571, 1572, 1590–92, 1594, 1596, 1601, 1604, 1610, 1611, 1613, 1614, 1618, 1630, 1632, 1633, 1637–40, 1663, 1664, 1668, 1669, 1673–76, 1678, 1679, 1681–90, 1693–97, 1699, 1701–04, 1706–56, 1761–69, 1771–1883 (294 docs.).

WARNHAM

Ep.I/24/128A, 1571, 1572, 1591, 1592, 1594, 1596, 1601, 1610, 1611, 1613, 1614, 1618, 1623, 1630, 1632–35, 1637–40, 1663, 1665–67, 1669–71, 1673–83, 1686–89, 1692, 1693, 1695–99, 1701–1812; **/128B,** 1813–51; **/128C,** 1852–54, 1856–89, 1891–94, 1896–98, 1908–10 (611 docs.).

WARNINGCAMP

Ep.I/24/129, 1571, 1572, 1590, 1592, 1601, 1610, 1611, 1613, 1618, 1633, 1634, 1637, 1639, 1640 (15 docs.).

WARTLING

Ep.II/16/194A, 1606–08, 1610, 1611, 1614–18, 1620–40, 1667, 1670–72, 1674–76, 1678–1812; **/194B,** 1813–94 (415 docs.).

WASHINGTON

Ep.I/24/130A, 1590–92, 1594, 1596, 1601, 1610, 1611, 1613, 1614, 1618, 1623, 1630, 1632–35, 1637–40, 1662–64, 1667–70, 1673, 1677, 1685–90, 1693–95, 1697–1763, 1765–1812; **/130B,** 1813–28, 1833–41, 1843–61, 1863, 1865–87, 1890–98 (390 docs.).

WESTBOURNE

Ep.I/24/131A, 1572, 1592, 1594, 1596, 1597, 1601, 1605, 1607, 1610, 1613, 1614, 1618, 1630, 1633, 1634, 1637–39, 1662–64, 1666, 1667, 1669, 1670, 1674–78, 1680, 1682–99, 1701–28, 1730–1812; **/131B,** 1813–24, 1827–40; **/131C,** 1841–70, 1891, 1902–04 (643 docs.).

WESTFIELD

Ep.II/16/195A, 1608, 1611–18, 1620–40, 1670–73, 1675–87, 1689–94, 1696–1812; **/195B,** 1813–79, 1881, 1883 (459 docs.).

WESTHAM

Ep.II/16/196A, 1596, 1597, 1606–18, 1620–23, 1625–40, 1667, 1668, 1678–98, 1700–1812; **/196B,** 1813–79 (436 docs.).

WESTHAMPNETT

Ep.I/24/132A, 1584, 1591, 1592, 1594, 1601, 1610, 1613, 1618, 1633, 1634, 1637, 1638, 1640, 1663, 1664, 1666, 1670, 1671, 1674–76, 1681–83, 1690, 1691, 1694, 1695, 1697–1700, 1703, 1705, 1706, 1708–11, 1715, 1716, 1719, 1721–29, 1731–33, 1735–39, 1741–1812; **/132B,** 1813–24, 1828–51, 1853, 1855–65, 1868–87, 1889–94, 1897–1901 (389 docs.).

WESTMESTON

Ep.II/16/197, 1606–18, 1620–26, 1628–39, 1664–66, 1670, 1675–77, 1679–1894, 1908 (409 docs.).

WHATLINGTON

Ep.II/16/198A, 1607, 1608, 1610, 1611, 1613–18, 1620–40, 1667, 1669–71, 1673–86, 1688–93, 1695–1812; **/198B,** 1813–94 (447 docs.).

WIGGONHOLT WITH GREATHAM

Ep.I/24/133A, 1592, 1594, 1596, 1601, 1607, 1610, 1611, 1613, 1614, 1618, 1623, 1630, 1632, 1633, 1635, 1637–40, 1662, 1666, 1669–99, 1701–63, 1765–1812; **/133B,** 1813–20, 1829–50, 1852–64, 1866–75, 1877, 1879–83, 1887–95 (305 docs.).

WILLINGDON

Ep.II/16/199A, 1593–95, 1597, 1598, 1606–18, 1620–41, 1664, 1665, 1667–83, 1685–97, 1699–1812; **/199B,** 1813–84, 1887–94 (407 docs.).

WILMINGTON

Ep.II/16/200A, 1616–18, 1620–41, 1665, 1668, 1671, 1672, 1674, 1678–1812; **/200B,** 1813–60, 1862–90 (438 docs.).

WINCHELSEA

Ep.II/16/201A, 1606–08, 1610–18, 1620, 1622–40, 1667, 1668, 1670, 1671, 1673, 1675–82, 1684–86, 1692, 1693, 1695–1812; **/201B,** 1813–93 (637 docs.).

Wisborough Green

Ep.I/24/134A, 1571, 1572, 1592, 1596, 1601, 1607, 1610, 1611, 1613, 1614, 1618, 1623, 1630, 1632–35, 1637–41, 1662–64, 1668–71, 1680–86, 1688–94, 1696–1812; **/134B,** 1813–34; **/134C,** 1835–60 (605 docs.).

Wiston

Ep.I/24/135, 1570–73, 1592, 1594, 1596, 1601, 1610, 1611, 1613, 1614, 1618, 1623, 1630, 1632–35, 1637–40, 1663, 1673–76, 1678, 1679, 1682, 1683, 1685–87, 1690, 1691, 1696–99, 1701–63, 1765, 1767–1903 (377 docs.).

Withyham

Ep.II/16/202A, 1606–28, 1630–41, 1664, 1667–79, 1681–1812; **/202B,** 1813–60; **/202C,** 1861–70, 1872–91, 1905–08 (785 docs.).

Withyham Hamlet

Ep.V/10/14, 1690–99, 1702, 1704–45 (57 docs.).

Withyam St. John

Ep.II/16/203, 1877–81, 1883–87, 1893 (47 docs.).

East Wittering

Ep.I/24/136, 1571, 1572, 1590–92, 1594–97, 1601, 1604, 1605, 1610, 1614, 1625, 1630, 1632–34, 1637–40, 1662, 1675, 1677, 1678, 1686, 1690, 1694–1868, 1876–89, 1891, 1892, 1894–96, 1898, 1901, 1904, 1908, 1909 (332 docs.)

West Wittering

Ep.I/24/137A, 1592, 1594, 1601, 1604, 1607, 1610, 1613, 1614, 1618, 1626, 1630, 1633, 1634, 1637, 1638, 1640, 1641, 1662, 1666, 1667, 1669, 1675, 1677–79, 1681, 1685–88, 1690, 1694, 1696–1812; **/137B,** 1813–69, 1883, 1885–1909 (393 docs.).

Wivelsfield

Ep.II/16/204A, 1608–18, 1620–22, 1624–41, 1665, 1666, 1671–78, 1680–1750, 1752–1812; **/204B,** 1813–84, 1890–92 (412 docs.).

Wivelsfield Hamlet

Ep.V/10/14, 1667–70, 1672–75, 1677–79, 1683, 1685–91, 1694–96, 1699, 1700, 1702–05, 1707, 1710–35, 1737–40, 1742, 1798 (59 docs.).

Woodmancote

Ep.II/16/205A, 1606, 1608–14, 1616–18, 1620–40, 1643, 1664–67, 1671, 1673–81, 1683–1812; **/205B,** 1813–84, 1887 (406 docs.).

Woolavington

Ep.I/24/138, 1571, 1572, 1592, 1594, 1610, 1611, 1618, 1622, 1633, 1634, 1637, 1639–41, 1662–65, 1667–72, 1675–77, 1679, 1681–83, 1692, 1693, 1696, 1698–1700, 1702–05, 1707, 1709, 1710, 1712–39, 1741–55, 1757–59, 1761–72, 1774–1871 (276 docs.).

Woolbeding

Ep.I/24/139, 1590–92, 1594, 1607, 1610, 1611, 1613, 1614, 1622, 1630, 1633, 1634, 1637, 1639, 1640, 1662–65, 1667–72, 1675–77, 1680–87, 1689–93, 1697, 1698, 1701–27, 1729–63, 1765–1867, 1875–1911 (304 docs.).

Worth

Ep.II/16/206A, 1606–18, 1620–40, 1670–75, 1677–1812; **/206B,** 1813–50; **/206C,** 1851–94 (756 docs.).

Worthing Christ Church

Ep.I/24/140, 1855–62, 1872, 1882, 1885–95, 1901–04 (84 docs.).

Worthing St. George

Ep.I/24/141, 1914–18 (12 docs.).

Yapton

Ep.I/24/142, 1572, 1593, 1594, 1604, 1605, 1610, 1611, 1613, 1614, 1618, 1629, 1630, 1632–34, 1637–40, 1662–64, 1666, 1668, 1672, 1675–78, 1681–1763, 1765–1858, 1860, 1861, 1904 (353 docs.).

APPENDIX II

ORDERS IN COUNCIL RELATING TO ALTERATIONS OF PARISH BOUNDARIES, 1837–1937

The Orders in Council, copies of which are kept in the Diocesan Registry, confirm the Schemes which (with maps attached) define the area of new districts and parishes, taken out of one or more existing parishes, or give the fullest details of alterations of boundaries. This list includes the creation of consolidated chapelries (c.c.), district chapelries (d.c.), particular districts (p.d.), new districts (n.d. *or* d.) and parishes (p.), and the extension (ext.) or diminution (dim.) of existing parishes. The Diocesan Registry indexes do not appear to be comprehensive; the *London Gazette* should also be consulted. For details of the relevant Church Building and New Parishes Acts see H. W. Cripps, *Law relating to the Church and Clergy* (1921), pp. 343–365.

Dio. Reg.[1] vol. p.	Parish	O. in C.	Out of/(to)
VI : 199	Aldrington, St. Leonard (ext.)	4. 5.35	Portslade; (A. St. Philip)
V : 93	St. Philip (d.c.)	5. 7.11	A. St. Leonard
VI : 199	St. Philip (ext.)	4. 5.35	A. St. Leonard
VI : 211	Aldwick, St. Richard (d.c.)	13. 8.35	Pagham
VI : 131	Bepton (ext.)	17.12.31	Linch; (Midhurst)

[1] This abbreviation is for the Diocesan Registry where copies of Orders in Council are bound in volumes. In a few cases Orders are noted which do not appear to have been included in the Registry series: a dash is in the first column in such instances.

Dio. Reg. vol. p.	Parish	O. in C.	Out of/(to)
VI : 176	Bexhill, St. Augustine (c.c.)	29. 6.34	B. St. Barnabas
IV : 155	St. Barnabas (d.)	23. 6.91	B. St. Peter
II : 38	St. Mark, Little Common (d.c.)	27. 8.57	B. St. Peter
IV : 269	St. Stephen (d.c.)	7. 8.00	B. St. Peter
V : 312	St. Stephen (ext.)	26. 5.25	B. St. Mark
VI : 194	Billingshurst (ext.)	29. 3.35	Pulborough
I : 318	Bodle Street Green, St. John E. (c.c.)	24. 9.55	Dallington; Hurstmonceux; Warbleton; Wartling
V : 183	Bognor, St. John (ext.)	22.12.15	S. Bersted
VI : 215	St. John (ext.)	3.10.35	Pagham
V : 208	Brighton, All Saints (d.c.)	16. 2.17	Brighton
IV : 1	All Souls (d.c.)	23. 8.83	Brighton
III : 212	The Annunciation (d.)	31. 7.80	Brighton
IV : 218	Chapel Royal (d.c.)	15. 1.97	Brighton
V : 230	St. Anne (d.c.)	7. 2.21	Brighton
III : 252	St. Bartholomew (d.)	15. 7.81	Brighton
III : 141	St. James (d.c.)	24. 3.76	Brighton
III : 61	St. John E. (d.c.)	9. 8.72	Brighton
IV : 53	St. Luke (d.c.)	12. 8.85	Brighton
VI : 192	St. Margaret (d.c.)	29. 3.35	Brighton
VI : 82	St. Mark, Kemp Town (c.c.)	15. 5.30	Brighton; Rottingdean
III : 176	St. Martin (d.c.)	26.10.75	Brighton
III : 312	St. Mary (c.c.)	28.10.79	Brighton
IV : 20	St. Mary Magdalen (d.)	26. 6.84	Brighton
IV : 37	St. Matthew (d.c.)	11. 8.84	Brighton
V : 292	St. Michael (c.c.)	12. 8.24	Brighton; B. St. Stephen; B. St. Nicholas
III : 230	St. Nicholas (d.c.)	30. 8.73	Brighton
IV : 87	SS. Nicholas and Paul	12. 7.87	exchange
III : 80	St. Paul (d.c.)	24. 3.73	Brighton
V : 13	St. Stephen (d.c.)	12. 8.07	Brighton
V : 277	St. Stephen (ext.)	21.11.22	Brighton
V : 252	St. Wilfrid (d.)	21. 4.22	Brighton; B. St. Luke
III : 2	Broadwater Down, St. Mark (c.c.)	26. 6.67	Frant
V : 233	St. Mark (ext.)	13.12.21	Frant
IV : 297	Burgess Hill, St. Andrew (d.)	11. 6.02	Ditchling; St. John's Common
VI : 308	Burwash Weald, St. Philip (c.c.)	23.10.77	Burwash; Heathfield; Mayfield
IV : 31	Buxted, St. Mary (d.)	11. 8.84	Buxted
———	Chichester, St. Paul (district parish)	10. 5.37	C. St. Peter the Gt.

Dio. Reg.			
vol. p.	*Parish*	*O. in C.*	*Out of/(to)*
III: 157	Chichester, 24.3.76, alteration of boundaries of SS. Bartholomew, Paul and Peter the Great		
VI : 131	Cocking (dim.)	17.12.31	(W. Lavington)
III: 41	Colgate, St. Saviour (c.c.)	21.12.71	Beeding; Horsham
III: 260	Copthorne, St. John (d.)	15. 7.81	Crawley Down All Saints; Worth, Burstow and Horne [Rochester]
IV : 290	West Crawley, St. Peter (d.c.)	4.11.01	Ifield
II : 223	Crawley Down, All Saints (d.c.)	1.11.62	Worth
IV : 184	Cuckfield,[1] St. Wilfrid (ext.)	23. 8.94	St. John's Common; Wivelsfield
V : 87	St. Wilfrid (ext.)	4. 5.11	C. Holy Trinity
I : 60	Upper Dicker, Holy Trinity (n.d.)	8. 8.45	Arlington; Chiddingly; Hellingly
II : 317	Duncton (add.d.)	20.11.65	Petworth
V : 162	Durrington (d.)	16. 7.14	W. Tarring
VI : 131	Easebourne (dim.)	17.12.31	(W. Lavington)
III: 287	Eastbourne, All Saints (c.c.)	3. 5.82	E. St. Saviour
IV : 252	All Saints (ext.)	2. 2.99	E. St. John
III: 245	All Souls (d.)	15. 7.81	E. Holy Trinity
IV : 137	All Souls (ext.)	30. 6.90	E. Christ Church
II : 248	Christ Church (d.c.)	3. 2.64	E. Holy Trinity
VI : 322	Christ Church (ext.)	12.12.73	Willingdon
I : 124	Holy Trinity (n.d.)	17. 6.47	E. St. Mary
V : 212	St. Andrew (d.c.)	14. 4.17	E. Christ Church
III: 306	St. Anne, Upperton (c.c.)	19. 7.83	E. Holy Trinity
VI : 220	St. Elizabeth (d.)	9.11.35	E. St. Mary; E. St. Michael; Willingdon
III: 9	St. John, Meads (c.c.)	5. 2.70	E. St. Mary; E. Holy Trinity
IV : 252	St. John, Meads (ext.)	2. 2.99	E. All Saints
V : 74	St. John, Meads (ext.)	23. 1.11	E. St. Mary
V : 82	St. Michael, Ocklynge (d.c.)	22. 3.11	E. St. Mary
VI : 1	St. Michael, Ocklynge (dim.)	22. 4.27	(E. St. Mary)
IV : 214	St. Peter (d.c.)	1. 8.96	E. St. Saviour
V : 221	St. Peter (ext.)	11. 3.20	E. St. Saviour
V : 316	St. Philip (c.c.)	26. 5.25	E. Christ Church; E. St. Anne; E. St. Michael
III: 3	St. Saviour (d.c.)	3. 8.67	E. Holy Trinity
IV : 175	St. Saviour (ext.)	9. 5.92	E. St. John
III: 127	Ebernoe, Holy Trinity (d.c.)	13. 5.75	Kirdford
II : 1	Eridge Green (d.)	30. 1.56	Frant; Rotherfield
III: 42	Eridge Green (ext.)	22. 4.72	Frant

[1] See Haywards Heath.

Dio. Reg.				
vol. p.		Parish	O. in C.	Out of/(to)
IV : 280		Fairwarp, Christ Church (c.c.)	24. 7.01	Buxted; High Hurst Wood Holy Trinity; Maresfield
V : 193		Fernhurst (ext.)	18. 8.16	Steep [Winchester]
I : 175		Forest Row, Holy Trinity (n.d.)	8. 1.50	E. Grinstead
——		Funtington: see Sennicots		
V : 1		East Grinstead, St. Mary (d.c.)	11.12.05	E.G. St. Swithun
IV : 70		New Groombridge, St. Thomas (d.c.)	16. 8.86	Withyham
VI : 287		Hadlow Down, St. Mark (c.c.)	21.6.1837	Buxted; Mayfield
III : 206		Hammerwood, St. Stephen (c.c.)	28. 6.80	E. Grinstead; Hartfield
IV : 131		Hastings, All Souls, Clive Vale (d.)	5. 7.89	H. All Saints
IV : 150		Christ Church, Blacklands (ext.)	23. 2.91	Ore
VI : 314		Christ Church, Blacklands (p.d.)	21. 7.81	H. Emmanuel; H. St. Mary Ore
III : 277		Holy Trinity (p.)	10. 3.82	H. St. Michael and Holy Trinity
IV : 84		Emmanuel (d.c.)	4. 2.75	H. St. Mary
——		Hastings, St. Andrew, assigned by deed by the Ecclesiastical Commissioners c.1870 (no Order in Council); out of reputed parish of St. Andrew.		
IV : 98		St. Clement, Halton (d.)	28. 6.39	H. St. Clement
IV : 42		St. Mary-in-the-Castle (d.c.)	30.12.84	
III : 13		St. Mary Magdalene [see St. Leonards]		
III : 15		St. Paul (p.)	23. 6.70	H. St. Mary Magdalene
IV : 142		St. Peter (d.c.)	15. 8.90	H. St. Paul
V : 60		St. Peter (ext.)	19. 7.10	H. St. Paul
II : 327		Haywards Heath, St. Wilfrid (d.c.)	16. 2.66	Cuckfield Holy Trinity
III : 111		Heene, St. Botolph (d.c.)	17.3 .75	W. Tarring
III : 298		Highbrook, All Saints (d.)	30.11.82	W. Hoathly
III : 40		High Hurst Wood, Holy Trinity (d.c.)	21.12.71	Buxted
III : 16		Hollington, St. John E. (d.c.)	19. 7.70	H.
IV : 303		St. John E. (ext.)	11. 6.02	H. St. Mary
VI : 11		Hove, St. Agnes (c.c.)	25. 7.27	H. St. Barnabas; Preston Good Shepherd
IV : 5		St. Barnabas (d.c.)	12.12.83	H. St. Andrew
IV : 48		St. Patrick (d.c.)	12. 8.85	H. St. Andrew
V : 299		St. Thomas A. (c.c.)	12. 8.24	H. St. Andrew; H. St. Patrick

Dio. Reg. vol. p.	Parish	O. in C.	Out of/(to)
V : 8	Hurst Green (c.c.)	9. 5.07	Etchingham; Salehurst
VI : 166	Jarvis Brook, St. Michael (p.)	14. 5.34	Rotherfield
VI : 156	Kingston-by-Lewes (dim.)	8. 8.32	(Lewes St. John B.)
VI : 120	Lancing, St. Michael (d.c.)	19. 5.31	L. St. James
VI : 131	West Lavington (ext.)	17.12.31	Cocking
VI : 156	Lewes, St. John B., Southover (ext.)	8. 8.32	Kingston-by-Lewes
IV : 58	Linch (ext.)	12.12.85	Stedham; Woolbeding
VI : 131	Linch (dim.)	17.12.31	(Bepton)
VI : 31	Littlehampton, St. James (d.c.)	21.12.28	L. St. Mary
III : 89	Loxwood (d.c.)	9. 8.73	Wisborough Green
VI : 131	Midhurst (ext.)	17.12.31	Bepton
III : 168	Milland [Tuxlith] (ext.)	13. 8.77	Rogate
VI : 109	Moulescoomb St. Andrew (d.)	19. 5.31	Falmer; Patcham
II : 223	Netherfield, St. John Baptist (d.c.)	1.11.62	Battle
IV : 163	North Mundham (ext.)	24.11.91	Pagham
I : 120	Nutley, St. James (n.d.)	17. 6.47	Maresfield
IV : 94	Ore, Christ Church (d.c.)	15. 9.87	O. St. Helen
VI : 215	Pagham (dim.)	3.10.35	(Bognor St. John)
IV : 235	Parham (ext.)	19. 5.98	Amberley
VI : 18	Peacehaven, The Ascension (d.)	3.11.27	Piddinghoe
III : 24	Portfield (d.)	14. 1.71	Oving
III : 76	Portfield (ext.)	24. 3.73	Oving
VI : 199	Portslade (dim.)	4. 5.35	(Aldrington)
VI : 304	Portslade-by-Sea, St. Andrew (d.c.)	23.10.76	Portslade
V : 273	Preston, Good Shepherd (c.c.)	13.10.22	P. St. Peter; Prestonville St. Luke
V : 172	St. Alban (d.c.)	3. 2.15	P. St. Peter
V : 225	St. Alban (ext.)	22. 7.20	P. St. Martin
IV : 248	St. Augustine (c.c.)	18. 7.98	P. St. Peter
V : 102	St. Matthias (d.c.)	28. 3.12	P. St. Peter
IV : 110	St. Saviour (d.c.)	17. 5.88	P. St. Peter
V : 216	Prestonville, St. Luke (d.c.)	22. 2.78	P. St. Peter
VI : 194	Pulborough (dim.)	29. 3.35	(Billingshurst)
III : 191	Roffey, All Saints (d.c.)	30.12.78	Horsham
IV : 319	Rye Harbour Holy Spirit (c.c.)	10. 2.05	Icklesham; Winchelsea St. Thomas; Lydd [Canterbury]
II : 262	St. John's Common, St. John E. (d.c.)	29. 6.65	Clayton; Keymer
IV : 45	St. Leonards, Christ Church (p.)	19. 5.85	St. L. St. Leonards; St. L. St. Mary Magdalene

Dio. Reg. vol. p.	Parish	O. in C.	Out of/(to)
VI : 67	St. Ethelburga (d.c.)	17.12.29	St. L. St. Leonard; St. Mary Bulverhythe (extra parochial)
VI : 302	St. Leonard (p.)	7.10.69	St. L. St. Leonard
III : 13	St. Mary Magdalene (p.)	23. 6.70	Hastings St. Mary
III : 14	St. Matthew, Silverhill (p.)	23.6.70	St. L. St. Leonard
IV : 303	St. Matthew, Silverhill (ext.)	11. 6.02	Hastings St. Mary
——	St. Paul	c.1870	St. L. St. Leonard
III : 271	Upper St. Leonards, St. John (p.)	26. 8.81	Hastings [parl. bor.]
III : 234	Sayers Common, Christ Church (d.c.)	1. 4.81	Hurstpierpoint
VI : 59	Scaynes Hill, St. Augustine (d.)	17.12.29	Lindfield
——	Sennicots, Funtington. No district. Built by Charles Baker (deed 10.5.1831).		
VI : 98	Sidley, All Saints (d.c.)	27.11.30	Bexhill St. Peter
III : 178	Southbourne, St. John E. (d.c.)	22. 2.78	Westbourne
VI : 181	Southwick, St. Peter (d.)	29. 6.34	Lancing; Portslade St. Andrew; Southwick St. Michael
I : 326	Stansted, Christ Church, Forestside (c.c.)	30. 1.56	Stoughton
I : 144	Staplefield Common, St. Mark (n.d.)	16.12.48	Cuckfield
II : 42	Tidebrook (c.c.)	6. 4.58	Mayfield; Wadhurst
IV : 122	Tunbridge Wells,[1] King Charles M. (c.c.)	28. 5.89	Broadwater Down, St. Mark; Tunbridge Wells Christ Church and Rusthall St. Paul [Rochester]
IV : 202	Turners Hill, St. Leonard (c.c.)	6. 3.96	Ardingly; Crawley Down All Saints; West Hoathly; Worth
——	Upper St. Leonards; see St. Leonards		
III : 178	Westbourne, St. John B.	22. 2.78	Westbourne
VI : 280	Whitehawk, St. Cuthman (d.)	2.2.1937	Brighton St. Wilfrid; Brighton St. Mark; Ovingdean
VI : 322	Willingdon (dim.)	12.12.73	(Eastbourne Christ Church)

[1] Dio. Canterbury.

Dio. Reg. vol. p.	Parish	O. in C.	Out of/(to)
III: 40	Withyham, St. John (d.c.)	21.12.71	W. St. Michael
I : 304	Worthing, Christ Church (d.c.)	21. 7.55	Broadwater
IV : 14	Holy Trinity (c.c.)	14. 4.84	Broadwater; W. Christ Church
IV : 114	St. Andrew (d.)	17. 5.88	Broadwater; W. Christ Church; W. Holy Trinity
III: 6	St. George (d.c.)	9.12.68	Broadwater
IV : 180	St. Paul (c.c.)	30. 4.94	Broadwater; W. St. George

APPENDIX III

BISHOPS OF CHICHESTER FROM 1396[1]

	elected/ (provided)	confirmed	consecrated/ (translated from)	temporalities restored	avoided (ante)/ [post]
Robert Rede, 1396	(5.10)		(Car.)	6. 3.97	6.15; d.
Stephen Patrington, 1417	(15.12)		(St.D.)		22.11.17; d.
Henry Ware, 1418	(6. 4)		17. 7.18	13. 5.18	19. 7.20; d.
John Kemp, 1421	(28. 2)		(Roch.)	21. 8.21	17.11.21; tr.Lon.
Thomas Polton, 1421	(17.11)		(Her.)	28. 7.22	27. 2.26; tr.Wor.
John Rickingale, 1426	(27. 2)		30. 6.26	1. 5.26	(6. 7.29); d.
Simon Sydenham, 1429	(14.10)		11. 2.31	24. 1.31	1.38; d.
Richard Praty, 1438	(21. 4)		27. 7.38	14. 7.38	8.45; d.
Adam Moleyns, 1445	(24. 9)		6. 2.46	3.12.45	9. 1.50; d.
Reginald Pecock, 1450	(23. 3)		(St.A.)	30. 5.50	[4.12.57]; res.
John Arundel, 1459	(8. 1)		3. 6.59	26. 3.59	18.10.77; d.
Edward Story, 1478	(11. 2)		(Car.)	27. 3.78	16. 3.03; d.
Richard Fitzjames, 1503	(29.11)		(Roch.)	29. 1.04	5. 6.06; tr.Lon.
Robert Sherburne, 1508	(18. 9)		(St.D.)	13.12.08	5.36; res.
Richard Sampson, 1536	3. 6	10. 6	11. 6.36	15. 6.36	9. 3.43; tr.Cov.
George Day, 1543	24. 4	5. 5	6. 5.43	10. 5.43	10.10.51; dep.
John Scory, 1552	nom. 23.5		(Roch.)	23. 5.52	8.53; dep.
George Day, 1553	restored August, 1553				2. 8.56; d.
John Christopherson, 1557	(7. 5)		21.11.57	21.11.57	(28.12.58); d.
William Barlow, 1559	congé: 22.6		[Bath]	27. 3.60	13. 8.68; d.
Richard Curtis, 1570	14. 4.	26. 4	21. 5.70	6. 6.70	30. 8.82; d.
Thomas Bickley, 1585	20.12	29. 1	30. 1.86		30. 4.96; d.
Anthony Watson, 1596	14. 6	14. 8	15. 8.96	3. 9.96	10. 9.05; d.

[1] For earlier Bishops of Chichester, see J. M. Horn (comp.), *John Le Neve, Fasti Ecclesiae Anglicanae, 1300–1541* (1964).

Name					
Lancelot Andrewes, 1605	16.10	31.10	3.11.05	27.12.09	6.11.09; tr.Ely
Samuel Harsnett, 1609	13.11	2.12	3.12.09	23.10.19	28. 8.19; tr.Nor.
George Carleton, 1619	8. 9	20. 9	(Ll.)		(27. 5.28); d.
Richard Montagu, 1628	14. 7	22. 8	24. 8.28	25. 9.28	12. 5.38; tr.Nor.
Brian Duppa, 1638	29. 5	13. 6	17. 6.38	20. 6.38	14.12.41; tr.Sal.
Henry King, 1642	5. 1	5. 2	6. 2.42		30. 9.69; d.
Peter Gunning, 1670	17. 2	3. 3	6. 3.70		4. 3.75; tr.Ely
Ralph Brideoake, 1675	9. 3	15. 4	18. 4.75	19. 4.75	5.10.78; d.
Guy Carleton, 1678	10.12	8. 1	(Br.)	16. 1.79	6. 7.85; d.
John Lake, 1685	10. 9	19.10	(Br.)		30. 8.89; d.
Simon Patrick, 1689	24. 9	12.10	13.10.89		2. 7.91; tr.Ely
Robert Grove, 1691	13. 7	29. 7	30. 8.91		25. 9.96; d.
John Williams, 1696	29.10	10.12	13.12.96		24. 4.09; d.
Thomas Manningham, 1709	21.10	10.11	13.11.09		24. 8.22; d.
Thomas Bowers, 1722	15. 9	6.10	7.10.22		23. 8.24; d.
Edward Waddington, 1724	17. 9	9.10	11.10.24		7. 9.31; d.
Francis Hare, 1731	2.11	25.11	(St.A.)		26. 4.40; d.
Matthias Mawson, 1740	13. 5	21.10	(Ll.)		15. 3.54; tr.Ely
William Ashburnham, 1754	22. 3	30. 3	31. 3.54	2. 4.54	4. 9.97; d.
John Buckner, 1797	27.10	28. 2	4. 3.98	13. 3.98	1. 5.24; d.
Robert James Carr, 1824	24. 5	4. 4	6. 6.24	10. 6.24	10. 9.31; tr.Wor.
Edward Maltby, 1831	26. 9	1.10	2.10.31	3.10.31	8. 6.36; tr.Dur.
William Otter, 1836	14. 9	1.10	2.10.36	5.10.36	20. 8.40; d.
Philip Nicholas Shuttleworth, 1840	14. 9	19. 9	20. 9.40	6.10.40	7. 1.42; d.
Ashhurst Turner Gilbert, 1842	3. 2	26. 2	27. 2.42	15. 3.42	21. 2.70; d.
Richard Durnford, 1870	28. 3		8. 5		14.10.95; d.
Ernest Roland Wilberforce, 1895	12.12	16. 1	(New).		9. 9.07; d.
Charles John Ridgeway, 1907	21.12		25. 1.08		1. 5.19; res.
Winfrid Oldfield Burrows, 1919	5. 6	9. 7	(Tr.)		13. 2.29; d.
George Kennedy Allen Bell, 1929	1. 5		11. 6.29		31. 1.58; res.
Roger Plumpton Wilson, 1958	4. 2		(Wak.)		

APPENDIX IV

BISHOPS OF LEWES

1909 Leonard Hedley Burrows
1914 Henry Edward Jones
1920 Henry Kemble Southwell
1926 Thomas William Cook
1929 William Champion
     Streatfeild

1929 Hugh Maudslay Hordern
1946 Geoffrey Hodgson Warde
1959 James Herbert Lloyd
     Morrell

APPENDIX V

ARCHDEACONS OF CHICHESTER FROM 1395[1]

1395 John Thomas
1398 William Read
1404 Thomas Harlyng
1409 John Thomas
1412 John Lindfield
1413 John Thomas
1439 John Morton
1439 John Faukes
1440 William Walesby
1444 William Normanton
1454 Simon de Gredon
1459 John Sprever
 — John Dogett (res. in 1478)
1478 Peter Husy
1481 Henry Boleyn
1481 John Cooke
1495 Gerard Burrell
1509 Robert Chapell
1512 William Norbury
1532 John Worthiall
1551 John Jewel
1555 Alban Langdale
1559 Richard Tremayne
1559 Thomas Spenser
1571 John Coldwell
1575 Thomas Gillingham
1580 John Longworth

1586 William Stone
1596 Henry Ball
1603 Thomas Pattinson
1608 Roger Andrewes
1635 Laurence Pay
1640 James Marsh
1643 Henry Hammond
1660 Jasper Mayne
1672 Oliver Whitby
1679 Josiah Pleydell
1708 James Barker
1736 Thomas Ball
1771 Thomas Holingbery
1792 John Buckner
1802 Charles Alcock
1803 Thomas Taylor
1808 Charles Webber
1840 Henry Edward Manning
1851 James Garbett
1879 John Russell Walker
1887 Francis John Mount
1903 Edward Leighton Elwes
1920 Benedict George Hoskyns
1934 Charles Philip Stewart
     Clarke
1945 Lancelot Mason

[1] For earlier Archdeacons of Chichester, see J. M. Horn (comp.), *John Le Neve, Fasti Ecclesiae Anglicanae, 1300–1541* (1964).

APPENDIX VI

ARCHDEACONS OF LEWES FROM 1395[1]

1395 John Bampton
1419 Lewis Coychurch
— Thomas Hanwell (occ. 1450, 1469)
1474 William Skylton
1475 John Dogett
1478 John Plente
1483 Simon Climping
1486 Thomas Oteley
1486 Richard Hill
1509 Edward Vaughan
1510 William Atwater
1512 William Cradock
1516 Oliver Pole
1520 Anthony Wayte
1527 Edward More
1531 Robert Buckenham
1542 John Shirry
1551 Richard Brisley
1558 Robert Tayler
1559 Edmund Weston
1570 Thomas Drant
1578 William Coell
1578 William Cotton
1598 John Mattock

1612 Richard Buckenham
1629 William Hutchinson
1643 Thomas Hooke
1660 Philip King
1667 Nathaniel Hardy
1670 Tobias Henshaw
1681 Joseph Sayer
1693 Richard Bowchier
1723 James Williamson
1737 Edmund Bateman
1751 Thomas D'Oyly
1770 John Courtail
1806 Matthias D'Oyly
1815 Edward Robert Raynes
1823 Thomas Birch
1840 Julius Charles Hare
1855 William Bruere Otter
1876 John Hannah
1888 Robert Shuttleworth Sutton
1912 Henry Kemble Southwell
1923 Francis Henry Dumville Smythe
1946 James Herbert Lloyd Morrell
1959 David Herbert Booth

APPENDIX VII

ARCHDEACONS OF HASTINGS

1912 Theodore Townson Churton
1915 Benedict George Hoskyns
1920 Arthur William Upcott
1922 Thomas William Cook

1928 Arthur Fawssett Alston
1938 Ernest Gordon Reid
1956 Guy Mayfield

[1] For earlier Archdeacons of Lewes, see J. M. Horn (comp.), *John Le Neve, Fasti Ecclesiae Anglicanae, 1300–1541* (1964).

APPENDIX VIII

DEANS OF CHICHESTER FROM 1390[1]

William of Lullington	1390
John Maydenhith	1397
John Haseley	1407
Henry Lovel	1410
Richard Talbot	c.1414
William Milton	c.1420
John Crucher	c.1426
John Waynflete	c.1455
John Cloos	1479
Robert Picherd	1501
Geoffrey Symeon	1504
John Young	c.1507
Thomas Larke	1517
William Fleshmonger	1518
Richard Caurden	1541
Giles Eyer	1549
Bartholomew Traheron	1551
William Pie	1553
Hugh Turnbull	1558
Richard Curtis	1567
Anthony Russhe	1570
Martin Culpeper	1577
William Thorne	1601
Francis Dee	1630
Richard Steward	1634
George Aglionby	1642 (ejected 1642)
Bruno Ryves	1646 (granted Deanery)
Bruno Ryves	1660 (installed)
Joseph Henshaw	1660
Joseph Gulston	1663
Nathaniel Crew	1669
Lambrocke Thomas	1671
George Stradling	1672
Francis Hawkins	1688
William Hayley	1699
Thomas Sherlock	1715
John Newey	1728
Thomas Hayley	1736
James Hargraves	1739
William Ashburnham	1742
Thomas Ball	1754
Charles Harward	1770
Combe Miller	1790
Christopher Bethell	1814
Samuel Slade	1824
George Chandler	1830
Walter Farquhar Hook	1859

[1] For earlier Deans of Chichester, see J. M. Horn (comp.), *John Le Neve, Fasti Ecclesiae Anglicanae, 1300–1541* (1964).

John William Burgon	1876
Francis Pigou	1888
Richard William Randall	1892
John Julius Hannah	1902
Arthur Stuart Duncan-Jones	1929
John Walter Atherton Hussey	1955

APPENDIX IX

CHANCELLORS OR VICARS-GENERAL OF THE DIOCESE FROM 1528[1]

1528	John Worthial	1671	Thomas Briggs
1554	Richard Brisley	1713	Francis Clerke
1558	Robert Tayler	1722	George Jordan
1560	Thomas Spenser	1754	Roger Pettiward
1561	Edmund Weston	1774	William Ashburnham
1563	Austin Bradbridge	1778	Drake Hollingbery
1566	Miles Bendes	1822	Henry Plimley
1570	Henry Worley	1841	Thomas Robinson Welch
1578	John Becon	1844	Robert Joseph Phillimore
1590	Anthony Blencow	1867	Robert Wintle Wintle
1606	John Drury	1892	Thomas Hutchinson
1614	Clement Corbett		Tristram
1627	William Nevill	1912	Alfred Bray Kempe
1640	Richard Chaworth	1922	Kenneth Mead Macmorran
1667	Thomas Croft	1960	Bryan Theodore Buckle

APPENDIX X

DEANS OF PAGHAM AND TARRING AND OF SOUTH MALLING[2]

		occurs
	from	to
Laurence Woodcock	6 May 1544	15 July 1553
John Igulden	11 June 1568	Nov. 1568
Richard Kitson	2 Aug. 1576	17 July 1602
Garrett Williamson	2 Oct. 1602	19 Apr. 1610

[1] The list in G. Hennessy, *Chichester Diocese Clergy Lists* (1900), p. 19, is unreliable, the author having confused Chancellors of the Diocese with Chancellors of the Cathedral.

[2] Earlier holders of the office for whom no documents have survived have been excluded.

(Bishop) Samuel Harsnett	29 Aug. 1610	29 Apr. 1619
John Cradock[1]	21 Oct. 1619	15 Oct. 1625
Francis Ringsted	10 Dec. 1625	9 June 1642
Thomas Croft	18 Jan. 1661/2	16 May 1663
Richard Chaworth	5 May 1666	
Thomas Briggs[2]	8 Mar. 1672/3	20 May 1713
John Bettesworth	9 June 1714	22 June 1763
Dennis Clarke	20 June 1764	17 July 1776
Andrew Coltee Ducarel	3 Dec. 1776	14 July 1784
William Scott [later kt.]	13 July 1785	11 July 1821
Maurice Swabey	25 Jan. 1822	8 June 1825
Herbert Jenner [later kt.]	21 June 1826	24 June 1835
Sherrard Beaumont Burnaby	20 May 1836	21 Aug. 1844[3]

APPENDIX XI

DEANS OF BATTLE[4]

1572 John Withers
1615 Thomas Bambridge
1629 Christopher Dowe
1664 William Watson
1689 William Simmonds
1731 Richard Nairne
1760 Thomas Nairne
1776 Johnson Lawson
1779 Thomas Ferris

1801 Thomas Birch
1836 John Littler
1863 Edward Neville Crake
1882 Edward Reid Currie
1920 Henry Francis
1924 Wilfrid Wadham Youard
1946 Alfred Thomas Arthur
    Naylor
1960 Francis Henry Outram

[1] Surrogate from 23 Oct. 1618.

[2] Surrogate earlier.

[3] End of peculiar jurisdiction.

[4] This list begins with holders of the office for whom records have survived or who are mentioned in records in classes other than Ep. VIII.

INDEX

Unless otherwise stated, all places in this index are in Sussex.

Attention is drawn to the fact that no indication is given in the index as to whether or not a man is in holy orders, nor of a name occurring more than once on a page.

In general, the dedication of the parish church is not given, and subsequent dedications in block capitals in the same entry indicate newer parishes.

An asterisk (*) against a name indicates an entry in the *Dictionary of National Biography*.

SEE ALSO LIST OF CONTENTS ON pp. iii–ix.

SEE ALSO AREAS OF JURISDICTION ON pp. xxii, xxiii.

Andrewes: Lancelot* (Bishop of Chichester), 235; registers of, 3, 4; Roger (Archdeacon of Chichester), 236
ANGMERING: 86; bishops' transcripts, 192; faculty papers, 58, 59
Apothecaries: 96; licences to, 100, 117; subscription by, 6, 100
Apparitors (Apparators): 38, 66, 114; accounts of, 167; appointment of, 137
Appeals (public appeals for money): 57, 59, 133, 137; see also Briefs; Subscriptions
APPLEDRAM (Apuldram): bishops' transcripts, 192; church building papers, 59; tithe, 84
Appleshaw (Hampshire): tithe, 84
Appointments: of administrators, 189; (grant of office) of bailiffs, 169, 170; of chaplains, 93; illegal appointment of a churchwarden, 74; of episcopal and other officials (officers), 3, 55–57, 137, 144; of guardians (of minors), 189; see also Parish clerks; Schoolmasters; Surrogates
Apprentices, Government: 72, 131
Appropriations of churches: 2, 5, 163
Archbishops: see Canterbury; Leighton, Robert (Glasgow); Whateley, Richard (Dublin)
Archdeacons: see Chichester; Ely; Hastings; Lewes; Oxford
Arches, Court of: see London
ARDINGLY: 232; bishops' transcripts, 192; faculty papers, 121
ARLINGTON: 229; bishops' transcripts, 192; vicarage (house), 76; vicars, 76
Articles of enquiry: Archbishop Whitgift's, 117; see also Churchwardens; Ministers; Visitation
ARUNDEL: 162, 187; bishops' transcripts, 193; faculty papers, 59; railway, 187; rural deanery, 27, 46; College of, 27; Holy Trinity Hospital, 2
Arundel, Earl of: 162
Arundel, John* (Bishop of Chichester): 234
ASHBURNHAM: bishops' transcripts, 193
Ashburnham, William: (Bishop of Chichester), 93, 235; register of, 4; consecration of, 8; restitution of temporalities, 97; domestic bills and receipts, 97; (Dean of Chichester), 238; (Chancellor of the diocese), 239
Ashfold (Wisborough Green): 185
ASHINGTON: bishops' transcripts, 193; faculty papers, 58; tithe, 81
Ashmole, Elias*: 163
Ashmolean MSS. (Oxford): 4, 95
ASHURST: bishops' transcripts, 193
Assessors' election papers: 128, 188
Assignations: of pensions, 2, 3; (instance) 53, 102, 103
Assignments: of insurance policy, 96; of residentiary houses, 4, 5
Astley (Shropshire): 98
Astrologer: 95
Attorney: letters of, 84; powers of, 81

Attree: see Lowndes and Attree; Senior and Attree
Atwater, William* (Archdeacon of Lewes): 237
Augmentation of livings: 1–3, 65, 71, 86, 87, 119, 136
Austin, John: 23, 73, 96
Aylward, Augustus A.: 75
Aylwin, ——: 21

Backer, Elizabeth: 21
Bacon, Robert: 74
Bailiffs: 169, 170
Baker, Charles: 57, 232
BALCOMBE: bishops' transcripts, 193; faculty papers, 121; rector, 137; schools in the rural deanery, 131
Ball: Henry (Archdeacon of Chichester), 236; Thomas (Archdeacon of Chichester), 236; Thomas (Dean of Chichester), 76, 238
Ballard, Richard: 74
Bambridge, Thomas (Dean of Battle): 240
Bampton, John (Archdeacon of Lewes): 237
Bank books: 96, 169
Bapchild (Kent): tithe, 84
Baptism: baptismal entries, 14, 138, 146; numbers of persons baptized, 70, 85, 94, 131; treatise on, 2; unbaptized infant, burial of, 74
Baptist Head Chambers (London): 181
Barber family pedigree: 93
BARCOMBE: bishops' transcripts, 193; church building papers, 132; curates, 73, 74; faculty papers, 121; proposed second church, 73; rectors, 73, 74; school, 73, 131
Bargham, prebend of: 12
Barker: James (Archdeacon of Chichester), 236; Robert, 130
BARLAVINGTON: bishops' transcripts, 193
Barlee, William: 73
Barlow, William* (Bishop of Chichester): 234; handwriting, 1–3; installation of, 3; register of, 3
Barnard, Edward: 22
Barngates (Aldingbourne): 170
BARNHAM: bishops' transcripts, 193; terrier, 46; tithe, 81
Barrow[-in-Furness] (Lancashire): St. George, 130
Bateman, Edmund (Archdeacon of Lewes): 237
Bath and Wells: Bishop of, 234; diocese of, 98
Battine, William: 22
BATTLE (Battell): 61, 128, 231; bishops' transcripts, 61, 128; church, 190, 191; faculty papers, 191; tithe, 191; Deans of Battle, list of, 240 (from which see under individual names); institution to the Deanery, 5; presentations to the Deanery, 10, 190; subscription by Deans, 8; cast of the Dean's seal, 190; records of the Dean of Battle's Pecu-

liar, 189–191; the Deanery (house), 190; the White House, 190
Bayly, W.: 93
Bayford, John and J. Heseltine: 99
Beaconsfield (Buckinghamshire): rectory, 129
Beaumont, Henry: 75
Beckett, Joseph Adkins: 74
BECKLEY: advowson, 11; bishops' transcripts, 193; church building papers, 132; faculty papers, 121
Becon, John* (Chancellor of the diocese): 239
BEDDINGHAM: bishops' transcripts, 193; church building papers, 133; tithe, 81, 84
BEEDING, LOWER: 229; bishops' transcripts, 194; faculty papers, 121; vicarage, 136
BEEDING, UPPER (Sele): bishops' trascripts, 194; faculty papers, 121
Belaney, Robert: 76
Bell, George Kennedy Allen (Bishop of Chichester): 235; enquiry, 88; seal matrix, 85
Bendes, Miles (Chancellor of the diocese): 239
Benefactions: see Charities
Benefices: admissions to, 1–3, 9, 37, 89, 96, 139, 145; exchanges of, 1; peculiar, 98; redeemed land tax on, 165, 166; sinecure, 70; spiritualities of, 89; temporalities of, 12, 89; union and disunion of, 2–5, 11, 60, 65, 76, 132, 134, 136, 148; see also Advowsons; Augmentation of livings; Collations; Inductions; Institutions; Patrons; Perpetual curacies; Plurality; Presentations; Resignations; Sequestration
Bennett, Richard: 189
BEPTON: 227, 231; bishops' transcripts, 194; tithe, 81
Berkeley, Capt.: 96
Berkshire courts: 78
BERSTED, SOUTH: 228; bishops' transcripts, 194; church building papers, 59, 154; churchwardens' presentments, 149; court papers relating to, 148; faculty papers, 153; schools in the rural deanery, 72; terriers, 150
BERWICK: bishops' transcripts, 194; church building papers, 132; faculty papers, 119
Bethell, Christopher* (Dean of Chichester): 238
Bettesworth, John (Dean of Pagham and Tarring and of South Malling): 240
Betton, Mr.: 94
BEXHILL: manor, 164, 170; schools in the rural deanery, 131; tithe, 81; Bexhill Hundred, 170; Bexhill pension, 164; ST. PETER: 90, 228, 232; bishops' transcripts, 194; faculty papers, 121; and St. Paul, 136; ST. AUGUSTINE: 228; ST. BARNABAS: 228; bishops' transcripts, 194; church building papers, 132; ST. MARK, Little Com-

mon, 90, 136, 228; bishops' transcripts, 194; faculty papers, 121; ST. STEPHEN, 228; see also Sidley
Bible, the: see Gospel of St. John; Job, Book of; Old Testament (sub Medieval); Scriptural passages
Bickley, Thomas* (Bishop of Chichester): 234; register of, 3
Biffin, J. C. H.: 96
BIGNOR: bishops' transcripts, 194; faculty papers, 58; tithe, 81
BILLINGSHURST: 164, 228, 231; bishops' transcripts, 194; faculty papers, 58, 59
Bills: domestic, 97; parliamentary, 73, 74, 76, 81, 84, 87, 174, 186
BINDERTON: bishops' transcripts, 201; tithe, 82, 84
Binding of particular interest: 101, 103, 104, 167, 170; see also Medieval; Public Record Office
BINSTED: bishops' transcripts, 195; faculty papers, 58
Biography of St. Wilfrid: 80
Birch, Thomas: (Archdeacon of Lewes) 237; (Dean of Battle) 191, 240
Birch's Lane or Place (London): 182
BIRDHAM: bishops' transcripts, 195; surveys of land in, 186; tithe, 81, 84; Birdham Common, 178, 185; Birdham Common inclosure, 178; Birdham Mill, 185; Hundred Steddle House (and House at Hundred Steddle), 184
Birmingham (Warwickshire): London and Birmingham Railway, 187
Bishop, Phoebe: 189
Bishops: of the province (of Canterbury), 98, 118; other than of Chichester and Lewes, see Bath and Wells; Bristol; Carlisle; Coventry; Durham; Ely; Exeter; Glasgow and Galloway; Hereford; Llandaff; Newcastle; Norwich; Oxford; Rochester; St. Asaph; St. David's; Salisbury; Selsey; Truro; Wakefield; Winchester; Worcester
Bishop's Acre (Amberley): 186
Bishop's Court (London): 180, 181
Bishop's Palace: see Chichester
Bishoprick, the (Horsham): 149
Bishops' transcripts: see Parish register transcripts
Bishops Wood (Slaugham): 185
Bishopston: manor, 170; prebend, 184
BISHOPSTONE: 164; bishops' transcripts, 195; church building papers, 132; faculty papers, 119, 121; tithe, 81, 167
Blatchington: 155
BLATCHINGTON, EAST: bishops' transcripts, 195; church building papers, 132
BLATCHINGTON (Bletchington), WEST: advowson, 5, 11; bishops' transcripts, 195; rector, 11; tithe, 81
Blencow, Anthony (Chancellor of the diocese): 239
Blomfield, Charles James* (Bishop of London): 73, 76
BODIAM: bishops' transcripts, 195;

Farm or Grange, 153, 183, 184, 186; Chichester Palace manor, 170; Chichester Harbour, 186; the Headacre, 149; (Mayor and) Corporation, 169, 186; Prebendal School, 12; statutes of the Prebendal School, 12, 80; Probate Registry, 98, 168; Sloe Fair Field, 169; Society of Friends, burials, 198; surveys of land in, 186; Vicars' Close, 51; the Vintry, 149; West Street, Butchers Row, 184;

ARCHDEACONRY:
114, 151, 153, 159; records of, 1–99; archdeacons, list of, 236 (*from which see under individual names*); archdeacons' accounts, 42, 167; archdeacon's registrar (*and* registry), 127, 167;

BISHOPS: 81, 85, 87, 137; list of, 234, 235 (*from which see under individual names*); other lists of, 5, 80; as freemen of Chichester, 80; Bishop's Palace (Chichester House), accounts for work and repairs done, 92, 165, 167; papers relating to, 92, 93; episcopal house of residence, 87; episcopal accounts, 97; election of bishops, 4, 234, 235; episcopal estates and manors, 162–187; registers of leases, 179, 183; income of bishops, 5, 70; episcopal mandates for induction, 12, 187; appointment of officials, 55–57; episcopal patronage (benefices), 11, 65, 98, 165, 179; episcopal possessions, valor of, 65; episcopal receipts, 97; lists of episcopal records (*and* note on), 5, 97; handlists and calendars of the records, 99; episcopal registers, 1–5; indexes, abstracts and copies of the registers, 5, 79, 80; bishop's secretary, 65, 74, 87; bishop's steward, 65, 174;

CATHEDRAL:
28, 57, 60, 65, 66, 79, 163; Chancellors, 5, 239; Cathedral clergy, 5, 69, 70, 79; dignitaries, 12, 38, 40, 70; lists of dignities, 165, 179; faculty papers, 145; Kalendar used in, 163; Library, 80; prebendaries, 12, 38, 40, 165 (*see also* Hova Villa; Highleigh); prebends, sinecure, 76 (*see also* Bargham; Bishopston; Highleigh; Sidlesham); sermon in, 79; statutes, 2, 6, 163; Treasurer, 77; visitation of, 26, 28, 34, 36–38;

CHANCELLORS (*or* vicar-general *or* official principal) of the diocese: 39, 55, 57, 66, 67; list of, 239 (*from which see under individual names*); accounts, 167; legal opinions, 15; subscription by, 6;

COURTS: Chichester consistory, 54, 69–71, 76–79, 98, 143; records of, 16–26; causes (*and* case, cause and court papers), 3–5, 11, 20–23, 32, 38, 72–75, 91, 105, 141, 148, 149, 156, 189, 191; list of court act books, 98; exhibits, 22, 23; court proceedings arising

from church inspections, 46; Pie Powder Court, 169;

DEANS: 38, 66; list of, 238, 239 (*from which see under individual names*); Dean's House, 58; election of, 3; decanal seal, 55; Dean of Chichester's Peculiar, 6, 8, 10, 13, 16, 26, 34, 37, 38, 55–57, 62, 63, 65, 69, 152, 153, 159; court, 54, 69, 141; Dean's manorial court, 144; records of the Peculiar, 138–145; registrar of the Peculiar, 144, 145;

DEAN AND CHAPTER (capitular): 12, 23, 65, 66, 68, 69, 79, 81, 85, 169; Chapter clerk, 56, 63; Chapter clerk's office, 168, 169; Chapter confirmation, 55, 137, 144; Chapter copyholds and estates, 147, 164, 166, 186; Chapter manors, steward of, 56; lease of Chapter property, 147; Chapter fees, 78; Chapter patronage (benefices), 40; lists of records of, 5, 99; Chapter seal, 55, 144;

DIOCESE:
diocesan papers, 97, 98; Diocesan Record Office at Chichester, establishment of, 99; diocesan registrar (*and* registry) (Chichester), 1, 5, 10, 23, 37, 45, 55–57, 62, 76, 79–81, 84, 85, 97, 98, 168, 169, 227; diocesan school inspectors, 72, 131;

SEE: in vacancy, 12, 14–16, 31, 33, 57, 109, 143, 147, 150, 153; revenue of, 97; restitution of temporalities, 97, 234, 235;

ALL SAINTS: assessment for the poor, 23; bishops' transcripts, 197; churchwardens' presentments, 149; court papers relating to, 148; faculty papers, 153; minister, 87; terriers, 150;

THE CLOSE: assessment for the poor, 23; bishops' transcripts, 198;

ST. ANDREW: 153; assessment for the poor, 23; bishops' transcripts, 197; churchwardens' presentments, 141;

ST. BARTHOLOMEW: 87, 153, 229; assessment for the poor, 23; bishops' transcripts, 198; churchwardens' presentments, 141; faculty papers, 145; perpetual curacy, 145; tithe, 82;

ST. JAMES' HOSPITAL: 27, 28; Mastership of, 10;

ST. MARTIN: 153; assessment for the poor, 23; bishops' transcripts, 198; churchwardens' presentments, 141; faculty papers, 145;

ST. MARY'S HOSPITAL: 4, 27, 28, 60, 79;

ST. OLAVE: assessment for the poor, 23; bishops' transcripts, 198; churchwardens' presentments, 141;

Constables: 54
Constantinople: 81
Conveyances: 5, 11, 57, 72, 118, 119, 155, 191
Convocation: election of proctors, 5, 108, 109, 112; mandate, 24; papers, 65–68; returns, 94
Cook(e): John, 77; Mrs. John, 77; John (Archdeacon of Chichester), 236; Thomas William (Archdeacon of Hastings), 188, 237; Thomas William (Bishop of Lewes), 236
COOMBES: bishops' transcripts, 200
Cooper: Godfrey Gilbert, 72; J.G., 72
Copperas stones (West Wittering): 184
COPTHORNE: 229; bishops' transcripts, 200
Copyholds: capitular, 166; enfranchisement, 166; episcopal, 165, 166; fines on, 167
Corbett, Clement* (Chancellor of the diocese): 239
Corn rents: 164–166
Correction causes: 16, 24, 105, 139, 147
Correspondence and letters: 8, 10, 11, 14, 15, 23, 26, 38, 45, 54, 55, 57, 59, 62, 66, 70–77, 88–94, 96, 97, 99, 105, 115, 126–131, 136, 137, 144, 145, 148, 149, 160–162, 165, 166, 174, 178, 183, 186–188, 190, 191
Cotton, William (Archdeacon of Lewes): 237
Court of High Commission: 90
Courts: see Berkshire; Canterbury; Chichester (Courts; Deans); Lewes; London; Oxford; Pagham; Sussex; Wales
Courtail, John (Archdeacon of Lewes): 76, 237
Coventry, Bishop of: 234
COWFOLD: bishops' transcripts, 200; churchwardens, 72; faculty papers, 121, 122; vicar, 72; Cowfold pension, 164
Coychurch, Lewis (Archdeacon of Lewes): 237
Cradock: John (Dean of Pagham and Tarring and of South Malling), 240; William (Archdeacon of Lewes) 237
Crake, Edward Neville (Dean of Battle): 240
CRAWLEY: 1; bishops' transcripts, 200; faculty papers, 120, 122
CRAWLEY, WEST: 229
CRAWLEY DOWN: 229, 232; augmentation of vicarage, 136; bishops' transcripts, 200; faculty papers, 122
Crew, Nathaniel* (Dean of Chichester): 238
Criminous clerk: 2
Crockford, John: 22
Croft, Thomas: (Chancellor of the diocese) 239; (Dean of Pagham and Tarring and of South Malling) 240
Crosse, Thomas Francis: 69
Crossingham, Robert: 22
CROWBOROUGH: bishops' transcripts, 200; ST. JOHN (now Withyham St. John):

233; bishops' transcripts, 226; faculty papers, 125
CROWHURST: bishops' transcripts, 200; church building papers, 133; faculty papers, 122
Crown: patronage (benefices), 165, 179; presentations, 1
The Crown: see London
Crucher, John (Dean of Chichester): 238
CUCKFIELD: 61, 116, 229, 230, 232; bishops' transcripts, 200; church building papers, 133; faculty papers, 119, 120, 122; for Cuckfield St. Wilfrid see Haywards Heath
Culpeper, Martin (Dean of Chichester): 238
Curacies (curates) (mainly stipendiary): passim; 37, 44, 68, 73, 112; 115, 118; augmentation of curacies, 71; licences to, 3–5, 7, 89, 90, 100, 159, 161, 190; lists of, 35, 65, 96, 98; nominations to, 88, 89, 96; papers relating to, 89; subscriptions by curates, 6–9, 89, 100; see also Perpetual curacies
Currey: Edmund Charles, 57, 75, 77, 129, 130; William, 130; solicitors, 128; see also Hunt & Currey; Moore & Currey
Currie, Edward Reid (Dean of Battle): 191, 240
Curteys (Curtis), Richard*: (Bishop of Chichester) 37, 65, 97, 234; installation of, 3; register of, 3; (Dean of Chichester) 3, 238
Curtis, E.: 75
Custumals (customaries, customs): 162–164; of Amberley manor, 173; of Streatham manor, 177, 178

D., J.: 93
DALLINGTON: 228; bishops' transcripts, 200; faculty papers, 120; rural deanery, 127, 187
DANEHILL: bishops' transcripts, 200; church building papers, 133; faculty papers, 122
Danny Park (Hurstpierpoint): 128
Darby, John: 189
Daubuz, J. B.: 73
Davison, Thomas: 56
Day: George* (Bishop of Chichester), 234; installation of, 3; register of, 3; John, 22
Day Books: 63, 130, 168
DEAN, EAST (West Sussex): bishops' transcripts, 201; church building papers, 60; for East Sussex see Eastdean
DEAN, WEST: bishops' transcripts, 201; church building papers, 60; tithe, 82, 84; for East Sussex see Westdean
'Deanry Debt Book': 158
Dear: Francis, 171; John, 167
Deaths, registers of: 116
Declarations: 6, 100, 138; against transubstantiation, 6; churchwardens', 127, 160, 188, 189; Bishop Lake's deathbed declaration 97; see also Oaths

EASTDEAN (East Sussex): bishops' transcripts, 201; church building papers, 133; tithe, 84
Easter offerings: 98
EASTERGATE: bishops' transcripts, 202; church building papers, 60; tithe, 82
Easton, Thomas: 22
EBERNOE: 229; bishops' transcripts, 202
Ecclesiastical Commissioners: 70, 98, 119, 174, 176, 178, 186, 230; estates, 166; records, 99
Ecclesiastical Courts: Act (1844), 128; Commissioners, 70
EDBURTON: bishops' transcripts, 203
Edinburgh: 93
Education: see Schoolmasters and Schools
Edwards, William: 159
EGDEAN: bishops' transcripts, 203
Eldridge: law suit relating to, 191
Elections: assessors' election papers, 128, 188; of bishops of Chichester, 4, 234, 235; of a churchwarden, 75; to Convocation, 65–69, 108, 109, 112; of Deans of Chichester, 3; monastic elections, 1, 2; confirmation of elections, 1, 234, 235
Elizabeth I (exchange of episcopal manors): 170
Ellis, John: 148
Ellman, Frederick: 128
ELSTED: bishops' transcripts, 203; church building papers, 60; rector, 76
Elwes, Edward Leighton (Archdeacon of Chichester): 236
Ely: archdeacons of the diocese, 130; bishops of, 93, 235; cathedral, 130; diocese of, 130
Endowments: of parish churches, 40; of schools, 71; of vicarages, 5
Enfranchisement of copyholds: 166
Enquiry: see Bell, George Kennedy Allen; Churchwardens; Ministers
Episcopal and Capitular Revenues Commission: 70
ERIDGE GREEN: 229; bishops' transcripts, 203
ETCHINGHAM: 231; bishops' transcripts, 203; church building papers, 133; faculty papers, 122; rural deanery, 187
Ewen(s): C., 96; William, 22
EWHURST: bishops' transcripts, 203; church building papers, 133; churchwardens, 74; curate, 74; faculty papers, 122; rectors, 72, 74
Examinations: ordinands' examination papers, 9; Oxford University Examination Statute, 95
Examiner (of the diocese): appointments of, 55, 144
Exchanges: of benefices, 1; of glebe, 118, 119; of land, 136, 137
Exchequer: proceedings, 167; suits, 150
Excommunications: 78, 104, 106; forms of excommunication, 148; lists of those excommunicated, 20, 33; excommunication books and papers, 20, 104, 156

Executors: 50, 116, 119; executors' accounts, 52; oath of, 26
Exeter, Bishop of: see Philpotts, Henry
Extra-diocesan papers: 79, 98, 99
Eyer, Giles (Dean of Chichester): 238

Fabric, church: passim; 43, 44, 46, 57, 61, 116, 136; reports on, 148
Faculties: 24, 37, 52, 63, 64, 71, 75, 77, 79, 99, 117, 125, 127, 129, 139, 147, 156; faculty papers, 57–59, 119–125, 129, 132, 144, 145, 153, 161, 191; faculty registers, 118, 119, 157
Faculties of appointment: 56, 137
Fair in Chichester: 169
FAIRLIGHT: bishops' transcripts, 203; church building papers, 133; faculty papers, 120
FAIRWARP: 90, 230
FALMER: 155, 231; bishops' transcripts, 203; church building papers, 136
Farlington (Hampshire): 87
Farrington [Farringdon] Street (London) railway: 187
Fast books: 97
Faukes, John (Archdeacon of Chichester): 236
Fearon, Joseph: 56
Fees: 63, 65, 67, 69–71, 78, 127, 130, 144, 167, 189
FELPHAM: bishops' transcripts, 203; curacy, 96; faculty papers, 58; sequestration, 91; tithe, 82
Fenn, John: 21
FERNHURST: 230; bishops' transcripts, 203; church building papers, 60
FERRING: bishops' transcripts, 203; faculty papers, 58; records of the manor of Ferring and Fure, 164, 170, 175–178; tithe, 82; Ferring Farm, 184
Ferris, Thomas (Dean of Battle): 240
Fetter Lane (London): 182
Fielder, Mary: 22
Filder, ——: 21
Finance: financial assistance for Westham school, 131; returns on parochial finances, 86, 98, 113, 188
FINDON: bishops' transcripts, 204; church building papers, 60; faculty papers, 59
Fines: 165, 167, 179
FIRLE, WEST: bishops' transcripts, 204; church building papers, 133; ruridecanal chapter, 131; schools in the rural deanery, 131; tithe, 81
First fruits: 86, 87
FISHBOURNE, NEW: bishops' transcripts, 204; churchwardens' presentments, 141; faculty papers, 145; rectory, 145; schools in the rural deanery, 72; Fishbourne Farm, 96
Fisher, John: 137
FITTLEWORTH: bishops' transcripts, 204; church building papers, 60; cottage in, 184; faculty papers, 58; inclosure award, 174; surveys of land in, 186; Fittleworth Mills, 185

Fitzjames, Richard* (Bishop of Chichester): 234; register of, 2
Fleet Street (London): 182
Fleshmonger, William (Dean of Chichester): 238
FLETCHING: 5; bishops' transcripts, 204; church building papers, 134; faculty papers, 120
FLIMWELL: augmentation of vicarage, 136; bishops' transcripts, 204; faculty papers, 122
FOLKINGTON: bishops' transcripts, 204; church building papers, 134; faculty papers, 122
FORD: bishops' transcripts, 204
Ford, John: 22
Foreigners, marriage with: 15
FOREST ROW: 73, 230; bishops' transcripts, 204; curate-in-charge, 73; faculty papers, 122; vicar, 74
FORESTSIDE: 232
Formularies: 125; civil, 78, 79, 84, 85; ecclesiastical, 47, 77–79, 85
Foster, Henry: 76
Foundation stone, laying of: 92
Fovargue: see Raper & Fovargue
Fowler, William: see Leeves
FRAMFIELD: 159; bishops' transcripts, 204; faculty papers, 122, 161
Francis, Henry (Dean of Battle): 240
Frankfürt: 80
Franklin, William: 21
FRANT: 86, 228, 229; bishops' transcripts, 204; church building papers, 134; faculty papers, 120; rector, 76; schools in the rural deanery, 131
Freeland, James Bennett: 5, 56, 73, 74, 81, 84, 167, 186, 187; papers, 79, 80
Freemen of Chichester: 80
France: marriage with French subjects, 15
Freshwater (Isle of Wight): tithe, 84
Friend, James: 74
FRISTON: bishops' transcripts, 205; faculty papers, 122
Frogley, Harriet: 96
Funeral accounts: 41
Furner, Thomas: 21
FUNTINGTON: bishops' transcripts, 205; church building papers, 60; faculty papers, 58; schools in the rural deanery, 72; tithe, 82, 84; see also Sennicots
Fure: see Ferring

Gadbury, John*: 95
Gallowes Heath (Broyle Farm, Chichester): 153
Garbett, James* (Archdeacon of Chichester): 76, 77, 236
Gas rate: 97
Gear, Thomas: 189
Geering, William: 76
Genealogical papers: 93
General Register Office: 118
George IV's support for the National Society: 71
Germany: see Frankfürt

Gibbons: Edward, 15; Joan, 15
Gilbert: Ashurst Turner* (Bishop of Chichester), 1, 40, 73–77, 93, 97, 98, 128, 129, 235; Oxford papers of, 95; Thomas, 189
Gillingham, Thomas (Archdeacon of Chichester): 236
Gilmore, John: 189
Gitten, Daniel: 21
Glasgow, Archbishop of: see Leighton, Robert
Glasgow and Galloway, Bishop of: see Trower, Walter John
Glebe (church land): 57, 65, 87, 132; exchanges of, 118, 119; see also Terriers
Gloucestershire: Record Office, 170; see also Cheltenham
Glover, Maria: 22
GLYNDE: bishops' transcripts, 205; church building papers, 134
Goble, ——: 21
Goodchild, Thomas Oliver: 160
Goodwood estate archives: 85
Gorham, Elizabeth: 189
GORING: bishops' transcripts, 205
Gospel of St. John: 80
Government apprentices: 72, 131
Grace, Henry Thomas: 137
GRAFFHAM: bishops' transcripts, 205
Grants of next presentation: 9, 11, 138
Gream: Robert, 76; Sarah Ann, 77
GREATHAM: bishops' transcripts, 225; church building papers, 61
Greek examination papers: 9
Green, George: 11
Greene: A. S., 129; solicitors, 128
Greystock, Mr.: 177
GRINSTEAD, EAST: 62, 230; bishops' transcripts, 205; church building papers, 134; churchwardens, 73; faculty papers, 120, 122; vicars, 73, 74; Lewes and East Grinstead Railway Co., 130; Sackville College, 73, 74; ST. MARY: 230
GRINSTEAD, WEST: bishops' transcripts, 205; recusants in, 55
GROOMBRIDGE, NEW: 230; bishops' transcripts, 205; church building papers, 134; faculty papers, 122
Grove, Robert* (Bishop of Chichester): 235; register of, 4
GUESTLING: bishops' transcripts, 205; church building papers, 134
Guild of Our Blessed Lady and St. Dunstan: 183
GULDEFORD, EAST: bishops' transcripts, 205
Gulston, Joseph (Dean of Chichester): 238
Gunning, Peter* (Bishop of Chichester): 235; register of, 3

HADLOW DOWN: 230; bishops' transcripts, 205; curate, 159
Haigh, Daniel Henry*: 73
HAILSHAM: bishops' transcripts, 206; church building papers, 134

High Wycombe: *see* Wycombe, High
HIGHBROOK: 230; bishops' transcripts, 207
Highleigh: prebend, 12; prebendaries, 40, 88
Hile: Edmund, 22; Sara, 22
Hill, Richard (Archdeacon of Lewes): 237
Hinde, Joseph: 76
Hoar, John: 22
HOATHLY, EAST: bishops' transcripts, 208; church building papers, 134; faculty papers, 122, 123
HOATHLY, WEST: 230, 232; bishops' transcripts, 208; church building papers, 134; faculty papers, 123
Hobbes, Francis: 148
Hodgson, John Fisher: 74
Hole Out of the Wall (London): 181
Holland, William: 11
Hol(l)ingbery: Drake (Chancellor of the diocese), 56, 239; Thomas (Archdeacon of Chichester), 236
HOLLINGTON: 136, 230; bishops' transcripts, 208; church building papers, 134; churchwardens, 75; rector, 75; ST. JOHN: 230 [(ext.) refers to Hastings St. Mary-in-the-Castle]; bishops' transcripts, 208; faculty papers, 123
Hollis, Elizabeth: 22
Holmes: Mr., 96; William Groome, 75
HOLTYE: faculty papers, 122
Home Office: 70; Home Secretary, 71
HOOE: bishops' transcripts, 208; faculty papers, 123
Hook, Walter Farquhar* (Dean of Chichester): 238
Hooke, Thomas (Archdeacon of Lewes): 237
Hoper: Messrs. G. & T., 97; George, 73, 128, 137, 159; J., 55; John, 128, 129; solicitors, 128, 129
HORAM: 189
Hordern, Hugh Maudslay (Bishop of Lewes): 236
Horne (Surrey): 229
Horoscope: 95
HORSHAM: 48, 62, 72, 229, 231; bishops' transcripts, 208; church building papers, 60; churchwardens, 74; faculty papers, 58, 59; Horsham Pew Case, 74; rural deanery, 72; schools in the rural deanery, 72; Society of Friends, 208; union chaplain, 93; vicar, 74; the Bishoprick, 149
HORSTED KEYNES: 130, 137; bishops' transcripts, 208; church building papers, 134; faculty papers, 123
HORSTED PARVA (Little Horsted): bishops' transcripts, 208; faculty papers, 123
Hoskyns, Benedict George: (Archdeacon of Chichester) 236; (Archdeacon of Hastings) 237
Hospitals: 43; *see also* Arundel; Chichester
HOUGHTON: 164; bishops' transcripts, 208; Chalk Pits, 185; Houghton Chace,

4; Houghton Parsonage, 184
House of Commons resolutions: 70, 71, 85
Household accounts: 167
Houses, residentiary: 4, 5
Hova Villa, prebendary of: 5
HOVE: 86; cemetery, 123; church building papers, 134; faculty papers, 123; HOLY TRINITY: bishops' transcripts, 209; ST. AGNES: 230; ST. ANDREW: 230; bishops' transcripts, 209; perpetual curate, 75; ST. BARNABAS: 230; faculty papers, 123; ST. JOHN: bishops' transcripts, 209; faculty papers, 123; ST. PATRICK: 230; bishops' transcripts, 209; faculty papers, 123; ST. PHILIP (formerly Aldrington St. Philip): 227; ST. THOMAS: 230
Howley, William* (Archbishop of Canterbury, 1828–48): 68
Huggate (Yorkshire): incumbent, 75
Hulle, William atte: 162
Humfrey, ——: 21
Hundred Steddle (Birdham): 184
HUNSTON: bishops' transcripts, 209; church building papers, 60; tithe, 82
Hunt: Bernard Hus(e)y, 57, 129; solicitors, 128
Hunt & Currey: 97
Hurst: John, 72, 73; Robert Henry, jun., 74
HURST GREEN: 231; faculty papers, 123
HURSTMONCEUX: 228; bishops' transcripts, 209
HURSTPIERPOINT: 232; bishops' transcripts, 209; faculty papers, 120; rector, 77; St. John's school, 76; schools in the rural deanery, 131; Danny Park, 128
Husey-Hunt: solicitors, 128
Hussey, John Walter Atherton (Dean of Chichester): 239
Husy, Peter (Archdeacon of Chichester): 236
Hutchinson, William (Archdeacon of Lewes): 237
Hutton, Thomas Palmer: 74
Hyland: Dennis, 22; Mrs., 189

ICKLESHAM: 231; augmentation of vicarage, 136; bishops' transcripts, 209; church building papers, 135; churchwardens, 75; faculty papers, 123; tithe, 23, 82; vicar, 75
IDEN: advowson, 11; bishops' transcripts, 209; presentation, 11
IFIELD: 229; bishops' transcripts, 209; church, 76; church building papers, 135; faculty papers, 123; Society of Friends, 209; vicar, 76
IFORD: bishops' transcripts, 209; faculty papers, 119, 123
Igulden, John (Dean of Pagham and Tarring and of South Malling): 239
Illuminated manuscripts: 1, 2, 155
Impropriations: 117
Inclosure: Commissioners, 165, 174; *see also* Amberley; Birdham; Fittleworth;

Languages: typographical specimens of oriental and other, 81; *see also* Greek; Latin

Larke, Thomas (Dean of Chichester): 238

Latin: court manuals, 78; examination papers, 9; poem, 95; speech, 95

LAUGHTON: bishops' transcripts, 210; church building papers, 135; faculty papers, 123

LAVANT, EAST: bishops' transcripts, 211; church, 148; churchwardens' presentments, 149; court papers relating to, 149; terriers, 150

LAVANT, MID: bishops' transcripts, 211

LAVANT, WEST: churchwardens' presentments, 149

LAVINGTON, WEST: 229, 231; bishops' transcripts, 211

Law Courts Chambers (London): 182

Lawson, Johnson (Dean of Battle): 240

Leader, Mary: 189

Leases: 4, 81, 87, 96, 99, 118, 147, 148, 153, 155, 164–166, 174, 191; registers of, 179, 183; Amberley leases, 174; London estate leases, 179–182; Sussex estate leases, 183–186

Ledgers: 168

Lees Buildings (London): 182

Leeves (*formerly* Fowler), William: 56, 76, 97

Legal opinions: 15, 81, 87, 91

Leighton, Robert* (Archbishop of Glasgow): 137

Leonard, Mary: 189

Letters: of collation, 89; dismissory, 88; patent, 4; testimonial, 9, 12, 38, 88, 89, 91; *see also* Administrations; Attorney; Correspondence; Institutions; Orders; Sequestration

Levett, Henry: 22

Levitt, Mr.: 118

LEWES: 81, 94, 96, 97, 117, 137, 164; archdeaconry, 6, 8, 26, 27, 40, 46–48, 54–57, 62–66, 68–71, 80, 85, 98; records of, 100–137; registrar of, 55, 71, 105, 111, 118, 128–131; deputy registrar of, 71, 98, 118, 137; archdeacons, 38, 66; list of, 237 (*from which see under individual names*): bishops, 127; list of, 236 (*from which see under individual names*); appointment of, 77; episcopal mandates for induction, 125, 187; County Court, 159; courts, 71, 78, 79; diocesan registry, 74, 77, 136; Probate Registry, 47; Lewes and East Grinstead Railway Co., 130; rural deanery, 127; schools in the rural deanery, 131; Society of Friends, burials, 211; no. 213, High Street, solicitors at, 128; House of Correction, 93; ALL SAINTS: bishops' transcripts, 211; Burial Board, 130; church building papers, 135; faculty papers, 119, 120, 123; rector, 77; ST. ANNE: bishops' transcripts, 211; faculty papers, 123; ST. JOHN BAPTIST, SOUTHOVER: 231; bishops' transcripts, 211; church building papers, 135;

faculty papers, 119, 120, 123; rector, 77; ruridecanal chapter,137; ST. JOHN-SUB-CASTRO: bishops' transcripts, 211; faculty papers, 120, 123; ST. MARK WESTOUT: bishops' transcripts, 211; ST. MARY: Convocation elections held at, 66; ST. MICHAEL: 129; bishops' transcripts, 211; church building papers, 135; faculty papers, 120, 123; ST. THOMAS-AT-CLIFFE: bishops' transcripts, 211; Burial Board, 130; church building papers, 135; faculty papers, 123, 161; parish clerk, 159

Lewin, T.: 76

Lewkenor, Richard: 21

Liber: A, 162; B, 162; C, 162; D, 163, 164; E, 163; P, 163; Y, 163; Liber (Libri) Cleri, 16, 17, 26–37, 107–111, 139, 147, 149, 151, 155–158, 187

Liberties: bishop's, 177; royal charters of, 163

Licences: 37, 57, 63, 98, 127; to chaplains, 93; to a painter, 3; to preach, 3, 4; royal licences, 2; to teach, 3–5; *see also* Apothecaries; Curacies; Dissenters; Marriage; Midwives; Non-Residence; Perpetual Curacies; Schoolmasters

Lichfield, diocese of: 98

Lickfold, William: 22

Lidsey (Aldingbourne): tithe, 170

LINCH: 227, 231; bishops' transcripts, 211

LINCHMERE: bishops' transcripts, 212

LINDFIELD: 232; bishops' transcripts, 212; faculty papers, 123, 161

Lindfield, John (Archdeacon of Chichester): 236

Lingfield (Surrey): church building papers, 99; perpetual curate, 74

LITLINGTON: bishops' transcripts, 212; manor, 170; tithe, 83

Little Common: *see* Bexhill St. Mark

Little Horsted: *see* Horsted Parva

Little White's Alley (London): 182

LITTLEHAMPTON: 231; bishops' transcripts, 212; church building papers, 60; faculty papers, 58, 59; tithe, 83; vicar, 75; Littlehampton Rectory, 184; ST. JAMES: 231

Littler, John (Dean of Battle): 191, 240

Llandaff, Bishops of: 235

Lloyd: ——, 22; Richard, 76

LODSWORTH: 96; bishops' transcripts, 212; schools in the rural deanery, 72

LONDON: 61, 75, 80, 92, 94, 97; bishops, 163, 234 (*see also* Blomfield, Charles James; Sherlock, Thomas); bishops, as provincial dean, 65, 66; courts (Admiralty, Arches, Audience and Episcopal), 21, 24, 73, 74, 77–79; court documents, 125; diocese, in vacancy, 67; Bishop of Chichester's estate records, 165, 179–183; registers of London leases, 179, 183; London and Birmingham Railway, 187; London, Brighton and South Coast Railway, 186; Direct London and Portsmouth Railway, 187; Tottenham to Farrington Street railway, 187; London Union on Church Matters, 72; Baptist Head Chambers, 181; Birch's Lane or Place, 182; Bishop's Court, 180, 181; Bond(s) Stables, 180, 181; Bowling Pin Alley, 182; Breams Buildings, 180–182; Chancery Lane, 179–183; Chancery Lane, widening of, 182; Chancery Lane House, 180; Chichester Rents, 180, 181; *City of Durham*, 181; Doctors' Commons, 78, 99, 129; Fetter Lane, 182; Fleet Street, 182; Hole Out of the Wall, 181; *King's Arms*, 182; the Law Courts Chambers, 182; Lees Buildings, 182; Little White's Alley, 182; Lonsdale Chambers, 182; no. 2, New Inn, 129; *Red Peruke*, 180, 181; Rolls Buildings, 182; St. Dunstan-in-the-West, 183; *St. John's Head* Tavern, 180; St. Mary Abchurch, 155; St. Pancras, Christ Church, curate, 74; Stokes's,181; Swan Court, 182; Symond's Inn, 179, 180, 182; Tenter Yard, 180, 181; *Three Crowns*, 180, 181; *White Swan*, 181; White's Alley, 180–182; White's Alley House, 180

Longworth, John (Archdeacon of Chichester): 236
Lonsdale Chambers (London): 182
Lovegrove, William: 73
Lovel, Henry (Dean of Chichester): 238
Lowdell, Stephen: 130
Lower Beeding: *see* Beeding, Lower
Lowndes, Mr.: 129
Lowndes and Attree: 129
LOXWOOD: 231; church building papers, 60
LULLINGTON: bishops' transcripts, 212; tithe, 84
Lullington, William of (Dean of Chichester): 238
LURGASHALL: bishops' transcripts, 212
Lydd (Kent): 231
LYMINSTER: bishops' transcripts, 212; faculty papers, 58

Mackarness, John Fielder* (Bishop of Oxford): 130
Macmorran, Kenneth Mead (Chancellor of the diocese): 239
MADEHURST: bishops' transcripts, 212; faculty papers, 58; tithe, 83
Maher, William: 93
MALLING, SOUTH: 129; bishops' transcripts, 213; church building papers, 135; faculty papers, 123; parish clerk, 159; parish officers, 129; perpetual curacy, 160; Ryders Wells, 130; Exempt Deanery of South Malling (Archbishop of Canterbury's Peculiar Jurisdiction), 27, 28, 62, 107, 113, 114, 116, 128, 150, 151; deans, list of, 239, 240 (*from which see under individual names*); records of, 154–161; lists of the records, 155, 159; registrars' corres-

pondence, 161; deputy registrar, 137
Maltby, Edward* (Bishop of Chichester): 72, 73, 235
Mandates: 1–4, 63, 102, 104, 127, 167; *see also* Convocation; Inductions; Installation
Manhood Hundred: 178; records of the manor, 170, 175, 176, 178
Manning, Henry Edward* (Archdeacon of Chichester): 73, 236
Manningham: law suit relating to, 163; Thomas* (Bishop of Chichester), 235; register of, 4
Manors: *see* Aldingbourne; Amberley; Bexhill; Bishopston; Cakeham; Chichester; Ferring; Litlington; Manhood Hundred; Ringmer; Selsey; Sidlesham; Streatham; Ticehurst; Tipnoke Hundred; Westergate; Willingdon
Mantle, —— : 21
Manuscripts: *see* Medieval
Manumissions: 2
Maps: 60, 189, 227; inclosure, 174, 178; tithe, 81; *see also* Plans
MARDEN, EAST: bishops' transcripts, 213; church building papers, 60; faculty papers, 58
MARDEN, NORTH: bishops' transcripts, 213
MARDEN, UP: bishops' transcripts, 213
MARESFIELD: 230, 231; bishops' transcripts, 213; church building papers, 135; faculty papers, 119, 123
MARK CROSS: bishops' transcripts, 213
Marriage: 70, 75, 107, 129; Acts (1822, 1823), 14; annulment of, 15; marriage licence affidavits, 14, 15, 101, 138, 139, 146, 154, 188, 190; marriage licence bonds, 14, 15, 101, 138, 139, 146; marriage licence papers, 15, 16; marriage licence registers, 13, 100, 154; marriage licences, 13, 14, 50, 51, 53, 64, 100, 106, 116, 117, 139, 143, 147, 151, 152, 156, 190
Marsh, James (Archdeacon of Chichester): 236
Martlett, —— : 21
Mason, Lancelot (Archdeacon of Chichester): 236
Matthewes, William: 22
Mattock, John (Archdeacon of Lewes): 237
Mawson, Matthias* (Bishop of Chichester): 235; as Bishop of Ely, 93; register of, 4
Maydenhith, John (Dean of Chichester): 238
MAYFIELD: 228, 230, 232; bishops' transcripts, 213; church building papers, 161; faculty papers, 123
Mayfield, Guy (Archdeacon of Hastings): 237
Mayne, Jasper* (Archdeacon of Chichester): 236
Mayor and Corporation of Chichester: 169
Mead, Elizabeth: 128

North Mead (Amberley): 185
NORTHCHAPEL: 96; bishops' transcripts, 214; church building papers, 60
NORTHIAM: 63; advowson, 11; bishops' transcripts, 214; church building papers, 135; faculty papers, 120, 124; parish clerk, 75
Norwich, Bishops of: 235
Nott, Anthony: 93
Nourse, William: 74
Nullity bonds: 15
Nurses: 77, 86
NUTHURST: bishops' transcripts, 214; faculty papers, 58; Alice Land, 148
NUTLEY: 231; bishops' transcripts, 214; church building papers, 135; faculty papers, 124
Nutting, Mrs. M. J.: 130

Oaths: 6, 26, 42, 56, 78, 98, 100, 117, 138, 142, 156, 158, 189; Oaths Act (1909), 98
Occupations: see Apothecaries; Astrologer; Butcher; Doctors; Midwives; Missionary; Nurses; Painter; Schoolmasters; Soldiers; Solicitors; Surgeons; Tanner; Timber merchant; Wine merchant; Yeomen
Office account books: 63, 64, 127, 128, 144, 153, 158, 159
Official principal of the diocese: see Chancellor of the diocese (sub Chichester)
Officials (officers): appointment of episcopal and others, 3, 55–57, 137, 144; subscription by, 7
Old Shoreham: see Shoreham, Old
Old Testament: see Job, Book of; Medieval
Oliffe (alias Mylles), William: 153
Oliver, Thomas: 21
Orders: letters of, 37, 38, 63, 88, 112, 127; registers of, 4, 26, 37, 103, 108, 109, 112
Orders in Council: 5, 70, 119, 136, 160, 189, 227–233
Ordinands: certificates of title, 88, 94; examination papers, 9; list of, 33; subscription by, 6–9
Ordination (sacrament): 37, 79; ordinations, 1–5; ordination papers, 88
Ordination of vicarages: 163
ORE: 230, 231; bishops' transcripts, 215; church building papers, 135; faculty papers, 120, 124; CHRIST CHURCH: 231
Oriental languages, typographical specimens of: 81
Osbaston, Cicely: 171
Osborne: John, 22; Richard, 22
Oteley, Thomas (Archdeacon of Lewes): 237
Otter: Alfred William, 56; William* (Bishop of Chichester), 235; William Bruere (Archdeacon of Lewes), 74, 75, 77, 237
Outram, Francis Henry (Dean of Battle): 240
Overington, James: 73

Overseers: accounts of, 23; rates, 23
OVING: 231; bishops' transcripts, 215; church building papers, 60; tithe, 83, 84; vicar, 11
OVINGDEAN: 232; bishops' transcripts, 215
Oxford: 92; archdeacon, see Clerke, Charles; bishops, see Mackarness, John Fielder; Wilberforce, Samuel; courts, 78; railway, 187; Bodleian Library (including Ashmolean MSS.), 4, 95, 163; Brasenose College, 95, 128; Chancellor of the university, 95; Sheldonian Theatre, 95; University College, 95; University Examination Statute, 95
Oxfordshire: see Chastleton

Page, Richard: 147
PAGHAM: 227, 228, 231; bishops' transcripts, 215; churchwardens' presentments, 149; court papers relating to, 149; survey of lands in, 23; terriers, 150; tithe, 23, 83; Exempt Deanery of Pagham and Tarring (Archbishop of Canterbury's Peculiar Jurisdiction), 6, 16, 26–30, 47, 55, 62, 65, 69, 143, 144, 157–160; deans, list of, 239, 240 (from which see under individual names); records of, 146–154; court, 54, 69
Painter, licence to a: 3
Pannett, Richard: 96
Papal documents: 139, 140
Papists: see Recusants
PARHAM: 231; bishops' transcripts, 215; church building papers, 60
Parish: boundaries, 189, 227–233; parish clerks, 73, 137 (see also Isfield; Lewes St. Thomas-at-Cliffe; Malling, South; Northiam; Pulborough); appointment of parish clerks, 26, 96, 159; councils, 69; parish papers, 95, 96, 137; lists of parish registers, 45, 115; parish register transcripts, 43, 45, 115, 116, 141, 149, 150, 158, 189, 192–227; parish rooms, 69; see also Charities
Parliament: parliamentary returns, 62, 69–71, 85, 131, 159; writ of summons to, 97; see also Acts; Surveys
Parochial library (Heathfield): 137
Parrington, Matthew: 75
Parsonage houses: 57, 59, 61, 80, 86, 119, 133, 136
PARTRIDGE GREEN: church building papers, 60
PATCHAM: 11, 74, 231; bishops' transcripts, 215; church building papers, 135; churchyard, 75; faculty papers, 124; vicar, 75
PATCHING: bishops' transcripts, 215; church building papers, 154; churchwardens' presentments, 149; court papers relating to, 149; terriers, 150
Patents: letters patent, 4; Lewes registrar's patent, 111
Patrick, Simon* (Bishop of Chichester):

173, 178, 183

Renunciations (by administrators and executors): 50, 142, 189

Renward, Thomas: 94

Repertory of the Endowment of Vicarages, A: 5

Reserved rents: 165, 166, 179

Residence of clergy: 65, 86, 112; returns of, 63, 98; *see also* Non-Residence

Residentiary houses: 4, 5

Resignations: 1–5, 9, 65, 68, 75, 90–92, 145, 159, 160; resignation bonds, 9, 105

Restitution of temporalities: 97, 234, 235

Returns: assessors' election returns, 128, 188; baptismal returns, 85, 131; of dissenters' meeting houses, 118; to Bishop Bell's enquiry, 88; financial returns, 86, 98, 113, 188; on maintenance of poor, 69; of non-conformists and recusants, 54, 55, 117, 118; of revenue of the see, 97; statistical returns, 85, 86, 94, 98; to Treasury, 61; *see also* Parliament

Rhodes, John: 138

Richard, St.*, will of: 163

Richards: Dr., 94; Griffith, 87

Rickingale, John* (Bishop of Chichester): 234

Ridgeway: Charles John (Bishop of Chichester), 77, 92, 235; John, 189

RINGMER: 117; bishops' transcripts, 217; church building papers, 135; faculty papers, 124, 161; manor courts, 158

Ringsted, Francis (Dean of Pagham and Tarring and of South Malling): 240

RIPE: bishops' transcripts, 217; church building papers, 135; faculty papers, 124; schools in the rural deanery, 131

Rochester: Bishops of, 234; diocese of, 5, 229, 232

RODMELL: bishops' transcripts, 217; rectory, 129, 145; tithe, 83

Roe, Samuel: 148

ROFFEY: 231; bishops' transcripts, 217

ROGATE: 231; bishops' transcripts, 217

Rogers, ——: 21

Rolls buildings (London): 182

Roman Catholic church, convert from: 79

Romanistic practices: 75, 76; *see also* Puseyism; Recusants

Romilly, John: 56

Roscamp, A. N. H.: 187

Rose: Edward, 146; Rose's Act (1813), 45

Rosseter, Mrs.: 129

ROTHERFIELD: 229, 231; bishops' transcripts, 217; faculty papers, 121, 124; rector, 76

ROTTINGDEAN: 228; bishops' transcripts, 217; faculty papers, 119, 124; Society of Friends, burials, 218

Row, Humfrey: 155

Rowland: John, 21; William, 21

Royal: commissions on ecclesiastical matters, 69; courts, 162; licences, 2; mandates, 1–3; orders relating to clergy non-residence, 105; *see also* Crown

RUDGWICK: 40; bishops' transcripts, 218; church building papers, 60; Rectory, 184; tithe, 83

RUMBOLDSWYKE: bishops' transcripts, 218; church building papers, 60; churchwardens' presentments, 141; faculty papers, 58; tithe, 84

Rural deans (*and* deaneries): 38, 40, 43, 44, 54 ("deane Ruralle"), 57, 61, 73, 96, 98, 126, 131, 132, 136, 137, 187; ruridecanal chapters, 72, 76, 131, 137; *see also* Arundel; Balcombe; Bersted, South; Bexhill; Boxgrove; Brighton; Burwash; Dallington; Eastbourne; Etchingham; Firle, West; Fishbourne, New; Frant; Funtington; Hastings; Horsham; Hurstpierpoint; Iping; Itchenor, West; Lewes; Lodsworth; Midhurst; Pevensey; Ripe, Rye; Selsey; Shermanbury; Southover (*sub* Lewes St. John Baptist); Storrington; Westham

Rush Lane (Aldingbourne): 185

RUSPER: 96; bishops' transcripts, 218; priory, 26

Russell, William: 74

Russhe, Anthony (Dean of Chichester): 238

Rusthall (Kent): 232

RUSTINGTON: bishops' transcripts, 218; church building papers, 60, 61

Ryders Wells (South Malling): 130

RYE: 62, 112; bishops' transcripts, 218; church building papers, 135; faculty papers, 119, 120; railway, 187; rural deanery, 187; Grammar School, 89; vicar, 137

RYE HARBOUR: 231

Ryves, Bruno* (Dean of Chichester): 238

Sackville College (East Grinstead): 73, 74

St. Asaph, Bishops of: 234, 235

St. David's: Bishops of, 234; diocese of, 98

St. Dunstan-in-the-West (London): 183

St. Giles-in-the-Fields (Middlesex): 97

St. John's Common: *see* Burgess Hill

St. John's Gospel: 80

St. John's Head Tavern: *see* London

ST. LEONARDS: church building papers, 135; railway, 187; CHRIST CHURCH: 231; bishops' transcripts, 218; faculty papers, 124; ST. ETHELBURGA: 232; ST. JOHN: *see* St. Leonards, Upper; ST. LEONARD: 231, 232; faculty papers, 124; ST. MARY MAGDALENE (formerly Hastings): 230, 231; bishops' transcripts, 218; ST. MATTHEW, Silverhill: 232; bishops' transcripts, 218; faculty papers, 124; ST. PAUL: 131, 232; bishops' transcripts, 218; faculty papers, 124; ST. PETER: faculty papers, 124

ST. LEONARDS, UPPER (formerly Hastings St. John): 232; faculty papers, 120, 124

St. Mary Abchurch (London): 155

St. Mary Bulverhythe (Hastings): 232
St. Mary's monastery (unidentified): 26
St. Olave (Southwark, Surrey): 155
SALEHURST: 231; advowson, 5; bishops' transcripts, 218; church building papers, 135; faculty papers, 119, 124
Salisbury, Bishops of: 235
Sampson, Richard* (Bishop of Chichester): 234; register of, 3
Sanden (Hertfordshire): rector, 75
Sandham, Robert: 138
Sawyer, James: 48
Sayer, Joseph (Archdeacon of Lewes): 237
SAYERS COMMON: 232; bishops' transcripts, 218
SCAYNES HILL: 232
Schoolmasters: 37, 43, 72, 73, 88, 112; appointment of, 93; licences to schoolmasters (and to teach), 3–7, 73, 93, 100, 143; subscription by, 6–9, 57, 100, 140
Schools: 43, 44, 71, 72, 76, 131, 132; diocesan school inspectors, 72, 131; education papers, 71, 72, 131, 132; schools charity, 94; Sunday Schools, 71; see also Barcombe; Brighton St. Margaret; Buxted; Chichester; Hastings; Hurstpierpoint; Iping; Lancing; Midhurst; Rye; Twineham; Uckfield; Westham
Scobell, John: 77
Scory, John* (Bishop of Chichester): 234; installation of, 3; register of, 3
Scotland: pew cases in, 74; see also Edinburgh
Scott: George Henry Cussans, 76; William (Dean of Pagham and Tarring and of South Malling), 240
Scrase: Clara, 131; Edward, 131
Scriptural passages supporting canon law: 7
Scriven, Thomas: 22
SEAFORD: bishops' transcripts, 219; church, 75; faculty papers, 119, 120, 124; tithe, 83
Seals: archidiaconal (Chichester), 55; archiepiscopal, 55; chapter, 55; Dean of Battle's seal (cast), 190; decanal (Chichester), 55; episcopal (Chichester), 55; seal matrices, 85, 131, 188
Secretary of State, return to: 70
SEDLESCOMBE (Seddlescombe): 189; bishops' transcripts, 219; church building papers, 135
Sele: see Beeding, Upper
Selhurst, William: 137
SELMESTON: augmentation of vicarage, 136; bishops' transcripts, 219; church building papers, 135; faculty papers, 124; tithe, 83; vicar, 76
SELSEY: 164; bishops' transcripts, 219; manor, 170; schools in the rural deanery, 72; tithe, 83; Bishops of, 97
Senior and Attree: 129
Sennicots (Funtington): 26, 61, 232
Sequestration: forms of, 78, 98; papers,

91, 105, 145; sequestration (and sequestrators) of benefices, 10, 50–52, 63, 64, 72, 73, 86, 100, 104, 129, 143, 179; sequestrators of the diocese, 55
Sergison, William: 93, 129
Sermons: 73, 79
Service, orders of: 86, 92; medieval service books, 2, 140, 147, 155; services, 86, 98, 116
Sewell, Thomas: 76
Sheephouse lands (Aldingbourne): 184
Sheldonian Theatre (Oxford): 95
Shepperton (Middlesex): rector, 74
Sherburne, Robert* (Bishop of Chichester): 12, 163, 234; accounts, 3; Donations, 2, 3; registers of, 2
Sherlock, Thomas* (Dean of Chichester; Bishop of London): 95, 238
SHERMANBURY: bishops' transcripts, 219; church building papers, 135; faculty papers, 119, 120, 124; schools in the rural deanery, 131, 132
Sherwin, William: 22
Ship money: 78
SHIPLEY: bishops' transcripts, 219; church rates, 5
Shirry, John (Archdeacon of Lewes): 237
Shoreham railway: 186
SHOREHAM, NEW: bishops' transcripts, 219; faculty papers, 124; vicar, 73
SHOREHAM, OLD: bishops' transcripts, 219; faculty papers, 124
Shropshire: see Astley
Shuttleworth, Philip Nicholas* (Bishop of Chichester): 235
Sidesmen: 29, 42
SIDLESHAM: 15, 164; advowson, 11; bishops' transcripts, 219; faculty papers, 58; manor, 170; poor rate, 24; prebend, 170; tithe, 83
SIDLEY (Bexhill): 232
Significavits: 104
Silverhill: see St. Leonards St. Matthew
Simmonds, William (Dean of Battle): 240
Simmons, Philadelphia: 159
Simony, oath against: 6
Sinecure: benefices, 70; prebends, 76
SINGLETON: bishops' transcripts, 220; church building papers, 60; tithe, 83, 84
Skylton, William (Archdeacon of Lewes): 237
Slade, Samuel (Dean of Chichester): 238
Slater, Anne: 189
SLAUGHAM: bishops' transcripts, 220; faculty papers, 119, 120, 124, 129; rector, 129; surveys of land in, 186; Bishops Wood in Slaugham Chace, 185
SLINDON: bishops' transcripts, 220; church, 148; church building papers, 61; churchwardens' presentments, 150; court papers relating to, 149; terriers, 150
SLINFOLD: 94; bishops' transcripts, 220; church building papers, 61; faculty papers, 58; tithe, 83
Smallpage, Katherine: 153

75; Birch v. Harrison, 191; Butler, Peckham and Peckham v. Bishop [Guy] Carleton, 162; Dowson v. Allen, 74; Freeland v. Neale, 74; Johnson v. Friend and Ballard, 74; Kemp v. Manningham, 163; Littler v. Eldridge, 191; Office v. Moss, 74; Rawlison v. Medwin and Hurst, 74; see also 21, 22 for appealed causes, 1579–1786

SULLINGTON: bishops' transcripts, 222; church building papers, 61; tithe, 83

Sumner, John Bird* (Archbishop of Canterbury, 1848–62): 76

Sunday Schools: 71

Supremacy, oaths of: 6, 78, 158

Surgeons: subscription by, 6

Surrey: 77, 97; see also Burstow; Dorking; Horne; Lingfield; Southwark

Surrogates: 13, 64, 127, 240; appointment of, 16, 57, 111, 129, 137, 144, 156; bonds, 57, 144; surrogation, 55

Surveys of episcopal estates: 167, 173–176, 178; 1647 Parliamentary Survey, 172, 173, 175–177

Suspension of incumbent: 90

Sussex: notes on the history of, 97; Sussex Advertiser, 97; Sussex Commission for Charitable uses, 39; Sussex Lunatic Asylum (Haywards Heath), burials, 207; Vice-Admiralty court papers, 84

SUTTON (West Sussex): bishops' transcripts, 222; church building papers, 61

SUTTON (with Seaford): tithe, 83

Sutton, Robert Shuttleworth: 68; (Archdeacon of Lewes) 237

Swabey, Maurice (Dean of Pagham and Tarring and of South Malling): 240

Swainson, Charles Anthony*: 68, 76

Swan Court (London): 182

Swayne, John: 76

Sydenham, Simon (Bishop of Chichester): 234

Symeon, Geoffrey (Dean of Chichester): 238

Symond's Inn (London): 179, 180, 182

Synods: episcopal, 26–28, 38, 92; synodals, 40, 78, 166; see also Procurations; Tenths

Talbot, Richard (Dean of Chichester): 238

TANGMERE: bishops' transcripts, 222; church, 148; church building papers, 154; churchwardens' presentments, 150; court papers relating to, 149; terriers, 150

Tanner: 148

Tarring, Exempt Deanery of: see Pagham

TARRING, WEST: 44, 148, 229, 230; bishops' transcripts, 222; church building papers, 154; churchwardens' presentments, 150; court papers relating to, 149; terriers, 150; vicar, 76

TARRING NEVILLE: bishops' transcripts, 207, 222

Tavern Acre (Amberley): 185

Taverns: see Public Houses

Taxation: of Pope Nicholas IV, 163; taxation books, 20

Tayler, Robert: (Archdeacon of Lewes) 237; (Chancellor of the diocese) 239

Taylor: Harriet, 129; John, 137; Thomas, 22; Thomas (Archdeacon of Chichester), 236

TELSCOMBE: bishops' transcripts, 222; church building papers, 136; faculty papers, 125

Temporalities: of the benefice, 12, 89; of the diocese, 97, 234, 235

Tenter Yard (London): 180, 181

Tenths: 40–42, 65, 86, 87, 165–167, 169; Queen's tenths, 137; see also Procurations; Synodals

Terriers: glebe (church), 46, 81, 83, 115, 119, 150, 162, 163; of episcopal land, 174–176, 178, 186

TERWICK: bishops' transcripts, 222

Testaments: see Wills (sub Probate)

Testimonial, letters: see Letters

THAKEHAM: bishops' transcripts, 222; church building papers, 61; curate, 73; rector, 73; Society of Friends, burials, 222

Theological MS.: 30

Thirty-Nine Articles, subscription to: 6

Thomas: John (Archdeacon of Chichester), 236; William, 22

Thompson, Sir Henry, bt: 76

Thorne, William* (Dean of Chichester): 238

THORNEY, WEST: bishops' transcripts, 223; church building papers, 61

Three Crowns: see London

TICEHURST: bishops' transcripts, 223; church building papers, 136; faculty papers, 125; manor, 170

TIDEBROOK: 232; bishops' transcripts, 223

Tilgate (Worth): 157

TILLINGTON: bishops' transcripts, 223; church building papers, 61; faculty papers, 58

Timber: merchant, 96; sale of, 97; woodcutting dispute, 4

The Times: 80

Tinkers (Amberley Manor): 184

Tipnoke Hundred: records of, 170, 177, 178

Tireman, Richard: 145

Tithe: 23, 96, 170; accounts, 81, 84, 167, 191; awards and maps, 71, 81; papers, 81–84, 191; tithe rent-charge, 73

Title: ordinands' certificates of, 88, 94

Tolls (Chichester Harbour): 186

Tolquhon family: 93

Tontine, the: 80

TORTINGTON: bishops' transcripts, 223

Tottenham (Middlesex): railway, 187

Traheron, Bartholomew (Dean of Chichester): 238

Transcripts of parish registers: see Parish

264

Translation of Bishops of Chichester: 234, 235

Transubstantiation, declaration against: 6

Treasurer of Chichester Cathedral: 77

Treasury: returns to, 61; *see also* the Tontine

Treatises: on baptism, 2; ecclesiastical formularies and treatises, 47, 77–79, 85; medieval, 2, 105

Tremayne, Richard* (Archdeacon of Chichester): 236

TREYFORD: 92; bishops' transcripts, 223

Trials, heresy: 16

Tristram, Thomas Hutchinson (Chancellor of the diocese): 130, 239

TROTTON: 45; bishops' transcripts, 223; tithe, 83, 84

Trower, Walter John (sometime Bishop of Glasgow and Galloway): 73

Truro, Bishop of: 235; *see also* Burrows, Winfrid Oldfield

Trusts (*and* trustees): 56, 81, 129

Tuck, Richard Holmes: 74

Tucker, D.: 75

Tufnell, Samuel Joliffe: 145

Tunbridge Wells (Kent) (now dio. Rochester): railway, 187; CHRIST CHURCH: 232; KING CHARLES THE MARTYR: 232

Turnbull, Hugh (Dean of Chichester): 238

Turner, Richard: 55

TURNERS HILL: 232; faculty papers, 125

TWINEHAM: 76; bishops' transcripts, 223; church building papers, 136; faculty papers, 125; school, 76

Tye: Agnes, 21; William, 76

Typography: 81

UCKFIELD: 136; bishops' transcripts, 223; faculty papers, 125; school, 131

UDIMORE: bishops' transcripts, 223; perpetual curate, 75; visitation return, 75

Union and disunion of benefices: *see* Benefices

Up Marden: *see* Marden, Up

Upcott, Arthur William (Archdeacon of Hastings): 137, 237

Upper: Beeding, Dicker, St. Leonards, *see under second word*

Upperton: *see* Eastbourne St. Anne

Upperton, Edward Fuller: 73

Upwaltham: *see* Waltham, Up

Valors: 65; valuations of episcopal estates, 174–176, 178, 186; valuation of livings in the King's Book, 118

Vaughan, Edward* (Archdeacon of Lewes): 237

Vavis, Anne: 189

Vicar-general: *see* Chancellor of the diocese (*sub* Chichester)

Vicarages: *passim*; endowment of, 5, 96; instruments constituting rectories and vicarages, 119, 136; ordination of, 163;

see also Augmentation; *and under names of individual benefices*

Vice-Admiralty court papers (Sussex): 84

Vincent, Frederick: 93

Vintry, the (Chichester): 149

Virger (verger): Dean's, 38, 40

Visitation: 1, 2, 79, 55, 88, 112, 115, 167; accounts, 42, 108, 113, 160, 167; address, 36; articles, 16; Bishop Bowers's Visitation Book, 46; of the Cathedral, 26, 28, 34, 36–38; injunctions for visitation of the Cathedral, 28, 36; fees, 113, 127, 187; papers, 38–40, 52, 126, 127, 149, 160, 187, 189; preachers (*or* who had not preached), 110, 126; proctors, 92; receipts, 160; returns, 74, 98; by a rural dean, 40; stewards for Chichester archidiaconal visitations, 12; *see also* Churchwardens; Liber Cleri; Ministers; Orders; Procurations

Vogan, Thomas: 76

Waddington, Edward* (Bishop of Chichester): 235; funeral accounts, 41; register of, 4

WADHURST: 232; bishops' transcripts, 224

Wakefield, Bishop of: 235

Wakeford, William: 144

WALBERTON: bishops' transcripts, 224; church building papers, 61; faculty papers, 58, 59; vicar, 76; Walberton Rectory, 184, 186

WALDRON: 189; bishops' transcripts, 224; faculty papers, 125

Wales: episcopal patronage in, 98; Welsh courts, 125

Walesby, William (Archdeacon of Chichester): 236

Walker, John Russell (Archdeacon of Chichester): 236

Wallis, William: 75

WALTHAM, UP: bishops' transcripts, 224

War: Civil, 163; 1939–1945, 80

WARBLETON: 228; bishops' transcripts, 224; church building papers, 136; faculty papers, 119, 125

Warde, Geoffrey Hodgson (Bishop of Lewes): 236

Ware, Henry (Bishop of Chichester): 234

WARMINGHURST: bishops' transcripts, 224

WARNHAM: bishops' transcripts, 224; faculty papers, 59

WARNINGCAMP: bishops' transcripts, 224

WARTLING: 228; bishops' transcripts, 224

Warwickshire: *see* Birmingham

WASHINGTON: bishops' transcripts, 224

Watersfield (Cold Waltham): 185

Watson: Anthony* (Bishop of Chichester), 118, 234; registers of, 3, 4; William (Dean of Battle), 240

Watts, Emily Maria: 189

Waynflete, John (Dean of Chichester): 238

Wayte, Anthony (Archdeacon of Lewes): 237
Webb, Benjamin: 74
Webber, Charles (Archdeacon of Chichester): 73, 236
Webster family: 190
Welch, Thomas Robinson (Chancellor of the diocese): 56, 239; seal matrix, 85
Wells: see Bath
West: Blatchington, Crawley, Dean (West Sussex), Firle, Grinstead, Hoathly, Itchenor, Lavant, Lavington, Stoke, Tarring, Thorney, Wittering, see under second word
WESTBOURNE: 232; bishops' transcripts, 225; faculty papers, 58; vicar, 74
WESTDEAN (East Sussex): bishops' transcripts, 201; faculty papers, 122; tithe, 82
Westergate: Common, 185; manor, 170
WESTFIELD: bishops' transcripts, 225; church building papers, 136; faculty papers, 125
WESTHAM: bishops' transcripts, 225; church building papers, 136; school, 131; schools in the rural deanery, 131
WESTHAMPNETT: bishops' transcripts, 225
WESTMESTON: 199; bishops' transcripts, 225; church building papers, 136
Weston, Edmund: (Archdeacon of Lewes) 237; (Chancellor of the diocese) 239
Whateley, Richard* (Archbishop of Dublin): 73
WHATLINGTON: bishops' transcripts, 225
Wheeler, William: 73
Whitby, Oliver (Archdeacon of Chichester): 236
White: Henry, 22; Richard, 22
White Swan: see London
White's Alley: see London
WHITEHAWK: 232
Whitgift, John* (Archbishop of Canterbury, 1583–1604): 117
Widows: 153; clergy (and orphans), 94, 114
WIGGONHOLT: bishops' transcripts, 225; church building papers, 61
Wilberforce: Ernest Roland (Bishop of Chichester), 77, 235; Samuel* (Bishop of Oxford), 73, 74
Wilfrid, St.*: 80
Wilkin, Richard: 137
William of Lullington (Dean of Chichester): 238
Williams, John* (Bishop of Chichester): 235; register of, 4
Williamson: Garrett (Dean of Pagham and Tarring and of South Malling), 239; James (Archdeacon of Lewes), 237
WILLINGDON: 229, 232; bishops' transcripts, 225; church building papers, 136; manor, 130; tithe, 83, 84
Willis, William: 76
Wills: see Probate
WILMINGTON: bishops' transcripts, 225;

faculty papers, 119, 125
Wilson, Roger Plumpton (Bishop of Chichester): 235
WINCHELSEA: 231; bishops' transcripts, 225; church building papers, 136
Winchester (Hampshire): Bishop of, 66; diocese of, 92, 230; Probate Registry, 49
Wine merchant's accounts: 148
Winston, Francis: 22
Wintle, Robert Wintle (Chancellor of the diocese): 75, 239
WISBOROUGH GREEN: 231; bishops' transcripts, 226; church building papers, 61; inclosure award, 174; surveys of land in, 186; tenement and land in, 184; tithe, 83; Ashfold, 185; Drungewick, 162; Mockbeggars, 184; Tinkers, 184; see also Amberley manor
WISTON: bishops' transcripts, 226; rector, 73
Withers, John (Dean of Battle): 240
WITHYHAM: 230, 233; bishops' transcripts, 226; faculty papers, 125; hamlet (part of Deanery of South Malling), bishops' transcripts, 226; ST. JOHN (formerly Crowborough St. John): 233; bishops' transcripts, 226; faculty papers, 125
Witnesses in consistory courts: 18, 19, 156
WITTERING, EAST: bishops' transcripts, 226; church building papers, 61; rector, 77; tithe, 83
WITTERING, WEST: bishops' transcripts, 226; church building papers, 61; Common, 185; messuages and lands in, 185; surveys of land in, 175; Cackham, resident of, 147; Cakeham Farm, 184; see also Cakeham
Wittersham (Kent): 94
WIVELSFIELD: 229; bishops' transcripts, 226; faculty papers, 125; hamlet (part of Deanery of South Malling), bishops' transcripts, 226
Wood: see Timber
Wood, Peter: 73
Woodard, Nathaniel*: 76
Woodcock, Laurence (Dean of Pagham and Tarring and of South Malling): 239
Woodhead, Capt. H. H.: 75
Woodland, Catherine: 22
WOODMANCOTE: bishops' transcripts, 226; faculty papers, 120, 125
Woods, Thomas: 22
WOOLAVINGTON: bishops' transcripts, 226
WOOLBEDING: 231; bishops' transcripts, 227
Woolgar: Nicholas, 21; William, 22
Wooll, John: 12
Worcester, Bishops of: 234, 235
Wordsworth, Christopher*: 73
Workhouses (union): Brighton, 93; Brede, 93; Horsham, 93
Worley, Henry (Chancellor of the diocese): 239

Worth: **157, 229, 232**; bishops' transcripts, **227**; church building papers, **136**; Tilgate, **157**
Worthial(l), John: (Archdeacon of Chichester), **236**; (Chancellor of the diocese) **239**
Worthing: **233**; bishops' transcripts, **227**; dissenters' meeting house, **95**; faculty papers, **58**; Holy Trinity: **233**; St. Andrew: **233**; St. George: **233**; bishops' transcripts, **227**; St. Paul: **90, 233**
Writs: **30, 37, 65**; of *levari facias*, **91, 117**; of summons to Parliament, **97**

Wycombe, High (Buckinghamshire): tithe, **84**
Wynne, John: **93**

Yapton: **148**; bishops' transcripts, **227**; faculty papers, **58, 59**; tithe, **83, 84**
Yeomen: **96, 137, 147**
Yonge, ——: **21**
Yorkshire: *see* Huggate; Pocklington
Youard, Wilfrid Wadham (Dean of Battle): **240**
Young: John (Dean of Chichester), **238**; Samuel, **155**

ADDENDA ET CORRIGENDA

p. 37, line 3 of I/19/1 *should read* archiepiscopal visitation of 1581, I/18/16).

p. 37, I/19/7, insert a comma after the word 'visitation'.

p. 42, line 19, *for* EP.I/22 *read* Ep.I/22.

p. 45, Ep.I/24A. It ought to have been noted here that a survey, 1813, giving lists (made by incumbents or curates) of parish registers and their place of deposit was required by the Act 52 Geo. III, c. 146.

p. 46, line 27, *for* transcript *read* typescript.

p. 74, line 19, transfer bracket from before 'vicar' to before the name 'John'.

p. 92, line 26, for *S.A.C.* read *Sussex Archaeological Collections.*

p. 101, line 5, the word 'Society' should be in italics.

p. 115, Ep.II/16A. A note here as given above for p. 45.

p. 115, line 27, *for* 1728 *read* 1729.

p. 128, footnote, *for* EP *read* Ep.

p. 160, line 16, add 'See note to Ep.II/32 (p. 127)'.

p. 171, line 6, add dates, 1648–1701.

p. 176, line 18, add, after 1483, a comma and the dates, 1671–1697.

p. 200, line 25, *for* Withiam *read* Withyham.

p. 205, after Graffham, insert 'Greatham *see* Wiggonholt'.

p. 218, line 26, *for* Magadalene *read* Magdalene.

p. 226, line 14, *for* Withyam *read* Withyham.

p. 228, last line, *for* 10.5.37 *read* 10.5.1837.

p. 230, line 46, *for* H. St. Mary *read* Hastings St. Mary-in-the-Castle.

p. 231, line 36, *for* P. St. Peter *read* Brighton St. Martin.

p. 234, line 26, after 'Curtis' insert '[Curteys]'.

p. 238, line 22, after 'Curtis' insert '[Curteys]'.

p. 239, line 14, insert '(Bishop)' before 'William Ashburnham'.

Readers will probably be aware of the extent of the Dunkin Collection in the British Museum (Add. MSS. 39326–39546). These 221 volumes were compiled by E. H. W. Dunkin from many sources, including the episcopal and capitular archives at Chichester. They relate mainly to Sussex clergy and families, but the variety of Dunkin's interests, and the importance of his work to those studying Sussex ecclesiastical records, can be seen by referring to the *British Museum Catalogue of Additions to the Manuscripts 1916–1920* (1933), pp. 32–40, a copy of which is available in the West Sussex Record Office Library.

PRINTED BY MOORE AND TILLYER LTD, AT THE REGNUM PRESS, CHICHESTER